ECOLOGICAL ECONOMICS

ECOLOGICAL ECONOMICS

Rakesh A. Joshi
Sukanta Sarkar

GenNext Publication

ISBN: 978-93-8022-301-8
Price: ₹ 1600/-

First Published, 2016

Published by

GeNext Publications
5, Ansari Road, Daryaganj
Delhi - 110002
E-mail: gennext@hotmail.com Ph.: 9212142040

Printed at : G. Print Process, Delhi

Cataloging in Publication Data–DK

Courtesy: D.K. Agencies (P) Ltd. <docinfo@dkagencies.com>

Joshi, Rakesh A., author.
Ecological economics / Rakesh A. Joshi, Sukanta Sarkar.
pages cm
Includes bibliographical references.
ISBN 9789380223018

1. Ecology--Economic aspects. 2. Environmental protection--Economic aspects. 3. Natural disasters--Economic aspects. 4. Pollution--Economic aspects. I. Sarkar, Sukanta, author. II. Title.

QH541.15.E25J67 2016 DDC 333.95 23

Contents

Foreword

Date: 12/10/2015

I am glad to know that Dr Rakesh Joshi and Dr Sukanta Sarkar have prepared manuscript of a book entitled *"Ecological Economics"* and the book is going to be published by the GenNext Publisher, New Delhi, India. Twenty seven chapters have concluded in this book. By reading the manuscript, I think most of the contemporary topics of ecological economics have been included in it. I am confident that this book will be very useful to the students and researchers of Planning, Sociology, Rural development, Environmental studies and Economics etc.

I wish academic endeavour of the authors of this book shall be fruitful and it will satisfy the academic queries of the readers.

With best wishes

Professor M A Rahman, PhD (USA)
Director, Centre for Global Environmental Culture (CGEC)
Coordinator, RCE Greater Dhaka and WWOOF Bangladesh
International University of Business Agriculture and Technology
Uttara Model Town, Dhaka, Bangladesh

Preface

Biodiversity is the term used to describe the variety of life found on Earth and all of the natural processes. This includes ecosystem, genetic and cultural diversity, and the connections between these and all species. Biological sources provide many industrial materials. These include fiber, oil, dyes, rubber, water, timber, paper and food. It plays an important role in drug discovery and medicinal resources. It is changing for the changes of climate. Climate change is the variation in global or regional climates over time. It reflects changes in the variability or average state of the atmosphere over time scales ranging from decades to millions of years.

In this connection, we want to place on record our deep appreciation to Professor Ajay Pathak, Vice-Chancellor, ICFAI University, Tripura, Agartala for providing valuable inputs. We desire to express our heartiest thank to Professor Md. A. Rahman, Department of Agriculture, International University of Business Agriculture and Technology, Dhaka, Bangladesh who despite his busy schedule and hectic academic engagements, all the time encouraged and supported us. We have also beholden to Dr N.G. Pendse, Department of Economics, Rani Durgabati University, Jabalpur who's erudite and scholarly tidbits for preparing such a vast work are still fresh in my mind. We also thanks to Dr Pradeep Kumar Pandey, Centre of Judicial Studies, Dibrugarh University, Assam; Dr Suman Kalan Chaudhury, Department of Business Administration, Berhampur University, Odisha; Dr D. Pulla Rao, Department of Economics, Andhra

University; Dr Vibhuti Patel, Professor cum Director, Centre for Study of Social Exclusion and Inclusive Policy, SNDT Women's University, Mumbai; Dr WakarAmin, Department of Social Work, University of Kashmir, J & K.; Dr Shazia Manzoor, Assistant professor Department of Social Work, University of Kashmir, J & K; Dr Pallab Kanti Ghoshal, Department of Commerce, Nataji Subhas College, Udaipur, for their valuable suggestions and moral support.

We are heartily grateful to Professor Ashish Kumar Shivastava and Professor L.S. Nigam, Pandit Ravishankar Shukla University, Raipur, Chhattisgarh who always encouraged us to carry on this constructive work. Further, we express our heartily thankfulness to each and every person who directly/indirectly helped us in preparing this work.

It is hoped that this book will be very useful for society in general and students of economics in particular. Comments and suggestions are most welcomed.

Dr Rakesh A. Joshi
Dr Sukanta Sarkar

Abbreviations

ACWC	:	Area Cyclone Warning Centres
ASEAN	:	Association of South-East Asian Nations
CAC	:	Command and Control
CITES	:	Convention on International Trade for Endangered Species
COD	:	Chemical Oxygen Demand
CRC	:	Central Relief Commissioner
CRF	:	Calamity Relief Fund
CSE	:	Centre for Science and Environment
CWC	:	Cyclone Warning Centre
DMIC	:	Disaster Management Information Centre
DOI	:	Department of the Interior
DRRO	:	District Relief and Rehabilitation Officer
EPA	:	Environmental Protection Agency
EUETS	:	European Union's Emission Trading Scheme
FWS	:	Fish and Wildlife Service
GIS	:	Geographical Information Systems
ICIMOD	:	International Centre for Integrated Mountain Development
IGY	:	International Geophysical Year
IMD	:	India Meteorological Department
IPCC	:	Intergovernmental Panel on Climate Change

MEA	:	Multilateral Environmental Agreements
MoEFCC	:	Ministry of Environment, Forest and Climate Change
MoFDM	:	Ministry of Food and Disaster Management
NAPCC	:	National Action Plan on Climate Change
NFMA	:	National Forest Management Act
NOAA	:	National Oceanic and Atmospheric Administration
NSRH	:	National Crisis Management Committee
ODS	:	Ozone-Depleting Substances
SACEP	:	South Asia Co-operative Environment Programme
SCFB	:	Self-Closing Flood Barrier
SFM	:	Sustainable Forest Management
UBCHA	:	UN Office for the Coordination of Humanitarian Affairs
UN	:	United Nations
UNCED	:	United Nations Conference on Environment and Development
UNDP	:	United Nations Development Programme
UNEP	:	United Nations Environment Programme
UNFCCC	:	United Nations Framework Convention on Climate Change
VFC	:	Village Forest Committee
WCDR	:	World Conference on Disaster Reduction
WFD	:	Water Framework Directive

Importance

Ecosystems are complex and ecological indicators can help describe them in simpler terms that can be understood and used by non-scientists to make management decisions. Biodiversity is the variety of different types of life found on Earth. It is a measure of the variety of organisms present in different ecosystems. It boosts ecosystem productivity where each species, no matter how small, all have an important role to play. Biological sources provide many industrial materials. These include fiber, oil, dyes, rubber, water, timber, paper and food. It plays an important role in drug discovery and medicinal resources. The earth's biodiversity is in grave danger. In the present era, human beings are the most dangerous cause of destruction of the earth's biodiversity. Biodiversity hotspot is a biogeography region with a significant reservoir of biodiversity that is under threat from humans.

Forests are vital for social, economic, ecological and environmental reasons. They play an important role in ecosystem processes (such as the biogeochemical and hydrological cycles), they provide habitat for wildlife and serve as sources of biodiversity, and they offer protection against soil erosion. Forests are a crucial link in the ecosystem. In addition to the direct use values, forests resources protect the environment in different ways, such as watershed protection, nutrient cycling, pollution control, micro-climatic regulation, and carbon sequestration. Forests are among the most effective systems for air pollution abatement and ground water recharge. In this era of global warming, forests help mitigate the effects of climate change, and maintain biodiversity and ecosystem functioning.

Climate change is the real fact in the twenty-first century. Climate change is the variation in global or regional climates over time. It reflects changes in the variability or average state of the atmosphere over time scales ranging from decades to millions of years. It is a long-term shift in weather conditions identified by changes in temperature, precipitation, winds, and other indicators. Global climate change has already had observable effects on the environment. Glaciers have shrunk, ice on rivers and lakes is breaking up earlier, plant and animal ranges have shifted and trees are flowering sooner. Climate change causes displacement of people in several ways, the most obvious and dramatic being through the increased number and severity of weather-related disasters which destroy homes and habitats causing people to seek shelter or livelihoods elsewhere.

During the last several decades, human activities have resulted in considerable reduction in the ozone layer of the atmosphere. Ozone depletion occurs when destruction of the stratospheric ozone is more than the production of the molecule. Ozone, while a minority constituent in Earth's atmosphere is responsible for most of the absorption of UVB radiation. The main public concern regarding the ozone hole has been the effects of increased surface UV radiation on human health. Increases in solar UV radiation could affect terrestrial and aquatic biogeochemical cycles, thus altering both sources and sinks of greenhouse and chemically-important trace gases.

Global warming and climate change are terms for the observed century-scale rise in the average temperature of the Earth's climate system and its related effects. Greenhouse gas is any gaseous compound in the atmosphere that is capable of absorbing infrared radiation, thereby trapping and holding heat in the atmosphere. Deforestation is the second largest anthropogenic source of carbon dioxide to the atmosphere, after fossil fuel combustion. Deforestation and forest degradation can cause wildlife to decline. The effects of climate change on human systems, mostly due to warming or shifts in precipitation patterns, or both, have been detected worldwide. Global warming is already having significant and costly effects on our communities, our health, and our climate.

Various phenomena like earthquakes, landslides, volcanic eruptions, floods, hurricanes, tornadoes, blizzards, tsunamis, and cyclones are all natural hazards. Disasters involve widespread human, material, economic or environmental impacts, which exceed the ability of the affected community or society to cope using its own resources. Disasters are events that have a huge impact on humans and/or the environment. It require government intervention. Disaster management does not avert or eliminate the threats; instead it focuses on creating plans to decrease the impact of disasters. India is highly vulnerable to natural disasters, losing about two per cent of the GDP on an average to disasters. India has been traditionally vulnerable to natural disasters on account of its unique geo-climatic conditions.

Flooding occurs in known floodplains when prolonged rainfall over several days, intense rainfall over a short period of time, or an ice or debris jam causes a river or stream to overflow and flood the surrounding area. Floods are the most common and widespread of all natural disasters. Earthquakes are one of the most destructive of natural hazards. Earthquake occurs due to sudden transient motion of the ground as a result of release of elastic energy in a matter of few seconds. Cyclone is a swirling atmospheric disturbance in which strong winds blow in a circle, and rotate in the same direction as rotation of the earth. Tsunami is a series of waves in a water body caused by the displacement of a large volume of water, generally in an ocean or a large lake.

Landslide is a geological phenomenon that includes a wide range of ground movements. Rock falls, deep failure of slopes and shallow. Drought is an extended period of deficient rainfall relative to the statistical multi-year average for a region. It is often referred to as a creeping phenomenon and its impacts vary from region to region. Forest fire is an uncontrolled fire occurring in nature. Sometimes, it is so large that it takes a long time for the fire fighting crews to gain control over the situation. Acid rain is a rain or any other form of precipitation that is unusually acidic, meaning that it possesses elevated levels of hydrogen ions.

Part I: Environmental Protection

1
Biodiversity

"If we're destroying our trees and destroying our environment and hurting animals and hurting one another and all that stuff, there's got to be a very powerful energy to fight that. I think we need more love in the world. We need more kindness, more compassion, more joy, more laughter. I definitely want to contribute to that." - **Ellen DeGeneres**

Earth is known for its biodiversity. Ecological indicators are used to communicate information about ecosystems and the impact human activity has on ecosystems to groups such as the public or government policy makers. Ecosystems are complex and ecological indicators can help describe them in simpler terms that can be understood and used by non-scientists to make management decisions.[1] Biodiversity is a term of science that has made its way into the civic vocabulary, from news reporting to middle school lesson plans on rain forests. To many, biodiversity simply refers to the number of different kinds of living things, or species richness. Scientists often add species abundance, or the number of individuals within a species or population, to the commonly understood definition.[2]

Biodiversity is the result of 3.5 billion years of evolution. The origin of life has not been definitely established by science. Some evidence suggests that life may already have been well-established only a few hundred million years after the formation of the Earth. During the last century, decreases in biodiversity have been increasingly observed. Rates of decline in biodiversity in this sixth mass extinction match or exceed rates of loss in the five previous mass extinction events in the fossil record. Conservation biology matured in the mid-twentieth century as ecologists, naturalists, and other scientists began to research and address issues pertaining to global biodiversity declines.[3]

The understanding of the importance of biodiversity has developed in the 20 years since the report of the World Commission on Environment and Development. There is increased recognition that people are part of, not separate from, the ecosystems in which they live, and are affected by changes in ecosystems, populations of species and genetic changes. As the basis for all ecosystem services, and the foundation for truly sustainable development, biodiversity plays fundamental roles in maintaining and enhancing the well-being of the world's more than 6.7 billion people, rich and poor, rural and urban alike.[4] Biodiversity provides the base for the livelihoods, cultures and economies of several hundred millions of people, including farmers, fisher folk, forest dwellers and artisans. It provides raw material for a diverse medicinal and health care systems. It provides the genetic base for the continuous up-gradation of agriculture, fisheries, and for critical discoveries in scientific, industrial and other sectors. The rapid erosion of biodiversity in the last few decades has impacted on the health of the land, water bodies and people.[5]

What is Biodiversity?

Biodiversity is the variety of different types of life found on Earth. It is a measure of the variety of organisms present in different ecosystems. This can refer to genetic variation, ecosystem variation, or species variation within an area, biome, or planet. It refers to the variety of life. It is seen in the number of species in an ecosystem or on the entire Earth. It gets used as a measure of the health of biological systems, and to see if there is a danger that too many species become extinct. Biologists most often define biodiversity as the totality of genes, species, and ecosystems of a region. There are three levels at which biological variety can been identified:

(a) **Species Diversity:** Every natural and man-made ecosystem is made up of a variety of animal and plant species. Some ecosystems such as tropical rainforests are very rich in the number of species as compared to other ecosystems such as the desert ecosystem.

(b) **Ecosystem Diversity**: There are a large variety of different ecosystems on the Earth. Distinctive ecosystems include natural landscapes like forests, grasslands, deserts, mountains etc. as well as aquatic ecosystems like rivers, lakes and seas.

(c) **Genetic Diversity**[6]: Every individual in a species differs widely from other individuals in its genetic makeup due to large number of combinations possible in the genes. This genetic variability is essential for healthy breeding population of a species.[7]

Importance of Biodiversity

Biodiversity is the term used to describe the variety of life found on Earth and all of the natural processes. This includes ecosystem, genetic and cultural diversity, and the connections between these and all species. It is helpful to think of an ecosystem. It helps in our day-to-day lives.[8] It is affected by climate change, with negative consequences for human well-being. Biodiversity makes an important contribution to both climate-change mitigation and adaptation. Consequently, conserving and sustainably managing biodiversity is critical to addressing climate change.[9]

Biodiversity boosts ecosystem productivity where each species, no matter how small, all have an important role to play. Ecosystems and their species perform important biological services. For example, green plants remove carbon dioxide and release oxygen into the atmosphere, which helps keep the environment healthy and fit for human life. Vegetation cover helps to protect soils from erosion. Ecosystems help maintain a healthy balance of gases in the atmosphere. Bacteria and fungi play a crucial role in recycling nutrients in ecosystems. Plants like reeds act as natural filters, helping to remove waste from surface waters and many bacteria can help break down low level pollutants. Wild species have been used as sources of drugs for thousands of years. Human societies have traditionally used plant and animal products like wool and fur for clothing, and wood for building construction and fuel.[10]

Biological sources provide many industrial materials. These include fiber, oil, dyes, rubber, water, timber, paper and food. It plays an important role in drug discovery and medicinal resources. Medicines from nature account for usage by 80 per cent of the world's population. Biodiversity enhances recreational activities like bird watching, fishing, trekking etc. It inspires musicians and artists. Biodiversity provides for variety of foods for the planet.[11]

Biodiversity is the origin of all species of crops and domesticated livestock and the variety within them. It is the foundation of ecosystem services essential to sustain agriculture and human well-being. Biodiversity and agriculture are strongly interrelated because while biodiversity is critical for agriculture, agriculture can also contribute to conservation and sustainable use of biodiversity.[12] It is important for all species' survival. We need a variety of habitats for all the different species because each species is adapted to a certain set of environmental conditions. All species depend on each other to survive, so if one becomes extinct another species that relies on it could go extinct as well.[13]

Even if we humans could find a way to overcome a catastrophic loss of biodiversity, our existence on Earth would certainly be changed. There's a very important economic aspect to biodiversity as well. In 1997, Cornell University scientists tallied the dollar value of all the services provided for humanity by life on Earth. Everything from ecotourism and pollination to soil formation and pharmaceuticals was taken into account. The total for services provided to humanity by Mother Nature came to US$2.9 trillion per year (another study concluded the total was US$33 trillion).[14]

Biodiversity as Global Perspectives

There are 80,000 species of edible plants known on Earth, but 90 per cent of the world's food comes from a mere 20 of these species. Edible plant species, both those we know of and those we do not offer a tremendous resource of possibilities that could greatly add to the security of food.[15] For many taxonomic groups, species inventories are more complete in temperate than in tropical countries. Considering that an overwhelmingly large proportion of the species waiting to be discovered are in the tropics, biologists make a statistical comparison of the temperate-tropical species richness of an exhaustively studied group of insects and extrapolate this ratio to other groups of animals and plants to come up with a gross estimate of the total number of species on earth.

Man has made remarkable advancements in many fields of science but when it comes to recording and scientifically describing different kinds of plants, animals and microorganisms, there remains much more to be explored and recorded than they are known.[16] Distribution of flora and fauna at any place is largely governed by the latitude, longitude, altitude, geology and climate of that region. Specific areas can be marked on the basis of distribution of distinctive flora and fauna and are known as Biogeographic zones. Each biogeographic zone has several habitats, biotic communities and ecosystems. In India, we are endowed with a rich diversity of the ten biogeographically distinct regions due to varying physical conditions and species groupings.[17]

Africa has rich and varied biological resources forming the continent's natural wealth on which its social and economic systems are based. In the West Indian Ocean islands such as Madagascar, there are five bird families and five primate families that live nowhere else on Earth. The Atlas Mountains in Northern Africa shelter rich pine and oak forests, and also a number of endemic and rare species such as the wild olive and the Saharan myrtle. In Egypt, some seven per cent of the country's bird population consists of migratory species which appear on a seasonal basis. The coastal areas of Egypt are situated along extremely important migratory routes for birds and there are very important wintering areas for water birds along the coast.

The Horn of Africa has the continent's highest number of endemic reptiles, alongside a number of endemic and threatened antelopes, such as the gerenuk, a species of long-necked antelope found in the dry bushy scrub in the Horn of Africa (Djibouti, Ethiopia, and Somalia). Basin, which covers Cameroon, the Central African Republic, the Congo, the Democratic Republic of the Congo Equatorial Guinea and Gabon, and, after the Amazon region, constitutes the world's second largest area of natural tropical rainforest. In Kenya, the forests have dwindled because large tracts of terrestrial and wetland ecosystems have been converted to farmland. The Congo basin forests measure nearly 200 million hectares in area and account for 30 per cent of the plant cover on the African continent and 19 per cent of the world's tropical rainforests. Africa is home to numerous wetlands of international significance, a number of which are listed in the Convention on Wetlands of International Importance, Especially as Waterfowl Habitat.

In terms of water resources, Africa is endowed with hundreds of lakes and rivers. There are 677 lakes in Africa, of which 88 are principal lakes. Africa has also some 80 transboundary rivers and lake basins, and the catchment areas of the 17 largest exceed 100,000 square kilometers. The largest freshwater lake in Africa and the second largest in the world is Lake Victoria. Lake Ichkeul in Tunisia, the last of a chain of lakes which in the past extended throughout the North African littoral, has seven freshwater rivers as tributaries. Furthermore, the River Nile constitutes a key biodiversity corridor across the arid Sahara desert, but is heavily affected by human activities in its lower reaches.[18]

Asia and the Pacific encompass some of the world's greatest biological, cultural and economic diversity. It covers 8.6 per cent of the Earth's total surface area and nearly 30 per cent of its land area. In 2008, Asia and the Pacific recorded the world's highest number of threatened species. In all, 13 of the 34 biodiversity hotspots designated by Conservation International are also to be found in this area (East Melanesian Islands, Himalayas, Indo-Burma, Japan, mountains of south-west China, New Caledonia, New Zealand, Philippines, Polynesia-Micronesia, south-west Australia, Sundaland, Wallacea, Western Ghats and Sri Lanka). Turning to coastal ecosystems, Asia and the Pacific contains a large proportion of the world's remaining mangrove forests and coral reefs; both systems continue, however, to suffer from various direct and indirect pressures.[19]

Southeast Asia is a bio-cultural hotspot encompassing about 20 per cent of global plant, animal and marine species. The region contains three mega diverse countries (Indonesia, Malaysia and the Philippines) where four of the world's 25 biodiversity hotspots are located. Its montane ecosystems are particularly noted for their high diversity of ferns, mosses and orchids. Although the number of species that has actually become extinct from the region is small, the relatively recent widespread deforestation and the associated fragmentation of natural habitats is expected to accelerate biodiversity decline in the coming years.[20]

India is one of 17 mega-diverse countries, as identified by Conservation International, and has four biodiversity hotspots. India contains 668 protected areas comprising of wildlife sanctuaries, national parks, tiger reserves, elephant reserves, community reserves, and conservation reserves. Conservation of various elements of biodiversity outside the protected area system is governed by a variety of legislations in a sectoral manner. Most of the wild biodiversity, mainly in the form of trees, are regulated through prevalent Central / State forest legislations such as the Indian Forest Act, 1927. In the overall management of forests and biodiversity, apart from the Working Plan, there is no information gathered at the sub-national level for assessing the health of forests, or to generate understanding about the functioning of an ecosystem.[21] India is one of the richest nations in terms of biological diversity. India owes this to its position in the tropical and subtropical latitudes.[22]

The natural world across Europe is suffering a crisis as serious as the threat of climate change. The losses threaten to undermine vital ecosystem services like clean water and fertile soils, which underpin both quality of life and the economy. Figures for the habitats and species awarded special protection under the EU habitats directive reveal that across 40 countries of Europe and the former Soviet Union, 50-85 per cent of habitats and 40-70 per cent of species were in an unfavourable condition, and many more could not be assessed because of a lack of information. Across Europe, the biggest declines from 1990 to 2000 had been for bogs and fenland, heath land and coastal habitats. Woodland, forests and lakes had grown, but these increases were dwarfed by the biggest habitat expansion, which was constructed, industrial, artificial habitats.[23]

The loss of biodiversity in Europe and elsewhere has been highlighted for several decades. There are an estimated approximately 250 mammal, 500 bird, 70 amphibian, 200 reptile, 220 freshwater fish, 200,000 invertebrate and 12,500 plant species in Europe. Recent European initiatives to coordinate data on biodiversity include the Species 20009 and Fauna Europea projects. Globally, the Global Biodiversity Information Facility coordinates biodiversity information, working in collaboration with existing programmes and with natural history museums and other organisations. There are many reports of biodiversity loss in Europe, most of which relate to the declining abundance of species or reduction in their distribution. Europe is extremely rich in habitats. Information on habitat quality is currently being assessed through various initiatives, such as the monitoring of habitats covered by Biodiversity Action Plans (BAPs) in the UK, with reporting every three years.[24]

Australia is one of the most biodiverse countries in the world. Many aspects of Australia's natural environment, such as the desert, the Great Barrier Reef, and distinctive native species such as the koala, kangaroos and eucalypts are central to Australians' national identities. Australian native animals adorn the national coat of arms and many of Australia's sporting codes have them as national team emblems. It is the most isolated inhabited continent and its geology is the oldest in the world. These factors, combined with its size and its long-term and geographical variations in climate make Australia one of the most biologically unique and diverse countries in the world. Australia's climate is geographically very variable compared to other countries, resulting in ecosystems ranging from deserts to tropical rainforests. Australia has more endemic species than are currently known for any other country. Eighty-seven per cent of Australia's mammals are endemic, as are approximately 45 per cent of birds, 86 per cent of vascular plants, 93 per cent of reptiles and 94 per cent of amphibians.[25]

North America's diminishing biological diversity has profound consequences. Because the loss is irreversible-species that are lost are lost forever. It have potential impact on the human condition, on the fabric of the continent's living systems, and on the process of evolution is immense. Some of the region's species depend on healthy, contiguous forest ecosystems. Habitat fragmentation and loss within these forests now threaten many migratory species. Birds are losing nesting, feeding, and resting areas. Mexico has adopted a three-pronged national strategy that includes management and sustainable use of wildlife, strengthening the National System of Protected Areas, and increasing knowledge through the National Commission for the Understanding and Use of Biodiversity. In the past 10 years, Mexico created 19 new biosphere reserves. Canada developed a biodiversity strategy in 1994. Federal legislation to protect threatened species is pending. A 2000 report on the nation's national parks called for urgent action to mitigate the impact of ongoing stresses. Since 1970, the amount of protected area has tripled. In the United States, both federal and states agencies invest huge amounts of their time and budgets in habitat and species protection.[26]

North America has a broad array of freshwater ecosystems because of the continent's complex geography and geological history. Within a multitude of habitats that include streams, large rivers, natural lakes, springs, and wetlands, rich assemblages of fishes reside, representing diverse taxonomic groups with unique ecological requirements. They face an unprecedented conservation crisis. In the last few decades, the proportion of inland fishes of North America, which are considered imperiled or extinct, increased from 20 to 40 per cent. Even in North America, where scientific knowledge of the fauna is advanced, new species are described every year. These discoveries are the combination of applied technologies, such as gene sequencing, which increase recognition of biodiversity at all levels, and the documentation of new, morphologically distinct forms and populations. Biological taxonomy is the discipline of classifying and naming organisms using an internationally accepted system or code. Seven hundred fish taxa are considered imperiled in North America's inland waters, currently, which represent 133 genera in 36 families. The majority of taxa are named species, followed by named subspecies, populations, undescribed species, and undescribed subspecies.[27]

Latin America and the Caribbean is the region with the greatest biological diversity on the planet and it hosts several of the world's mega diverse countries. The region holds almost one half of the world's tropical forests, 33 per cent of its total mammals, 35 per cent of its reptilian species, 41 per cent of its birds and 50 per cent of its amphibians. The biological diversity of Latin America and the Caribbean constitutes one of its essential features. In recent years the pace of deforestation has slowed in some parts of the region, including the Brazilian Amazon forest and Mexico. Cumulative deforestation of the Brazilian Amazon is nevertheless substantial, representing more than 17 per cent of the original forest area.

Latin America and the Caribbean hold more than 30 per cent of all the planets available freshwater and some 40 per cent of its total renewable water resources. Almost one quarter of the world's inland water fish species are found in Latin America and the Caribbean region. Human pressures on freshwater resources and water pollution have adversely affected catches, with negative effects for local populations who depend on this source of protein for their nutrition. The eastern Atlantic coast of South America, the western coast of Central America, and the Caribbean are the worst affected shorelines in the region. Some of the most degraded ecosystems in Latin America and the Caribbean are mangroves, wetlands and coral reefs, resulting in the loss of valuable ecosystem services, such as sewage treatment by mangrove wetlands systems and the eco-tourism essential for many Caribbean economies. Such region is the world's richest genetic reservoir, for which ecosystems are vital as sources of new useful traits in food crops, active components for pharmaceutical products, potential industrial applications, and useful genes and their corresponding functions.[28]

Twenty four bird species breed in Antarctica, with the continent's five species of penguin making up 80 per cent of the entire bird biomass in most parts of Antarctica. Despite the extreme conditions in Antarctica, two species of flowering plants and more than 300 species of lichen, 75 species of moss, several fungi species, and around 360 species of terrestrial and freshwater algae exist in ice-free areas. The four populations of penguins that live and breed on the Antarctic continent are under escalating pressure. Antarctica and the Southern Ocean are home to a large number of different whales. The albatross is one of the world's most spectacular birds. They spend most of their time at sea in Australia and New Zealand and can live up to 60 years. Antarctic krill are small, prawn-like crustaceans and one of the world's most abundant multi-celled animals. Over 100 million birds breed around the rocky Antarctic coastline and offshore islands.[29]

Reasons for Loss of Biodiversity

The earth's biodiversity is in grave danger. In the present era, human beings are the most dangerous cause of destruction of the earth's biodiversity. Habitat destruction is a major cause for biodiversity loss. Habitat loss is caused by deforestation, overpopulation, pollution and global warming. Species can also be threatened by genetic pollution, uncontrolled hybridisation and gene swamping. Global warming is also becoming a major cause for loss of biodiversity.[30]

Extinction is a natural part of life on Earth. Over the history of the planet most of the species that ever existed, evolved and then gradually went extinct. Species go extinct because of natural shifts in the environment that take place over long periods of time, such as ice ages. Today, species are going extinct at an accelerated and dangerous rate, because of non-natural environmental changes caused by human activities. Some of the activities have direct effects on species and ecosystems, such as: Habitat loss/ degradation, Over exploitation, Spread of Non-native Species/ Diseases. Some human activities have indirect but wide-reaching effects on biodiversity, including: Climate change, Pollution.[31]

Today's threats to species and ecosystems are the greatest recorded in recent history and virtually all of them are caused by human mismanagement of biological resources often stimulated by misguided economic policies and faulty institutions. Increased insatiable demand for resources results to land use changes hence loss to genetic diversity, species reduction and increased ecosystem changes such as random population changes, disease outcrops, habitat fragmentation among others resulting in biodiversity losses. Chemical pollution is a threat to biodiversity. Species in habitats are increasingly being harmed by industrial activities and pollution from excessive use of agro-chemicals such as DDT, oil spills, acid precipitation etc.

Biodiversity Hotspots

Biodiversity hotspot is a biogeographic region with a significant reservoir of biodiversity that is under threat from humans. Only a small percentage of the total land area within biodiversity hotspots is now protected. Several international organisations are working in many ways to conserve biodiversity hotspots.[32] It is a biogeographic region that is both a significant reservoir of biodiversity and is threatened with destruction. The term biodiversity hotspot specifically refers to 25 biologically rich areas around the world that have lost at least 70 per cent of their original habitat. The remaining natural habitat in these biodiversity hotspots amounts to just 1.4 per cent of the land surface of the planet, yet supports nearly 60 per cent of the world's plant, bird, mammal, reptile, and amphibian species.[33]

There are 25 Biodiversity Hotspots in the world mostly located in the Tropics. The loose definition is that it is a biogeographic region with a significant reservoir of biodiversity that is under threat from humans. Norman Myers in 1988 had first identified ten tropical forest hotspots characterised both by exceptional levels of plant endemism and by serious levels of habitat loss, in one of his seminal papers. To qualify as a hotspot, a region must meet two strict criteria: it must contain at least 1,500 species of vascular plants as endemics, and it has to have lost at least 70 per cent of its original habitat.[34]

Biodiversity hotspots are areas that support natural ecosystems that are largely intact and where native species and communities associated with these ecosystems are well represented. There are areas with a high diversity of locally endemic species, which are species that are not found or are rarely found outside the hotspot. The identification of biodiversity hotspots was a two-stage process. The experts first identified areas with many endemic species. They then assessed each of these areas for current conservation pressures and the possibility of future threats to biodiversity. Areas with many endemic species where the levels of stress or future threat were considered to be high were identified as hotspots. The hotspots were identified to increase public awareness of the cost-effectiveness of strategic and timely action to conserve biodiversity. Conservation International, a non-profit environmental organisation based in Washington DC, has identified more than 30 biodiversity hotspots around the world, including one in the southwest of Western Australia.[35]

Increasing population pressure and over-exploitation of the biotic resources is taking their toll on biodiversity leading to its loss. Now, due to better infrastructure, contact of these areas with humans has increased. Temperature changes can also alter the water cycle and the availability of nitrogen and other nutrients. Basically, the temperature variations which are now occurring affect all parts of forest ecosystems, some more than others. The fragmentation of forests is a general consequence of the haphazard logging and agricultural land conversion which is occurring everywhere, but especially in tropical forests. Catastrophic events like floods, droughts, cyclones, volcanoes, fires, etc. cause severe biodiversity loss from time-to-time.[36] There are four main reasons why species are being threatened in these biodiversity hotspots:

1. ***Habitat destruction:*** Activities such as logging of wood, increased agriculture, increased human habitation has led to destruction of forests and pollution of rivers. These factors are causing species ranges to reduce and habitats to become choppy.
2. ***Resource mismanagement:*** Increased tourism without proper regulation has led to pollution and environmental degradation.
3. ***Poaching:*** Large mammals such as the tiger, rhinoceros and the elephant once faced the distinct possibility of complete extinction due to rampant hunting and poaching.
4. ***Climate change:*** It affects the existing biodiversity.[37]

India has two biodiversity hot spots, namely:

1. **Himalaya (Eastern Himalayas):** Phyto-geographically, the Eastern Himalaya forms a distinct floral region and comprises of Nepal, Bhutan, states of East and North-East India, and a contiguous sector of Yunnan province in

South-Western China. The area has long been recognised as a rich centre of primitive flowering plants and is popularly known as the 'Çradle of Speciation'. The area is also rich in wild relatives of plants of economic significance e.g. rice, banana, citrus, ginger, chilli, jute and sugarcane.

2. **Western Ghats**: The Western Ghats region, which is spread into six states of India, is considered to be one of the most important bio-geographic zones of India, as it is one of the richest centres of endemism. Due to varied topography and microclimatic regimes, some areas within the region are considered to be active zones of speciation. The region has 490 arborescent taxa, of which as many as 308 are endemic. About 1,500 endemic species of dicotyledonous plants are reported from the Western Ghats.[38]

Effects of Biodiversity Loss

Biological diversity is the resource upon which families, communities, nations and future generations depend. It is the link between all organisms on earth, binding each into an interdependent ecosystem, in which all species have their role. Biodiversity underpins the health of the planet and has a direct impact on all our lives.[39] Biodiversity in forests is very important to the ecosystem of that forest. Every ecosystem around the world is relient on biodiversity. Ecosystems in forests can be considered fragile because of the use the humans have for the forests. While it is evident that biodiversity is the heart of all ecosystems, it is often forgotten when decisions are made concerning the future of forests. Ecosystems are destroyed when biodiversity is forgotten because certain species are dependent on other species.[40]

Animals are being affected greatly by the decline of biodiversity. Mammals like polar bears and seals will be greatly affected by changes in biodiversity. Polar bears are depending on sea ice to hunt seals and to move from one area to another. Polar bears are unlikely to survive as a species if there is an almost complete loss of summer sea-ice cover, which is projected to occur before the end of this century by some climate models. Humans are causing an increase in the speed of animals becoming extinct. The World Wide Fund for Nature mentions that the "Earth is unable to keep up in the struggle to regenerate from the demands we place on it." People need to realise that they are harming the environment and that they are capable of reversing the effects.[41]

Losses in biodiversity in rainforests cause significant changes in ecosystem functioning. Species interactions are perhaps the most important aspect of ecosystem functioning. Species are interacting at some level with all the other organisms in the system, forming highly complex interlocking systems. Most of the research into the interrelationships between biodiversity and ecosystem functions has been done on plants, which affect soil processes, decomposition, water retention and many other ecosystem functions.[42]

The impact of biodiversity on any single ecosystem process is non-linear and saturating, such that change accelerates as biodiversity loss increases. Diverse communities are more productive because they contain key species that have a large influence on productivity, and differences in functional traits among organisms increase total resource capture. Loss of diversity across trophic levels has the potential to influence ecosystem functions even more strongly than diversity loss within trophic levels. Much work has shown that food web interactions are key mediators of ecosystem functioning, and that loss of higher consumers can cascade through a food web to influence plant biomass. Functional traits of organisms have large impacts on the magnitude of ecosystem functions, which give rise to a wide range of plausible impacts of extinction on ecosystem function.[43]

Habitat fragmentation is the loss and subdivision of a habitat and the corresponding increase in other habitats in the landscape. Habitat fragmentation not only affects species, but also affects the processes that drive biodiversity. Poor agricultural practices also degrade soil quality and promote the loss of topsoil. Furthermore, agriculture has resulted in local reductions and extirpations of fauna associated with agricultural lands. After habitat loss, overharvesting has had the greatest effect on biodiversity. In fact, overharvesting and habitat loss often occur simultaneously, as removal of an organism from its environment can have irreversible impacts on the environment itself.[44]

The importance of stability in community ecology is clear. An unstable ecosystem will be more likely to lose species. If there is indeed a link between diversity and stability, it is likely that losses of diversity could feedback on themselves, causing even more losses of species. Productivity has a less clear importance in community ecology. Beyond the value biodiversity has in regulating and stabilising ecosystem processes, there are direct economic consequences of losing diversity in certain ecosystems and in the world as a whole. Losing species means losing potential foods, medicines, industrial products, and tourism, all of which have a direct economic effect on people's lives.[45]

Conservation of Biodiversity

Biodiversity as genetic species and as intact ecosystems can be best preserved in-situ by setting aside an adequate representation of wilderness as Protected Areas. These include national parks and wildlife sanctuaries which receive protection from governmental and international agencies.[46] Conservation of biological diversity and sustainable use of its components came into the limelight in 1972. In 1973, UNEP identified conservation of biodiversity as a priority area. There were negotiations for a legally binding instrument to address biological diversity and its loss to enhance fairness and equity in sharing of the benefits of biodiversity. This led to the opening of the Convention on Biological Diversity in 1992; Rio de Janeiro under the United Nations Conference on Environment and Development/Earth Summit.[47]

The provision of ecosystem services in the future will be influenced by multiple and interacting environmental change drivers. There is more than one way to conserve biodiversity. In situ and ex situ are the Latin words for on-site and offsite. In situ conservation occurs in nature, for instance in a protected area, traditional farm, nature reserve or national park. Ex-situ conservation occurs when a specimen of a species is set in artificial conditions such as in a zoo or a botanical garden. In situ conservation helps to guarantee the survival of a species in its natural habitat. While protected areas and parks remain a cornerstone for biodiversity conservation worldwide, conservation efforts are not limited to these places. Large productive landscapes with no specific conservation objective can contain lots of biodiversity while offering food, shelter and other ecosystem services for humanity.[48]

International biodiversity conventions and conservation organisations are: African Convention on Conservation of nature and natural resources; The Ramsar Convention on Wetlands of international importance; International Union for the Conservation of nature (World Conservation Union); Convention on International trade for endangered species (CITES); International Convention for the Protection on birds; International Board for Plant genetic resources; World Resources Institute; World Wide Fund for Nature; Convention on Conservation of migratory species of wild animals; International Convention for the Regulation of whaling; and UNESCO programme on Man and biosphere.[49]

There are several ways in which ecosystem services can be measured and monitored. Provisioning services, such as food or drinking water production, are usually monitored in a very straightforward way through their produced quantities. Valuation of ecosystem services aims to better inform decision-making, ensuring that policy appraisals more comprehensively take into account costs and benefits related to the natural environment. Valuing ecosystem services in monetary terms is often difficult and controversial, particularly for many regulating and supporting services for which the benefits to people are not direct and easily recognised.[50]

The conservation of intrinsic and utilitarian values associated with biodiversity will require the cooperation of private landowners, with participation enhanced through incentive mechanisms. There are three major reasons why the role of private landowners and incentives are important: the location of listed and at-risk species, the need for conservation tools that are complementary to regulation and the lack of markets for public goods like species and habitat conservation. The conservation of intrinsic and utilitarian values associated with biodiversity will require the cooperation of private landowners, with participation enhanced through incentive mechanisms. There are three major reasons why the role of private landowners and incentives are important: the location of listed and at-risk species, the need for conservation tools that are complementary to regulation and the lack of markets for public goods like species and habitat conservation.[51]

Formal policies and programmes for conservation and sustainable utilisation of biodiversity resources date back to several decades. The concept of environmental protection is enshrined in the Indian constitution in Articles 48a and 51a (g). Major Central Acts relevant to biodiversity include: Environment Protection Act, 1986; Fisheries Act, 1897; Forest Act, 1927; Forest (Conservation) Act, 1980; Wildlife (Protection) Act 1972 and Wildlife (Protection) Amendment Act 1991. The various Central

Acts are supported by a number of state laws and statutes concerning forests and other natural resources. The policies and strategies directly relevant to biodiversity include National Forest Policy amended in 1988, National Conservation Strategy and Policy Statement for Environment and Sustainable Development, National Agricultural Policy, National Land Use Policy, National Fisheries Policy, National Policy and Action Strategy on Biodiversity, National Wildlife Action Plan and Environmental Action Plan.[52]

References

1. Economic indicator (2015) (Available at https://en.wikipedia.org/wiki/Ecological_indicator)
2. Robert Costello, On the Web: Measuring Biodiversity across North America, (Available at http://www.mnh.si.edu/mna/Resources/BiodiversityLessonPlan.pdf)
3. Biodiversity (2015) (Available at https://en.wikipedia.org/wiki/Biodiversity)
4. http://www.unep.org/geo/geo4/report/05_Biodiversity.pdf
5. Dilip Surkar, Conserving Biodiversity in India (Available at http://www.vigyanprasar.gov.in/Radioserials/Conserving_Biodiversity2.pdf)
6. Biodiversity (2015) (Available at https://simple.wikipedia.org/wiki/Biodiversity)
7. Dr Nitasha Malhotra, The importance of biodiversity (Available at http://ags.geography.du.ac.in/Study%20Materials_files/Nitasha%20Malhotra_KNC.pdf)
8. What is Biodiversity? (Available at http://www.ecokids.ca/dev/eco_info/topics/biodiversity/index.cfm)
9. Climate Change and Biodiversity, Available at https://www.cbd.int/climate/
10. Why biodiversity is is important? (Available at http://www.greenschoolsireland.org/biodiversity/why-is-biodiversity-important.364.html)
11. What is biodiversity? (Available at http://www.conserve-energy-future.com/what-is-biodiversity.php)
12. See https://www.cbd.int/agro/importance.shtml
13. Why is biodiversity important? (Available at http://www.pc.gc.ca/eng/pn-np/ns/cbreton/natcul/natcul1/d/iii.aspx)
14. Biodiversity and conservation, chapter 15 (Available at http://www.ncert.nic.in/ncerts/l/lebo115.pdf)
15. See http://www.cnhp.colostate.edu/biodiversity.asp
16. Biodiversity and its conservation, unit 4 (Available at http://mait4us.weebly.com/uploads/9/3/5/9/9359206/unit4.pdf)
17. *Ibid.*
18. State of biodiversity in Africa (Available at https://www.cbd.int/iyb/doc/celebrations/iyb-egypt-state-of-biodiversity-in-africa.pdf)
19. State of biodiversity in Asia and Pacific (Available at http://www.unep.org/delc/Portals/119/regional%20brief%20for%20Asia%20and%20Pacific.pdf)
20. Suneetha M. Subramanian, Alexandros Gasparatos, Ademola K. Braimoh and Wendy Elliott (2011), Unraveling the drivers of Southeast Asia's

biodiversity loss (Available at http://unu.edu/publications/articles/unraveling-the-drivers-of-southeast-asia-biodiversity-loss.html#info)

21. Conservation of biodiversity and ecosystem services by REDD+ project in India (Available at http://www.moef.nic.in/assets/redd-bk4.pdf)
22. Grade 12 Biology, Unit 5: Conservation of Biodiversity (Available at http://www.edu.gov.mb.ca/k12/cur/science/found/gr12_bio/unit5.pdf)
23. Threat to European biodiversity 'as serious as climate change (Available at http://www.theguardian.com/environment/2009/apr/24/europe-biodiversity-loss)
24. Trends in Biodiversity in Europe and the Impact of Land-use Change (Available at https://www.pik-potsdam.de/news/public-events/archiv/alter-net/former-ss/2007/02-09.2007/watt/literature/trends-in-biodiversity-in-europe_proof.pdf)
25. Australia's biodiversity (Available at http://www.abs.gov.au/AUSSTATS/abs@.nsf/Lookup/1301.0Feature+Article12009 %E2%80%9310)
26. See http://www.cec.org/Page.asp?PageID=122&ContentID= 1911&SiteNodeID=361
27. See http://www.actionbioscience.org/biodiversity/walsh.html
28. State of biodiversity in Latin America and Caribbean (Available at http://www.unep.org/delc/Portals/119/LatinAmerica_ StateofBiodiv.pdf)
29. http://www.wwf.org.au/our_work/saving_the_natural_ world/oceans_and_marine/priority_ocean_places/antarctica_and_southern_ocean/biodiversity/
30. What is biodiversity? (Available at http://www.conserve-energy-future.com/what-is-biodiversity.php)
31. What is Biodiversity? (Available at http://www.nwf.org/Wildlife/Wildlife-Conservation/Biodiversity.aspx)
32. Biodiversity Hotspots (Available at https://en.wikipedia.org/wiki/Biodiversity_hotspot)
33. http://www.sciencedaily.com/terms/biodiversity_hotspot.htm
34. Biodiversity hotspots (Available at http://www.gktoday.in/biodiversity-hotspots/)
35. http://www.environment.gov.au/biodiversity/conservation/hotspots
36. Puja Mondal, Biodiversity Hotspots: Meaning and Hotspots found in India (Available at http://www.yourarticlelibrary. com/biodiversity/biodiversity-hotspots-meaning-and-hotspots-found-in-india/30153/)
37. Biodiversity hotspots in India (Available at http://www.biodiversityofindia.org/index.php?title=Biodiversity_ hotspots_in_India)
38. Biodiversity hotspots in India (Available at http://www.gktoday.in/biodiversity-hotspots-in-india/)
39. See http://wwf.panda.org/about_our_earth/biodiversity/biodiversity_and_you/
40. Role of biodiversity in Asian forest (Available at http://www4.ncsu.edu/~mnhutche/World%20Forestry/)
41. See http://blogs.longwood.edu/biodiversity/
42. Consequence of biodiversity loss (Available at http://www.rainforestconservation.org/rainforest-primer/2-biodiversity/g-recent-losses-in-biodiversity/4-consequences-of-biodiversity-loss/)
43. Biodiversity loss and its impact on humanity (Available at http://snre.umich.edu/cardinale/wp-content/uploads/2012/04/Cardinale-et-al-Nature-2012.pdf)
44. See http://redpath-museum.mcgill.ca/Qbp/3.Conservation/impacts.htm

45. Ecological effects of biodiversity (Available at https://en.wikipedia.org/wiki/Ecological_effects_of_biodiversity)
46. Dr Nitasha Malhotra, The importance of biodiversity (Available at http://ags.geography.du.ac.in/Study%20Materials_files/Nitasha%20Malhotra_KNC.pdf)
47. Thecla M. Mutia, Biodiversity conservation (Available at http://www.os.is/gogn/unu-gtp-sc/UNU-GTP-SC-10-0805b.pdf)
48. Biodiversity conservation and sustainability development (Available at http://www.fao.org/docrep/017/i3157e/i3157e10.pdf)
49. Thecla M. Mutia, Biodiversity conservation (Available at http://www.os.is/gogn/unu-gtp-sc/UNU-GTP-SC-10-0805b.pdf)
50. Paula A. Harrison and the RUBICODE consortium, Conservation of Biodiversity and Ecosystem Services in Europe: From Threat to Action (Available at http://www.rubicode.net/rubicode/RUBICODE_Brochure_Final.pdf)
51. Incentives for Biodiversity Conservation: An Ecological and Economic Assessment (Available at http://www.defenders.org/publications/incentives_for_biodiversity_conservation.pdf)
52. Conserving Biodiversity in India (Available at http://www.vigyanprasar.gov.in/Radioserials/Conserving_ Biodiversity2.pdf)

2

Climate Change

"If we each take responsibility in shifting our own behaviour, we can trigger the type of change that is necessary to achieve sustainability for our race or this planet. We change our planet, our environment, our humanity every day, every year, every decade, and every millennia."

– Yehuda Berg

Climate is the long-term pattern of weather in a particular area. The climate of a location is affected by its latitude, terrain, and altitude, as well as nearby water bodies and their currents. Climates can be classified according to the average and the typical ranges of different variables, most commonly temperature and precipitation. The Intergovernmental Panel on Climate Change glossary definition is as follows: Climate in a narrow sense is usually defined as the average weather, or more rigorously, as the statistical description in terms of the mean and variability of relevant quantities over a period ranging from months to thousands or millions of years. The classical period is 30 years, as defined by the World Meteorological Organisation. These quantities are most often surface variables such as temperature, precipitation, and wind. Climate in a wider sense is the state, including a statistical description, of the climate system.[1]

Different parts of the world have different climates. Some parts of the world are hot and rainy nearly every day. They have a tropical wet climate. Others are cold and snow-covered most of the year. A region's climate is something like a person's personality. There are three climate types in the tropical group: tropical wet; tropical monsoon; and tropical wet and dry. Regions lying within the dry climate group occur where precipitation is low, including cool, high latitudes. Regions with mild and continental climates are also called temperate regions. Both climate types have distinct cold seasons. Areas with continental climates have colder winters, longer-lasting snow, and shorter growing seasons. The two polar climate types, tundra and ice cap, lie within the Arctic and Antarctic Circles near the North and South Poles. Climate does not change from day to day like weather, but it does change over time. Climate change can happen for many reasons.[2]

What is Climate Change?

Climate change is the variation in global or regional climates over time. It reflects changes in the variability or average state of the atmosphere over time scales ranging from decades to millions of years. These changes can be caused by processes internal to the Earth, external forces or, more recently, human activities. Earth has undergone periodic climate shifts in the past, including four major ice ages. These consisting of glacial periods where conditions are colder than normal, separated by interglacial periods.[3]

It is a change in the statistical distribution of weather patterns when that change lasts for an extended period of time. It may refer to a change in average weather conditions, or in the time variation of weather around longer-term average conditions. It is caused by factors such as biotic processes, variations in solar radiation received by Earth, plate tectonics, and volcanic eruptions.[4]

Causes of Climate Change

Climate change is a long-term shift in weather conditions identified by changes in temperature, precipitation, winds, and other indicators. It can involve both changes in average conditions and changes in variability, including, for example, extreme events. Factors that cause climate change can be divided into two categories–those related to natural processes and those related to human activity. In addition to natural causes of climate change, changes internal to the climate system, such as variations in ocean currents or atmospheric circulation, can also influence the climate for short periods of time.[5]

Earth's temperature depends on the balance between energy entering and leaving the planet's system. Many factors, both natural and human, can cause changes in Earth's energy balance, including: Changes in the greenhouse effect, which affects the amount of heat retained by Earth's atmosphere; Variations in the sun's energy reaching Earth; and Changes in the reflectivity of Earth's atmosphere and surface.[6]

There are a number of natural factors responsible for climate change. Some of the more prominent ones are continental drift, volcanoes, ocean currents, the earth's tilt, and comets and meteorites. When a volcano erupts it throws out large volumes of sulphur dioxide, water vapour, dust, and ash into the atmosphere. The gases and dust particles partially block the incoming rays of the sun, leading to cooling. Sulphur dioxide combines with water to form tiny droplets of sulphuric acid. Changes in the tilt of the earth can affect the severity of the seasons - more tilt means warmer summers and colder winters; less tilt means cooler summers and milder winters.[7]

Humans are increasingly influencing the climate and the earth's temperature by burning fossil fuels, cutting down rainforests and farming livestock. This adds enormous amounts of greenhouse gases to those naturally occurring in the atmosphere, increasing the greenhouse effect and global warming. CO_2 is the greenhouse gas most commonly produced by human activities and it is responsible for 64 per cent of man-made global warming. Other greenhouse gases are emitted in smaller quantities, but they trap heat far more effectively than CO_2 and in some cases are thousands of times stronger. Methane is responsible for 17 per cent of man-made global warming, nitrous oxide for six per cent.[8]

Effects of Climate Change

Global climate change has already had observable effects on the environment. Glaciers have shrunk, ice on rivers and lakes is breaking up earlier, plant and animal ranges have shifted and trees are flowering sooner. Scientists have high confidence that global temperatures will continue to rise for decades to come, largely due to greenhouse gasses produced by human activities.[9]

Climate change is already beginning to transform life on Earth. Around the globe, seasons are shifting, temperatures are climbing and sea levels are rising.[10] The most vulnerable ecosystems include coastal ecosystems, alpine areas, rainforests, fragmented terrestrial ecosystems and areas vulnerable to fire or low freshwater availability.

Climate change may lead to dramatic increases in prevalence of a variety of infectious diseases. Though many infectious diseases are affected by changes in climate, vector-borne diseases, such as malaria, dengue fever and leishmaniasis, present the strongest causal relationship. Increased precipitation can increase mosquito population indirectly by expanding larval habitat and food supply. Malaria kills approximately 300,000 children annually, poses an imminent threat through temperature increase. Climate change may dramatically impact habitat loss, for example, arid conditions may cause the collapse of rainforests, as has occurred in the past.

Climate change causes displacement of people in several ways, the most obvious and dramatic being through the increased number and severity of weather-related disasters which destroy homes and habitats causing people to seek shelter or livelihoods elsewhere. Effects of climate change such as desertification and rising sea levels gradually erode livelihood and force communities to abandon traditional homelands for more accommodating environments. Individual and social factors such as gender, age, education, ethnicity, geography and language lead to differential vulnerability and capacity to adapt to the effects of climate change.[11]

Global warming is likely to be the greatest cause of species extinctions this century. The Intergovernmental Panel on Climate Change says a 1.5°C average rise may put 20-30 per cent of species at risk. If the planet warms by more than 3°C, most ecosystems will struggle. Climate change is having serious and unpredictable impacts on the world's water systems through more flooding and droughts. The Intergovernmental Panel on Climate Change has warned that: The impacts of climate change in the polar regions over the next 100 years will exceed impacts forecast for other regions, and will have globally significant consequences. For endangered species such as orangutans in Borneo and Indonesia, which are already at risk because of deforestation, forest conversion and illegal hunting – one of the first effects of climate change is likely to be food shortages caused by unusual rainfall patterns.[12]

The changing climate impacts society and ecosystems in a broad variety of ways. For example, climate change can increase or decrease rainfall, influence agricultural crop yields, affect human health, cause changes to forests and other ecosystems, or even impact our energy supply.[13] The impacts of climate change on health will depend on many factors. These factors include the effectiveness of a community's public health and safety systems to address or prepare for the risk and the behaviour, age, gender, and economic status of individuals affected. Impacts will likely vary by region, the sensitivity of populations, the extent and length of exposure to climate change impacts, and society's ability to adapt to change. Climate change will likely lead to more frequent, more severe, and longer heat waves in the summer as well as less severe cold spells in the winter.[14]

Climate change is already having a significant impact on ecosystems, economies and communities. Rising average temperatures do not simply mean balmier winters. Some regions will experience more extreme heat while others may cool slightly. Flooding, drought and intense summer heat could result. Violent storms and other extreme weather events could result from the increased energy stored in our warming atmosphere. One of the most serious impacts of climate change is how it will affect water resources around the world.[15] Changes in nature have serious implications for people and our economic system. The insurance industry estimates the potential economic damage, caused by the impacts of global warming, to be hundreds of billions of dollars each year.

Climate change will have a significant impact on food availability, food accessibility, food utilisation and food systems stability in many parts of the world. Climate change poses a significant risk of increased crop failure, loss of livestock and will impact on local food security. Climate change will have major and unpredictable effects on the world's water systems, including an increase in floods and droughts. Extremes in droughts and flooding will become more common, causing displacement and conflict. Less fresh water means less agriculture, food and income.[16] Rapid climate change and accelerating biodiversity loss risks human security.[17]

The Antarctic climate has changed throughout time and on a wide range of temporal scales. Southern Ocean bottom temperatures have changed dramatically over the past 60 Ma, as has been demonstrated by palaeotemperature studies of benthic foraminifera isolated from deep-sea sediment cores. Demonstrating long-term changes in the biodiversity of marine systems is hindered by the paucity of data and the overwhelming effects of man's activities, even in Antarctica. Important insights into the potential effects of future climate change come from examining historical changes in the fauna, and from comparison of the two Polar Regions. To understand the impact of climate change on the Antarctic ecosystem as a whole, one needs to understand the structure of the food web.[18]

Deforestation

Deforestation is the removal of a forest or stand of trees where the land is thereafter converted to a non-forest use. It occurs for many reasons: trees are cut down to be used or sold as fuel or timber, while cleared land is used as pasture for livestock, plantations of commodities and settlements. According to the United Nations Framework Convention on Climate Change secretariat, the overwhelming direct cause of it is agriculture. Subsistence farming is responsible for 48 per cent of deforestation; commercial agriculture is responsible for 32 per cent of deforestation; logging is responsible for 14 per cent of deforestation and fuel wood removals make up five per cent of deforestation.

Deforestation is one of the major causes to the environmental degradation which is affected by the agents like small farmers, ranches, loggers and plantation companies. Conversion of forests to agricultural land to feed growing needs of people. Since industrialisation and urbanisation needs land to grow, so major amount of forest lands are cut for that purpose. For building big dams, large scale devastation of forests takes place which breaks the natural ecological balance of the region. Overgrazing occurs when plants are exposed to intensive grazing for extended periods of time, or without sufficient recovery periods. Overgrazing reduces the usefulness, productivity, and biodiversity of the land and is one cause of desertification and erosion.[19]

Deforestation is a contributor to global warming, and is often cited as one of the major causes of the enhanced greenhouse effect. Tropical deforestation is responsible for approximately 20 per cent of world greenhouse gas emissions. In deforested areas, the land heats up faster and reach a higher temperature, leading to localised upward motions that enhance the formation of clouds and ultimately produce more rainfall. The water cycle is affected by deforestation. Deforestation reduces the content of water in the soil and groundwater as well as atmospheric moisture. The dry soil leads to lower water intake for the trees to extract. It reduces soil cohesion, so that erosion, flooding and landslides ensue. Deforestation generally increases rates of soil erosion, by increasing the amount of runoff and reducing the protection of the soil from tree litter.[20] It on a human scale results in decline in biodiversity. The forest products industry is a large part of the economy in both developed and developing countries.[21]

In recent history, large-scale destruction of the forests began with the British who wished to utilise the timber and the natural resources for the expansion and continuation of the empire. Vast tracks of forest were chopped to create the vast railway network. The other major cause of deforestation immediately after independence was agricultural expansion, often state-sponsored. Much of the rich moist deciduous forests of the humid Terai region in northern Uttar Pradesh, for example, were cleared to provide land to immigrants from the newly created Pakistan.[22]

Green House Gases

The greenhouse effect is the process by which radiation from a planet's atmosphere warms the planet's surface to a temperature above what it would be in the absence of its atmosphere. Earth's natural greenhouse effect is critical to supporting life. Human activities, primarily the burning of fossil fuels and clearing of forests, have intensified the natural greenhouse effect, causing global warming. The existence of the greenhouse effect was argued for by Joseph Fourier in 1824. The argument and the evidence was further strengthened by Claude Pouillet in 1827 and 1838, and reasoned from experimental observations by John Tyndall in 1859. The effect was more fully quantified by Svante Arrhenius in 1896. By their percentage contribution to the greenhouse effect on Earth the four major gases are: water vapour, 36–70 per cent; carbon dioxide, 9–26 per cent; methane, 4–9 per cent; and ozone, 3–7 per cent.[23]

The exchange of incoming and outgoing radiation that warms the Earth is often referred to as the greenhouse effect because a greenhouse works in much the same way. Incoming UV radiation easily passes through the glass walls of a greenhouse and is absorbed by the plants and hard surfaces inside. Weaker IR radiation, however, has difficulty passing through the glass walls and is trapped inside, thus warming the greenhouse. Carbon dioxide and other greenhouse gases act like a blanket, absorbing IR radiation and preventing it from escaping into outer space. The net effect is the gradual heating of Earth's atmosphere and surface, a process known as global warming.[24]

Greenhouse gas is any gaseous compound in the atmosphere that is capable of absorbing infrared radiation, thereby trapping and holding heat in the atmosphere. By increasing the heat in the atmosphere, greenhouse gases are responsible for the greenhouse effect, which ultimately leads to global warming. The gases in the atmosphere that absorb radiation are known as "greenhouse gases" because they are largely responsible for the greenhouse effect. The greenhouse effect, in turn, is one of the leading causes of global warming. The most significant greenhouse gases are water vapour, carbon dioxide, methane and nitrous oxide, according to the Environmental Protection Agency. Fluorinated gases including hydrofluorocarbons, per fluorocarbons and sulphur hexafluoride, are created during industrial processes and are also considered greenhouse gases. Chlorofluorocarbons, once used as refrigerants and aerosol propellants until they were phased out by international agreement, are also greenhouse gases.[25]

Greenhouse gases absorb energy allowing less heat to escape back to space, and 'trapping' it in the lower atmosphere. Atmospheric concentrations of both the natural and man-made gases have been rising over the last few centuries due to the industrial revolution. As the global population has increased and our reliance on fossil fuels has been firmly solidified, so emissions of these gases have risen.[26]

Heat Wave

Heat wave is a prolonged period of excessively hot weather, which may be accompanied by high humidity, especially in oceanic climate countries. A definition based on Frich et al.'s, Heat Wave Duration Index is that a heat wave occurs when the daily maximum temperature of more than five consecutive days exceeds the average maximum temperature by 5°C (9°F), the normal period being 1961–1990. Heat waves form when high pressure aloft strengthens and remains over a region for several days up to several weeks. Global warming boosts the probability of extreme weather events, like heat waves, far more than it boosts more moderate events.[27]

Heat waves typically occur between March and June, and in some rare cases even extend till July. The extreme temperatures and resultant atmospheric conditions adversely affect people living in these regions as they cause physiological stress, sometimes resulting in death. The health impacts of Heat Waves typically involve dehydration, heat cramps, heat exhaustion and/or heat stroke.[28] The cumulative effect of the persistent heat will prove extra dangerous for residents and animals who do not find ways to keep cool. Residents are reminded to drink plenty of water, wear light clothing and never leave kids or pets unattended in a sealed car. Strenuous activities should be avoided during the midday and afternoon hours, the hottest times of the day. If that is not possible, be sure to take frequent breaks.[29]

Global Warming

Global warming and climate change are terms for the observed century-scale rise in the average temperature of the Earth's climate system and its related effects. Scientific understanding of global warming is increasing. The Intergovernmental Panel on Climate Change reported in 2014 that scientists were more than 95 per cent certain that most of global warming is caused by increasing concentrations of greenhouse gases and other human activities.[30] It is the increase of Earth's average surface temperature due to effect of greenhouse gases, such as carbon dioxide emissions from burning fossil fuels or from deforestation, which trap heat that would otherwise escape from Earth. This is a type of greenhouse effect.[31]

Global warming is the term used to describe a gradual increase in the average temperature of the Earth's atmosphere and its oceans, a change that is believed to be permanently changing the Earth's climate.[32] It is primarily a problem of too much carbon dioxide in the atmosphere which acts as a blanket, trapping heat and warming the plane. Certain waste management and agricultural practices aggravate the problem by releasing other potent global warming gases, such as methane and nitrous oxide.[33] The effects of global warming are the environmental and social changes caused by human emissions of greenhouse gases.

Possible Solutions

Climate change is the most severe *problem* we are facing today, it is more serious even than the threat of terrorism. Uses of non-renewable resources may be burning of coal, oil and, eventually, natural gas. This is perhaps the most daunting challenge as denizens of richer nations literally eat, wear, work, play and even sleep on the products made from such fossilised sunshine. There are no perfect solutions for reducing dependence on fossil fuels. For example, carbon neutral biofuels can drive up the price of food and lead to forest destruction, and while nuclear power does not emit greenhouse gases, it may be a way. Uses of renewable resources should be increase. Transportation is the leading source of greenhouse gas emissions. One way to dramatically curtail transportation fuel needs is to move closer to work, use mass transit, or switch to walking, cycling or some other mode of transport that does not require anything other than human energy.

The easiest way to cut back on greenhouse gas emissions is simply to buy less stuff. Citizens of many developed countries are profligate wasters of energy, whether by speeding in a gas-guzzling sport-utility vehicle or leaving the lights on when not in a room. More efficient refrigerators, airconditioners and other appliances can be use. Every year, 33 million acres of forests are cut down. Timber harvesting in the tropics alone contributes 1.5 billion metric tonnes of carbon to the atmosphere. That represents 20 per cent of human-made greenhouse gas emissions and a source that could be avoided relatively easily. There should be aforestation.[34]

Many and varied solutions to climate change have been proposed, including individual frugality, energy conservation measures, renewable energy, and carbon sequestration. Emission of greenhouse gases may be reducing. Carbon dioxide is mostly emitted from the consumption of energy from fossil fuels, changing the way we produce and use energy is our starting point in trying to reduce emissions.[35] The European Union has long led the way, implementing a cap and trade system in 2005. Australia just recently set a carbon tax and plans to join the EU emissions trading market. In the USA, nine northeastern states have a modest cap and trade system, and California is poised to implement a much more ambitious system in 2013. British Columbia has implemented a successful carbon tax, but the USA and Canada do not have national carbon pricing systems.[36]

References

1. Climate (Available at https://en.wikipedia.org/wiki/Climate)
2. See http://education.nationalgeographic.com/encyclopedia/climate/
3. Climate (Available at https://en.wikipedia.org/wiki/Climate)
4. Climate change (Available at https://en.wikipedia.org/wiki/Climate_change)
5. Causes of Climate Change (Available at http://www.climatechange.gc.ca/default.asp?lang=en&n=65CD73F4-1)
6. Causes of climate change (Available at http://www.epa.gov/climatechange/science/causes.html)
7. Causes of climate change (Available at http://edugreen.teri.res.in/explore/climate/causes.htm)
8. Causes of climate change (Available at http://ec.europa.eu/clima/change/causes/index_en.htm)
9. The current and future consequences of global change (Available at http://climate.nasa.gov/effects/)
10. See http://www.nature.org/ourinitiatives/urgentissues/global-warming-climate-change/threats-impacts/
11. Effects of global warming on humans (Available at https://en.wikipedia.org/wiki/Effects_of_global_warming_ on_humans)
12. The effects of climate change (Available at http://www.wwf.org.uk/what_we_do/tackling_climate_change/impacts_of_climate_change/)
13. Climate Change Impacts and Adapting to Change (Available at http://www.epa.gov/climatechange/impacts-adaptation/)
14. Human Health Impacts (Available at http://www.epa.gov/climatechange/impacts-adaptation/health.html)
15. See http://www.davidsuzuki.org/issues/climate-change/science/impacts/impacts-of-climate-change/
16. See http://wwf.panda.org/about_our_earth/aboutcc/problems/
17. See http://www.globalissues.org/article/172/climate-change-affects-biodiversity

18. Rhys E. Green, Mike Harley, Lera Miles, Jorn Scharlemann, Andrew Watkinson and Olly Watts, Global Climate Change and Biodiversity, Available at http://jncc.defra.gov.uk/pdf/MJHGlobalclimatechange_14.08.03.pdf
19. Puja Mondal, Deforestation in India: Causes and Consequences of Deforestation in India (Available at http://www.yourarticlelibrary.com/environment/deforestation/deforestation-in-india-causes-and-consequences-of-deforestation-in-india/30096/)
20. See http://www.globalchange.umich.edu/globalchange2/current/lectures/deforest/deforest.html
21. *Ibid.*
22. Deforestation in India: Overview and proposed case studies (Available at http://enviroscope.iges.or.jp/modules/envirolib/upload/1508/attach/1ws-9-pankaji.pdf)
23. Greenhouse effect (Available at https://en.wikipedia.org/wiki/Greenhouse_effect)
24. Marc Lallanila (2015), What is greenhouse gas effects (Available at http://www.livescience.com/37743-greenhouse-effect.html)
25. Marc Lallanila (2015), Greenhouse Gas Emissions: Causes andSources (Available at http://www.livescience.com/37821-greenhouse-gases.html)
26. See https://www.ncdc.noaa.gov/monitoring-references/faq/greenhouse-gases.php
27. Heat wave (Available at https://en.wikipedia.org/wiki/Heat_wave)
28. From official website of National Disaster Management Authority.
29. Eric Leister (2015), Dangerous Heat Wave from Poland to Ukraine and Romania This Week (Available at http://www.accuweather.com/en/weather-news/dangerous-heat-wave-from-polan/51607149)
30. Global warming (Available at https://en.wikipedia.org/wiki/Global_warming)
31. See http://www.nmsea.org/Curriculum/Primer/Global_ Warming/fossil_fuels_and_global_warming.htm
32. See http://www.livescience.com/topics/global-warming/
33. Global warming causes (Available at http://www.climatehotmap.org/about/global-warming-causes.html)
34. David Biello (2007), 10 Solutions for Climate Change (Available at http://www.scientificamerican.com/article/10-solutions-for-climate-change/)
35. Climate Change Solutions (Available at http://www. ourclimate.net/)
36. See http://www.skepticalscience.com/solving-climate-problem-step-by-step.html

3

Ozone Depletion

"The only way to save a rhinoceros is to save the environment in which it lives, because there's a mutual dependency between it and millions of other species of both animals and plants."

–David Attenborough

Ozone is made up of oxygen and is produced naturally in the atmosphere. As the presence of ozone gets reduced in the atmosphere, it causes the ozone layer to get thinner and thinner. The more ozone layer gets thin, the bigger gets the size of ozone hole. Ozone layer is a deep layer in earth's atmosphere that contains ozone which is a naturally occurring molecule containing three oxygen atoms. These ozone molecules form a gaseous layer in the Earth's upper atmosphere called stratosphere. This lower region of stratosphere containing relatively higher concentration of ozone is called Ozonosphere. The ozonosphere is found 15-35 km (9 to 22 miles) above the surface of the earth. The ozone layer was discovered in 1913 by the French physicists Charles Fabry and Henri Buisson. The ozone layer has the capability to absorb almost 97-99 per cent of the harmful ultraviolet radiations that sun emit and which can produce long-term devastating effects on humans beings as well as plants and animals.[1]

Ozone is constantly produced and destroyed in a natural cycle. The overall amount of ozone is essentially stable.

This balance can be thought of as a stream's depth at a particular location. Although individual water molecules are moving past the observer, the total depth remains constant.[2] In 1969, Dutch chemist Paul Crutzen published a paper that described the major nitrogen oxide catalytic cycle affecting ozone levels. Crutzen demonstrated that nitrogen oxides can react with free oxygen atoms, thus slowing the creation of ozone (O_3), and can also decompose ozone into nitrogen dioxide (NO_2) and oxygen gas (O_2).[3]

In the stratosphere ozone is produced as a result of the dissociation of oxygen molecule by the intense UV component of the sunshine. Stratospheric ozone is gradually broken down to O and O_2 by the absorption of short wavelength UV radiations, but are created simultaneously when this atomic oxygen combines with other oxygen molecules, thus there exists equilibrium between the rates of creation and destruction. The growing body of scientific evidence which is clear that this equilibrium was disturbed by the introduction of man made substances that increase the rate of conversion of O_3 back to O_2.[4]

What is Ozone Depletion?

During the last several decades, human activities have resulted in considerable reduction in the ozone layer of the atmosphere. Ozone depletion occurs when destruction of the stratospheric ozone is more than the production of the molecule. The scientists have observed reduction in stratospheric ozone since early 1970s. It is found to be more prominent in Polar Regions.[5] Severe depletion creates the so-called ozone hole that can be seen in images of total Antarctic ozone made using satellite observations. In most years the maximum area of the ozone hole is bigger than the area of the Antarctic continent itself.

Identification of Ozone Hole

The Antarctic ozone hole is an area of the Antarctic stratosphere in which the recent ozone levels have dropped to as low as 33 per cent of their pre-1975 values. The ozone hole occurs during the Antarctic spring, from September to early December, as strong westerly winds start to circulate around the continent and create an atmospheric container.[6] In 1985, a group of scientists made an unsettling discovery: a marked decrease in stratospheric ozone over the South Pole, in the

Antarctic. The depletion appeared during the southern hemisphere's spring (October and November) and then filled in. Soon after the Antarctic hole was found, Canadian scientists discovered that the ozone layer above the Arctic is also thinning significantly.[7]

The British Antarctic Survey announced the discovery of a massive hole in the ozone over Antarctica. The British had been monitoring stratospheric O_3 over Antarctica for decades, used ground-based detectors. They had first noticed a puzzling seasonal drop in O_3 levels each spring since 1977. The team reported that each October (Antarctic spring), O_3 levels dropped by as much as 40 per cent below 1960's baseline levels before recovering by November.[8] The stratospheric ozone layer forms a thin shield in the upper atmosphere, protecting life on Earth from the sun's ultraviolet rays. It has been called the Earth's sunscreen.

Causes of Ozone Depletion

Scientific evidence indicates that stratospheric ozone is being destroyed by a group of manufactured chemicals, containing chlorine and/or bromine. These chemicals are called ozone-depleting substances (ODS). The main ODS are chlorofluorocarbons (CFCs), hydrochlorofluorcarbons (HCFCs), carbon tetrachloride and methyl chloroform. Halons also play a large role. Hydro fluorocarbons (HFCs) are being developed to replace CFCs and HCFCs, for uses such as vehicle air conditioning.[9] ODS are broken down by sunlight in the stratosphere, producing halogen atoms, which subsequently destroy ozone through a complex catalytic cycle. Ozone destruction is greatest at the South Pole where very low stratospheric temperatures in winter create polar stratospheric clouds. Ice crystals formed in these clouds provide a large surface area for chemical reactions, accelerating catalytic cycles.[10]

Chlorofluorocarbons and other halogenated ozone depleting substances are mainly responsible for man-made chemical ozone depletion. The total amount of effective halogens in the stratosphere can be calculated and are known as the equivalent effective stratospheric chlorine. CFCs were invented by Thomas Midgley, Jr. in the 1920s. They were used in air-conditioning and cooling units, as aerosol spray propellants prior to the 1970s, and in the cleaning processes of delicate electronic equipment.[11]

Chlorofluorocarbons, Halons and Freons found commonly in aerosol cans and released by many electronic appliances, these were seen to decrease the level of ozone in the stratosphere. All of these gases contain chlorine, which is a major cause behind the thinning of the ozone layer. The destruction of the ozone layer is primarily caused when the amount of gases that contain chlorine begins to increase in the environment. CFC's are not washed back to the earth and are not even destroyed in reaction with other chemicals which means that they can remain the atmosphere for large period of time may be from 20 to 120 years or more. As a result, they are transported back to stratosphere, where they are eventually broken down by UV rays from the sun, releasing free chlorine.[12]

Effects of Ozone Depletion

Ozone is responsible for most of the absorption of UVB radiation. The main public concern regarding the ozone hole has been the effects of increased surface UV radiation on human health. As the ozone hole over Antarctica has in some instances grown so large as to affect parts of Australia, New Zealand, Chile, Argentina, and South Africa, environmentalists have been concerned that the increase in surface UV could be significant. Ozone depletion would magnify all of the effects of UV on human health, both positive (including production of Vitamin D) and negative (including sunburn, skin cancer, and cataracts). The most common forms of skin cancer in humans, basal and squamous cell carcinomas have been strongly linked to UVB exposure. Another form of skin cancer, malignant melanoma, is much less common.[13]

Several of the world's major crop species are particularly vulnerable to increased UV, resulting in reduced growth, photosynthesis and flowering. These species include wheat, rice, barley, oats, corn, soybeans, peas, tomatoes, cucumbers, cauliflower, broccoli and carrots. In particular, plankton (tiny organisms in the surface layer of oceans) is threatened by increased UV radiation. Plankton is the first vital step in aquatic food chains. Decreases in plankton could disrupt the fresh and saltwater food chains, and lead to a species shift in Canadian waters.[14] Increases in solar UV radiation could affect terrestrial and aquatic biogeochemical cycles, thus altering both sources and sinks of greenhouse and chemically-important trace gases e.g., carbon dioxide, carbon monoxide, carbonyl sulphide and possibly other gases, including ozone. Synthetic polymers, naturally occurring biopolymers, as well as some other materials of commercial interest are adversely affected by solar UV radiation. Today's materials are somewhat protected from UVB by special additives.[15]

Australians suffer the highest rates of skin cancer in the world. Each year, around 1,200 Australians die from what is an almost totally preventable disease. Everyone can develop skin cancer; however, some people may be at higher risk than others, due to a range of factors. Ultraviolet radiation levels in Australia are higher than in Europe, even during summer. Being located close to the ozone hole over the Antarctic means much higher, more severe levels of UV radiation get through to ground level. During summer, the earth's orbit brings Australia closer to the sun than Europe during its summer, resulting in an additional seven per cent solar UV intensity.[16]

Preventive Measures

Afforestation is the best way of prevention. Peoples should be encouraged to plant more number of trees, where trees can absorb the gases like chlorofluorocarbons like chlorine, carbon dioxide and other harmful gases. Using eco-friendly products reduces environmental pollution, so that the pollution causing sources becomes automatically reduced. Regulation of laws and strict enforcing of laws on industries may prevent release the harmful pollutants into the atmosphere. By creating the public awareness among peoples, they can realise the importance of natural resources and thus we can prevent the depletion of ozone.[17]

Efforts to find a replacement for CFCs have been somewhat successful. The efforts seem to be working. Reports show that by 2049, the ozone will recover to 1979 thickness, which is when scientists believe the hole began to form. Many scientists believe the Montreal Protocol is responsible for this joyous recovery.[18]

Government Policy

The Vienna Convention for the protection of the Ozone layer in 1985 and the Montreal Protocol on Substances that deplete the ozone layer in 1987 were the starting points of global cooperation for protection of the ozone layer in the stratosphere. Basic measures for reduction of controlled substances include reduction in the short-term and replacement with alternatives and transitation technologies in the middle and long term.[19]

One hundred and ninety four nations, including Canada, have signed an international agreement to end the production of chlorofluorocarbons, halons and other ozone-depleting substances. The agreement is called the Montreal Protocol on Substances that Deplete the Ozone Layer (1987). The protocol has been amended several times, to speed up ODS phase-out dates and to include more types of ODS. The federal and provincial/territorial governments share responsibility for protecting the ozone layer. Under the Montreal Protocol, the federal government is responsible for controlling the import, manufacture, use, sale and export of ODS.[20]

Electronic appliances emit CFC even when they are not in use. So always unplug the electronic instruments when they are not in use. Prefer buying energy-efficient appliances like fluorescent bulbs. Replace your old refrigerators and air-conditioners as they are the major contributors of CFC in the atmosphere. Plant trees, as they absorb UV rays greatly and thus protect the environment. So aforestation can play vital role.[21]

Following the International Geophysical Year (IGY) in 1957 World Meteorological Organisation (WMO, 1992) assumed the responsibilities of ozone observation and the Global Ozone Observing System (GO3OS) was established. At present GO3OS plays a key role in the international systematic observation of the ozone layer. The network of GO3OS conducts the observation by a variety of instruments, at ground based and balloon born stations. These include: (a) Dobson Spectrophotometer, (b) Brewer Spectrophotometer and (c) Ozonometer.[22] In 1995, the United Nations named September 16 the International Day for the Protection of the Ozone Layer.

Vienna Conference

The Vienna Conference was the first international conference on ozone layer depletion. It was held in Vienna, Austria in 1985 when a hole in the stratospheric ozone layer was observed in the South Pole marked by increased UV-B infiltration over

Antarctica. On the basis of the Vienna Convention, the Montreal Protocol on Substances that Deplete the Ozone Layer was negotiated and signed by 24 countries and by the European Economic Community in September 1987. The Protocol called for the Parties to phase down the use of CFCs, halons and other man-made ODCs. It acts as a framework for the international efforts to protect the ozone layer. However, it does not include legally binding reduction goals for the use of CFCs, the main chemical agents causing ozone depletion.

The Vienna Convention for the Protection of the Ozone Layer

Article 1: Definitions: For the purposes of this Convention: (1) "The ozone layer" means the layer of atmospheric ozone above the planetary boundary layer. (2) "Adverse effects" means changes in the physical environment or biota, including changes in climate, which have significant deleterious effects on human health or on the composition, resilience and productivity of natural and managed ecosystems, or on materials useful to mankind. (3) "Alternative technologies or equipment" means technologies or equipment the use of which makes it possible to reduce or effectively eliminate emissions of substances which have or are likely to have adverse effects on the ozone layer. (4) "Alternative substances" means substances which reduce, eliminate or avoid adverse effects on the ozone layer. (5) "Parties" means, unless the text otherwise indicates, Parties to this Convention. (6) "Regional economic integration organisation" means an organisation constituted by sovereign States of a given region which has competence in respect of matters governed by this Convention or its protocols and has been duly authorised, in accordance with its internal procedures, to sign, ratify, accept, approve or accede to the instruments concerned. (7) "Protocols" means protocols to this Convention.

Article 2: General obligations: 1. The Parties shall take appropriate measures in accordance with the provisions of this Convention and of those protocols in force to which they are party to protect human health and the environment against adverse effects resulting or likely to result from human activities which modify or are likely to modify the ozone layer. 2.To this end the Parties shall, in accordance with the means at their disposal and their capabilities: (a) Co-operate by means of systematic observations, research and information exchange in order to better understand and assess the effects of human activities on the ozone layer and the effects on human health and the environment from modification of the ozone layer; (b) Adopt appropriate legislative or administrative measures and co-operate in harmonising appropriate policies to control, limit, reduce or prevent human activities under their jurisdiction or control should it be found that these activities have or are likely to have adverse effects resulting from modification or likely modification of the ozone layer; (c) Co-operate in the formulation of agreed measures, procedures and standards for the implementation of this Convention, with a view to the adoption of protocols and annexes; and (d) Co-operate with competent international bodies to implement effectively this Convention and protocols to which they are party. 3. The provisions of this Convention shall in no way affect the right of Parties to adopt, in accordance with international law, domestic measures additional to those referred to in paragraphs 1 and 2 above, nor shall they affect additional domestic measures already taken by a Party, provided that these measures are not incompatible with their obligations under this Convention., and 4. The application of this article shall be based on relevant scientific and technical considerations.

Article 3: Research and systematic observations: 1. The Parties undertake, as appropriate, to initiate and co-operate in, directly or through competent international bodies, the conduct of research and scientific assessments on: (a) The physical and chemical processes that may affect the ozone layer; (b) The human health and other biological effects deriving from any modifications of the ozone layer, particularly those resulting from changes in ultra-violet solar radiation having biological effects; (c) Climatic effects deriving from any modifications of the ozone layer; (d) Effects deriving from any modifications of the ozone layer and any consequent change in UV-B radiation on natural and synthetic materials useful to mankind; (e) Substances, practices, processes and activities that may affect the ozone layer, and their cumulative effects; (f) Alternative substances and technologies; (g) Related socio-economic matters. 2. The Parties undertake to promote or establish, as appropriate, directly or through competent international bodies and taking fully into account national legislation and relevant ongoing activities at both the national and international levels, joint or complementary programmes for systematic observation of the state of the ozone layer and other relevant parameters, and 3. The Parties undertake to co-operate, directly or through competent international bodies, in ensuring the collection, validation and transmission of research and observational data through appropriate world data centres in a regular and timely fashion.

Article 4: Co-operation in the legal, scientific and technical fields: 1. The Parties shall facilitate and encourage the exchange of scientific, technical, socio-economic, commercial and legal information relevant to this Convention as further elaborated in annex II. Such information shall be supplied to bodies agreed upon by the Parties. Any such body receiving information regarded as confidential by the supplying Party shall ensure that such information is not disclosed and shall aggregate it to protect its confidentiality before it is made available to all Parties. 2. The Parties shall co-operate, consistent with their national laws, regulations and practices and taking into account in particular the needs of the developing countries, in promoting, directly or through competent international bodies, the development and transfer of technology and knowledge. Such co-operation shall be carried out particularly through: (a) Facilitation of the acquisition of alternative technologies by other Parties; (b) Provision of information on alternative technologies and equipment, and supply of special manuals or guides to them; (c) The supply of necessary equipment and facilities for research and systematic observations; and (d) Appropriate training of scientific and technical personnel.

Article 5: Transmission of information: The Parties shall transmit, through the secretariat, to the Conference of the Parties established under Article 6 information on the measures adopted by them in implementation of this Convention and of protocols to which they are party in such form and at such intervals as the meetings of the parties to the relevant instruments may determine.

Article 6: Conference of the Parties: 1. A Conference of the Parties is hereby established. The first meeting of the Conference of the Parties shall be convened by the secretariat designated on an interim basis under Article 7 not later than one year after entry into force of this Convention. Thereafter, ordinary meetings of the Conference of the Parties shall be held at regular intervals to be determined by the Conference at its first meeting. 2. Extraordinary meetings of the Conference of the Parties shall be held at such other times as may be deemed necessary by the Conference, or at the written request of any Party, provided that, within six months of the request being communicated to them by the secretariat, it is supported by at least one-third of the Parties. 3. The Conference of the Parties shall by consensus agree upon and adopt rules of procedure and financial rules for itself and for any subsidiary bodies it may establish, as well as financial provisions governing the functioning of the secretariat. 4. The Conference of the Parties shall keep under continuous review the implementation of this Convention, and, in addition, shall: (a) Establish the form and the intervals for transmitting the information to be submitted in accordance with Article 5 and consider such information as well as reports submitted by any subsidiary body; (b) Review the scientific information on the ozone layer, on its possible modification and on possible effects of any such modification; (c) Promote, in accordance with Article 2, the harmonisation of appropriate policies, strategies and measures for minimising the release of substances causing or likely to cause modification of the ozone layer, and make recommendations on any other measures relating to this Convention; (d) Adopt, in accordance with Articles 3 and 4, programmes for research, systematic observations, scientific and technological co-operation, the exchange of information and the transfer of technology and knowledge; (e) Consider and adopt, as required, in accordance with Articles 9 and 10, amendments to this Convention and its annexes; (f) Consider amendments to any protocol, as well as to any annexes thereto, and, if so decided, recommend their adoption to the parties to the protocol concerned; (g) Consider and adopt, as required, in accordance with Article 10, additional annexes to this Convention; (h) Consider and adopt, as required, protocols in accordance with Article 8; (i) Establish such subsidiary bodies as are deemed necessary for the implementation of this Convention; (j) Seek, where appropriate, the services of competent international bodies and scientific committees, in particular the World Meteorological Organisation and the World Health Organisation as well as the Coordinating Committee on the Ozone Layer, in scientific research, systematic observations and other activities pertinent to the objectives of this Convention, and make use as appropriate of information from these bodies and committees; (k) Consider and undertake any additional action that may be required for the achievement of the purposes of this Convention. 5. The United Nations, its specialised agencies and the International Atomic Energy Agency, as well as any State not party to this Convention, may be represented at meetings of the Conference of the Parties by observers. Any body or agency, whether national or international, governmental or non-governmental, qualified in fields relating to the protection of the ozone layer which has informed the secretariat of its wish to be represented at a meeting of the Conference of the Parties as an observer may be admitted unless at least one-third of the Parties present object. The admission and participation of observers shall be subject to the rules of procedure adopted by the Conference of the Parties.

Article 7: Secretariat: 1. The functions of the secretariat shall be: (a) To arrange for and service meetings provided for in Articles 6, 8, 9 and 10; (b) To prepare and transmit reports based upon information received in accordance with Articles 4 and 5, as well as upon information derived from meetings of subsidiary bodies established under Article 6; (c) To perform the functions assigned to it by any protocol; (d) To prepare reports on its activities carried out in implementation of its functions under this Convention and present them to the Conference of the Parties; (e) To ensure the necessary co-ordination with other relevant international bodies, and in particular to enter into such administrative and contractual arrangements as may be required for the effective discharge of its functions; and (f) To perform such other functions as may be determined by the Conference of the Parties. 2. The secretariat functions will be carried out on an interim basis by the United Nations Environment Programme until the completion of the first ordinary meeting of the Conference of the Parties held pursuant to Article 6. At its first ordinary meeting, the Conference of the Parties shall designate the secretariat from amongst those existing competent international organisations which have signified their willingness to carry out the secretariat functions under this Convention.

Article 8: Adoption of protocols: 1. The Conference of the Parties may at a meeting adopt protocols pursuant to Article 2. 2. The text of any proposed protocol shall be communicated to the Parties by the secretariat at least six months before such a meeting.

Article 9: Amendment of the Convention or protocols: 1. Any Party may propose amendments to this Convention or to any protocol. Such amendments shall take due account, *inter alia*, of relevant scientific and technical considerations. 2. Amendments to this Convention shall be adopted at a meeting of the Conference of the Parties. Amendments to any protocol shall be adopted at a meeting of the Parties to the protocol in question. The text of any proposed amendment to this Convention or to any protocol, except as may otherwise be provided in such protocol, shall be communicated to the Parties by the secretariat at least six months before the meeting at which it is proposed for adoption. The secretariat shall also communicate proposed amendments to the signatories to this Convention for information. 3. The Parties shall make every effort to reach agreement on any proposed amendment to this Convention by consensus. If all efforts at consensus have been exhausted, and no agreement reached, the amendment shall as a last resort be adopted by a three-fourths majority vote of the Parties present and voting at the meeting, and shall be submitted by the Depositary to all Parties for ratification, approval or acceptance. 4. The procedure mentioned in paragraph 3 above shall apply to amendments to any protocol, except that a two-thirds majority of the parties to that protocol present and voting at the meeting shall suffice for their adoption. 5. Ratification, approval or acceptance of amendments shall be notified to the Depositary in writing. Amendments adopted in accordance with paragraphs 3 or 4 above shall enter into force between parties having accepted them on the ninetieth day after the receipt by the Depositary of notification of their ratification, approval or acceptance by at least three-fourths of the Parties to this Convention or by at least two-thirds of the parties to the protocol concerned, except as may otherwise be provided in such protocol. Thereafter the amendments shall enter into force for any other Party on the ninetieth day after that Party deposits its instrument of ratification, approval or acceptance of the amendments. 6. For the purposes of this article, "Parties present and voting" means Parties present and casting an affirmative or negative vote.

Article 10: Adoption and amendment ofannexes: 1. The annexes to this Convention or to any protocol shall form an integral part of this Convention or of such protocol, as the case may be, and, unless expressly provided otherwise, a reference to this Convention or its protocols constitutes at the same time a reference to any annexes thereto. Such annexes shall be restricted to scientific, technical and administrative matters. 2. Except as may be otherwise provided in any protocol with respect to its annexes, the following procedure shall apply to the proposal, adoption and entry into force of additional annexes to this Convention or of annexes to a protocol: (a) Annexes to this Convention shall be proposed and adopted according to the procedure laid down in Article 9, paragraphs 2 and 3, while annexes to any protocol shall be proposed and adopted according to the procedure laid down in Article 9, paragraphs 2 and 4; (b) Any party that is unable to approve an additional annex to this Convention or annex to any protocol to which it is party shall so notify the Depositary, in writing, within six months from the date of the communication of the adoption by the Depositary. The Depositary shall without delay notify all Parties of any such notification received. A Party may at any time substitute an acceptance for a previous declaration of objection and the annexes shall thereupon enter into force for that Party; (c) On the expiry of six months from the date of the circulation of the communication by the Depositary, the annex shall become effective for all Parties to this Convention or to any protocol concerned which have not submitted a notification in accordance with the provision of subparagraph (b) above. 3. The proposal, adoption and entry into force of amendments to annexes to this Convention or to any protocol shall be subject to the same procedure as for the proposal, adoption and entry into force of annexes to the Convention or annexes to a protocol. Annexes and amendments thereto shall take due account, *inter alia,* of relevant scientific and technical considerations. 4. If an additional annex or an amendment to an annex involves an amendment to this Convention or to any protocol, the additional annex or amended annex shall not enter into force until such time as the amendment to this Convention or to the protocol concerned enters into force.

Article 11: Settlement of disputes: 1. In the event of a dispute between Parties concerning the interpretation or application of this Convention, the parties concerned shall seek solution by negotiation. 2. If the parties concerned cannot reach agreement by negotiation, they may jointly seek the good offices of, or request mediation by, a third party. 3. When ratifying, accepting, approving or acceding to this Convention, or at any time thereafter, a State or regional economic integration organisation may declare in writing to the Depositary that for a dispute not resolved in accordance with paragraph 1 or paragraph 2 above, it accepts one or both of the following means of dispute settlement as compulsory: (a) Arbitration in accordance with procedures to be adopted by the Conference of the Parties at its first ordinary meeting; (b) Submission of the dispute to the International Court of Justice. 4. If the parties have not, in accordance with paragraph 3 above, accepted the same or any procedure, the dispute shall be submitted to conciliation in accordance with paragraph 5 below unless the parties otherwise agree. 5. A conciliation commission shall be created upon the request of one of the parties to the dispute. The commission shall be composed of an equal number of members appointed by each party concerned and a chairman chosen jointly by the members appointed by each party. The commission shall render a final and recommendatory award, which the parties shall consider in good faith. 6. The provisions of this Article shall apply with respect to any protocol except as provided in the protocol concerned.

Article 12: Signature: This Convention shall be open for signature by States and by regional economic integration organisations at the Federal Ministry for Foreign Affairs of the Republic of Austria in Vienna from 22 March 1985 to 21 September 1985, and at United Nations Headquarters in New York from 22 September 1985 to 21 March 1986.

Article 13: Ratification, acceptance or approval: 1. This Convention and any protocol shall be subject to ratification, acceptance or approval by States and by regional economic integration organisations. Instruments of ratification, acceptance or approval shall be deposited with the Depositary. 2. Any organisation referred to in paragraph 1 above which becomes a Party to this Convention or any protocol without any of its member States being a Party shall be bound by all the obligations under the Convention or the protocol, as the case may be. In the case of such organisations, one or more of whose member States is a Party to the Convention or relevant protocol, the organisation and its member States shall decide on their respective responsibilities for the performance of their obligation under the Convention or protocol, as the case may be. In such cases, the organisation and the member States shall not be entitled to exercise rights under the Convention or relevant protocol concurrently. 3. In their instruments of ratification, acceptance or approval, the organisations referred to in paragraph 1 above shall declare the extent of their competence with respect to the matters governed by the Convention or the relevant protocol. These organisations shall also inform the Depositary of any substantial modification in the extent of their competence.

Article 14: Accession: 1. This Convention and any protocol shall be open for accession by States and by regional economic integration organisations from the date on which the Convention or the protocol concerned is closed for signature. The instruments of accession shall be deposited with the Depositary. 2. In their instruments of accession, the organisations referred to in paragraph 1 above shall declare the extent of their competence with respect to the matters governed by the Convention or the relevant protocol. These organisations shall also inform the Depositary of any substantial modification in the extent of their competence.3. The provisions of Article 13, paragraph 2, shall apply to regional economic integration organisations which accede to this Convention or any protocol.

Article 15: Right to vote: 1. Each Party to this Convention or to any protocol shall have one vote. 2. Except as provided for in paragraph 1 above, regional economic integration organisations, in matters within their competence, shall exercise their right to vote with a number of votes equal to the number of their member States which are Parties to the Convention or the relevant protocol. Such organisations shall not exercise their right to vote if their member States exercise theirs, and vice versa.

Article 16: Relationship between the Convention and its protocols: 1. A State or a regional economic integration organisation may not become a party to a protocol unless it is, or becomes at the same time, a Party to the Convention. 2. Decisions concerning any protocol shall be taken only by the parties to the protocol concerned.

Article 17: Entry into force: 1. This Convention shall enter into force on the ninetieth day after the date of deposit of the twentieth instrument of ratification, acceptance, approval or accession. 2. Any protocol, except as otherwise provided in such protocol, shall enter into force on the ninetieth day after the date of deposit of the eleventh instrument of ratification, acceptance or approval of such protocol or accession thereto.3. For each Party which ratifies, accepts or approves this Convention or accedes thereto after the deposit of the twentieth instrument of ratification, acceptance, approval or accession, it shall enter into force on the ninetieth day after the date of deposit by such Party of its instrument of ratification, acceptance, approval or accession. 4. Any protocol, except as otherwise provided in such protocol, shall enter into force for a party that ratifies, accepts or approves that protocol or accedes thereto after its entry into force pursuant to paragraph 2 above, on the ninetieth day after the date on which that party deposits its instrument of ratification, acceptance, approval or accession, or on the date which the Convention enters into force for that Party, whichever shall be the later, and 5. For the purposes of paragraphs 1 and 2 above, any instrument deposited by a regional economic integration organisation shall not be counted as additional to those deposited by member States of such organisation.

Article 18: Reservations: No reservations may be made to this Convention.

Article 19: Withdrawal: 1. At any time after four years from the date on which this Convention has entered into force for a Party that Party may withdraw from the Convention by giving written notification to the Depositary. 2. Except as may be provided in any protocol, at any time after four years from the date on which such protocol has entered into force for a party that party may withdraw from the protocol by giving written notification to the Depositary. 3. Any such withdrawal shall take effect upon expiry of one year after the date of its receipt by the Depositary, or on such later date as may be specified in the notification of the withdrawal. 4. Any Party which withdraws from this Convention shall be considered as also having withdrawn from any protocol to which it is party.

Article 20: Depositary: 1. The Secretary-General of the United Nations shall assume the functions of depositary of this Convention and any protocols. 2. The Depositary shall inform the Parties, in particular, of: (a) The signature of this Convention and of any protocol, and the deposit of instruments of ratification, acceptance, approval or accession in accordance with Articles 13 and 14; (b) The date on which the Convention and any protocol will come into force in accordance with Article 17; (c) Notifications of withdrawal made in accordance with Article 19; (d) Amendments adopted with respect to the Convention and any protocol, their acceptance by the parties and their date of entry into force in accordance with Article 9; (e) All communications relating to the adoption and approval of annexes and to the amendment of annexes in accordance with Article 10; (f) Notifications by regional economic integration organisations of the extent of their competence with respect to matters governed by this Convention and any protocols, and of any modifications thereof. (g) Declarations made in accordance with Article 11, paragraph 3.

Article 21: The original of this Convention, of which the Arabic, Chinese, English, French, Russian and Spanish texts are equally authentic, shall be deposited with the Secretary-General of the United Nations.

Montreal Protocol

According to wikipedia, the Montreal Protocol is an international treaty designed to protect the ozone layer by phasing out the production of numerous substances that are responsible for ozone depletion. It was agreed on 16 September 1987, and entered into force on 1 January 1989, followed by a first meeting in Helsinki, May 1989. The stated purpose of the treaty is that the signatory states "Recognising that worldwide emissions of certain substances can significantly deplete and otherwise modify the ozone layer in a manner that is likely to result in adverse effects on human health and the environment. Determined to protect the ozone layer by taking precautionary measures to control equitably total global emissions of substances that deplete it with the ultimate objective of their elimination on the basis of developments in scientific knowledge".

The provisions of the Protocol include the requirement that the Parties to the Protocol base their future decisions on the current scientific, environmental, technical, and economic information that is assessed through panels drawn from the worldwide expert communities. Since the Montreal Protocol came into effect, the atmospheric concentrations of the most important chlorofluorocarbons and related chlorinated hydrocarbons have either leveled off or decreased. It also offers major incentives for non-signatory nations to sign the agreement. The treaty negotiators justified the sanctions because depletion of the ozone layer is an environmental problem most effectively addressed on the global level.

The Montreal Protocol includes a unique adjustment provision that enables the Parties to the Protocol to respond quickly to new scientific information and agree to accelerate the reductions required on chemicals already covered by the Protocol. The Parties to the Montreal Protocol have amended the Protocol to enable, among other things, the control of new chemicals and the creation of a financial mechanism to enable developing countries to comply. It targets 96 chemicals in thousands of applications across more than 240 industrial sectors. The Multilateral Fund has provided more than US$2.5 billion in financial assistance to developing countries to phase out production and consumption of ozone depleting substances since the Protocol's inception in 1987.

The Montreal Protocol stipulates that the production and consumption of compounds that deplete ozone in the stratosphere—chlorofluorocarbons (CFCs), halons, carbon tetrachloride, and methyl chloroform—are to be phased out by 2000 (2005 for methyl chloroform).

The Montreal Protocol on Substances that Deplete the Ozone Layer

Article 1: Definitions: For the purposes of this Protocol: "Convention" means the Vienna Convention for the Protection of the Ozone Layer, adopted on 22 March 1985. "Parties" means, unless the text otherwise indicates, Parties to this Protocol. "Secretariat" means the Secretariat of the Convention. "Controlled substance" means a substance in Annex A, Annex B, Annex C or Annex E to this Protocol, whether existing alone or in a mixture. It includes the isomers of any such substance, except as specified in the relevant Annex, but excludes any controlled substance or mixture which is in a manufactured product other than a container used for the transportation or storage of that substance."Production" means the amount of controlled substances produced, minus the amount destroyed by technologies to be approved by the Parties and minus the amount entirely used as feedstock in the manufacture of other chemicals. The amount recycled and reused is not to be considered as "production". "Consumption" means production plus imports minus exports of controlled substances. "Calculated levels" of production, imports, exports and consumption means levels determined in accordance with Article 3. "Industrial rationalisation" means the transfer of all or a portion of the calculated level of production of one Party to another, for the purpose of achieving economic efficiencies or responding to anticipated shortfalls in supply as a result of plant closures.

Article 2: Control Measures: 1. Incorporated in Article 2A. 2. Replaced by Article 2B. 3. Replaced by Article 2A. 4. Replaced by Article 2A. 5. Any Party may, for one or more control periods, transfer to another Party any portion of its calculated level of production set out in Articles 2A to 2F, and Article 2H, provided that the total combined calculated levels of production of the Parties concerned for any group of controlled substances do not exceed the production limits set out in those Articles for that group. Such transfer of production shall be notified to the Secretariat by each of the Parties concerned, stating the terms of such transfer and the period for which it is to apply. Any Party not operating under paragraph 1 of Article 5 may, for one or more control periods, transfer to another such Party any portion of its calculated level of consumption set out in Article 2F, provided that the calculated level of consumption of controlled substances in Group I of Annex A of the Party transferring the portion of its calculated level of consumption did not exceed 0.25 kilograms per capita in 1989 and that the total combined calculated levels of consumption of the Parties concerned do not exceed the consumption limits set out in Article 2F. Such transfer of consumption shall be notified to the Secretariat by each of the Parties concerned, stating the terms of such transfer and the period for which it is to apply. 6. Any Party not operating under Article 5, that has facilities for the production of Annex A or Annex B controlled substances under construction, or contracted for, prior to 16 September 1987, and provided for in national legislation prior to 1 January 1987, may add the production from such facilities to its 1986 production of such substances for the purposes of determining its calculated level of production for 1986, provided that such facilities are completed by 31 December 1990 and that such production does not raise that Party's annual calculated level of consumption of the controlled substances above 0.5 kilograms per capita. 7. Any transfer of production pursuant to paragraph 5 or any addition of production pursuant to paragraph 6 shall be notified to the Secretariat, no later than the time of the transfer or addition. 8. (a) Any Parties which are Member States of a regional economic integration organisation as defined in Article 1 (6) of the Convention may agree that they shall jointly fulfil their obligations respecting consumption under this Article and Articles 2A to 2I provided that their total combined calculated level of consumption does not exceed the levels required by this Article and Articles 2A to 2I; (b) The Parties to any such agreement shall inform the Secretariat of the terms of the agreement before the date of the reduction in consumption with which the agreement is concerned; (c) Such agreement will become operative only if all Member States of the regional economic integration organisation and the organisation concerned are Parties to the Protocol and have notified the Secretariat of their manner of implementation. 9. (a) Based on the assessments made pursuant to Article 6, the Parties may decide whether: (i) Adjustments to the ozone depleting potentials specified in Annex A, Annex B, Annex C and/or Annex E should be made and, if so, what the adjustments should be; and (ii) Further adjustments and reductions of production or consumption of the controlled substances should be undertaken and, if so, what the scope, amount and timing of any such adjustments and reductions should be; (b) Proposals for such adjustments shall be communicated to the Parties by the Secretariat at least six months before the meeting of the Parties at which they are proposed for adoption; (c) In taking such decisions, the Parties shall make every effort to reach agreement by consensus. If all efforts at consensus have been exhausted, and no agreement reached, such decisions shall, as a last resort, be adopted by a two-thirds majority vote of the Parties present and voting representing a majority of the Parties operating under Paragraph 1 of Article 5 present and voting and a majority of the Parties not so operating present and voting; (d) The decisions, which shall be binding on all Parties, shall forthwith be communicated to the Parties by the Depositary. Unless otherwise provided in the decisions, they shall enter into force on the expiry of six months from the date of the circulation of the communication by the Depositary. 10. Based on the assessments made pursuant to Article 6 of this Protocol and in accordance with the procedure set out in Article 9 of the Convention, the Parties may decide: (a) whether any substances, and if so which, should be added to or removed from any annex to this Protocol, and (b) the mechanism, scope and timing of the control measures that should apply to those substances; 11. Notwithstanding the provisions contained in this Article and Articles 2A to 2I Parties may take more stringent measures than those required by this Article and Articles 2A to 2I.

Article 2A: CFCs: 1. Each Party shall ensure that for the twelve-month period commencing on the first day of the seventh month following the date of entry into force of this Protocol, and in each twelve-month period thereafter, its calculated level of consumption of the controlled substances in Group I of Annex A does not exceed its calculated level of consumption in 1986. By the end of the same period, each Party producing one or more of these substances shall ensure that its calculated level of production of the substances does not exceed its calculated level of production in 1986, except that such level may have increased by no more than ten per cent based on the 1986 level. Such increase shall be permitted only so as to satisfy the basic domestic needs of the Parties operating under Article 5 and for the purposes of industrial rationalisation between Parties.2. Each Party shall ensure that for the period from 1 July 1991 to 31 December 1992 its calculated levels of consumption and production of the controlled substances in Group I of Annex A do not exceed 150 per cent of its calculated levels of production and consumption of those substances in 1986; with effect from 1 January 1993, the twelve-month control period for these controlled substances shall run from 1 January to 31 December each year.3.Each Party shall ensure that for the twelve-month period commencing on 1 January 1994, and in each twelve-month period thereafter, its calculated level of consumption of the controlled substances in Group I of Annex A does not exceed, annually, twenty-five per cent of its calculated level of consumption in 1986. Each Party producing one or more of these substances shall, for the same periods, ensure that its calculated level of production of the substances does not exceed, annually, twenty-five per cent of its calculated level of production in 1986. However, in order to satisfy the basic domestic needs of the Parties operating under paragraph 1 of Article 5, its calculated level of production may exceed that limit by up to ten per cent of its calculated level of production in 1986. 4. Each Party shall ensure that for the twelve-month period commencing on 1 January 1996, and in each twelve-month period thereafter, its calculated level of consumption of the controlled substances in Group I of Annex A does not exceed zero. Each Party producing one or more of these substances shall, for the same periods, ensure that its calculated level of production of the substances does not exceed zero. However, in order to satisfy the basic domestic needs of the Parties operating under paragraph 1 of Article 5, its calculated level of production may exceed that limit by a quantity equal to the annual average of its production of the controlled substances in Group I of Annex A for basic domestic needs for the period 1995 to 1997 inclusive. This paragraph will apply save to the extent that the Parties decide to permit the level of production or consumption that is necessary to satisfy uses agreed by them to be essential.5. Each Party shall ensure that for the twelve-month period commencing on 1 January 2003 and in each twelve-month period thereafter, its calculated level of production of the controlled substances in Group I of Annex A for the basic domestic needs of the Parties operating under paragraph 1 of Article 5 does not exceed eighty per cent of the annual average of its production of those substances for basic domestic needs for the period 1995 to 1997 inclusive.6. Each Party shall ensure that for the twelve-month period commencing on 1 January 2005 and in each twelve-month period thereafter, its calculated level of production of the controlled substances in Group I of Annex A for the basic domestic needs of the Parties operating under paragraph 1 of Article 5 does not exceed fifty per cent of the annual average of its production of those substances for basic domestic needs for the period 1995 to 1997 inclusive. 7. Each Party shall ensure that for the twelve-month period commencing on 1 January 2007 and in each twelve-month period thereafter, its calculated level of production of the controlled substances in Group I of Annex A for the basic domestic needs of the Parties operating under paragraph 1 of Article 5 does not exceed fifteen per cent of the annual average of its production of those substances for basic domestic needs for the period 1995 to 1997 inclusive.8.Each Party shall ensure that for the twelve-month period commencing on 1 January 2010 and in each twelve-month period thereafter, its calculated level of production of the controlled substances in

Group I of Annex A for the basic domestic needs of the Parties operating under paragraph 1 of Article 5 does not exceed zero. For the purposes of calculating basic domestic needs under paragraphs 4 to 8 of this Article, the calculation of the annual average of production by a Party includes any production entitlements that it has transferred in accordance with paragraph 5 of Article 2, and excludes any production entitlements that it has acquired in accordance with paragraph 5 of Article 2.

Article 2B: Halons: 1. Each Party shall ensure that for the twelve-month period commencing on 1 January 1992, and in each twelve-month period thereafter, its calculated level of consumption of the controlled substances in Group II of Annex A does not exceed, annually, its calculated level of consumption in 1986. Each Party producing one or more of these substances shall, for the same periods, ensure that its calculated level of production of the substances does not exceed, annually, its calculated level of production in 1986. However, in order to satisfy the basic domestic needs of the Parties operating under paragraph 1 of Article 5, its calculated level of production may exceed that limit by up to ten per cent of its calculated level of production in 1986. 2. Each Party shall ensure that for the twelve-month period commencing on 1 January 1994, and in each twelve-month period thereafter, its calculated level of consumption of the controlled substances in Group II of Annex A does not exceed zero. Each Party producing one or more of these substances shall, for the same periods, ensure that its calculated level of production of the substances does not exceed zero. However, in order to satisfy the basic domestic needs of the Parties operating under paragraph 1 of Article 5, its calculated level of production may, until 1 January 2002 exceed that limit by up to fifteen per cent of its calculated level of production in 1986; thereafter, it may exceed that limit by a quantity equal to the annual average of its production of the controlled substances in Group II of Annex A for basic domestic needs for the period 1995 to 1997 inclusive. This paragraph will apply save to the extent that the Parties decide to permit the level of production or consumption that is necessary to satisfy uses agreed by them to be essential. 3. Each Party shall ensure that for the twelve-month period commencing on 1 January 2005 and in each twelve-month period thereafter, its calculated level of production of the controlled substances in Group II of Annex A for the basic domestic needs of the Parties operating under paragraph 1 of Article 5 does not exceed fifty per cent of the annual average of its production of those substances for basic domestic needs for the period 1995 to 1997 inclusive. 4. Each Party shall ensure that for the twelve-month period commencing on 1 January 2010 and in each twelve-month period thereafter, its calculated level of production of the controlled substances in Group II of Annex A for the basic domestic needs of the Parties operating under paragraph 1 of Article 5 does not exceed zero.

Article 2C: Other fully halogenated CFCs: 1. Each Party shall ensure that for the twelve-month period commencing on 1 January 1993, its calculated level of consumption of the controlled substances in Group I of Annex B does not exceed, annually, eighty per cent of its calculated level of consumption in 1989. Each Party producing one or more of these substances shall, for the same period, ensure that its calculated level of production of the substances does not exceed, annually, eighty per cent of its calculated level of production in 1989. However, in order to satisfy the basic domestic needs of the Parties operating under paragraph 1 of Article 5, its calculated level of production may exceed that limit by up to ten per cent of its calculated level of production in 1989. 2. Each Party shall ensure that for the twelve-month period commencing on 1 January 1994, and in each twelve-month period thereafter, its calculated level of consumption of the controlled substances in Group I of Annex B does not exceed, annually, twenty-five per cent of its calculated level of consumption in 1989. Each Party producing one or more of these substances shall, for the same periods, ensure that its calculated level of production of the substances does not exceed, annually, twenty-five per cent of its calculated level of production in 1989. However, in order to satisfy the basic domestic needs of the Parties operating under paragraph 1 of Article 5, its calculated level of production may exceed that limit by up to ten per cent of its calculated level of production in 1989. 3. Each Party shall ensure that for the twelve-month period commencing on 1 January 1996, and in each twelve-month period thereafter, its calculated level of consumption of the controlled substances in Group I of Annex B does not exceed zero. Each Party producing one or more of these substances shall, for the same periods, ensure that its calculated level of production of the substances does not exceed zero. However, in order to satisfy the basic domestic needs of the Parties operating under paragraph 1 of Article 5, its calculated level of production may, until 1 January 2003 exceed that limit by up to fifteen per cent of its calculated level of production in 1989; thereafter, it may exceed that limit by a quantity equal to eighty per cent of the annual average of its production of the controlled substances in Group I of Annex B for basic domestic needs for the period 1998 to 2000 inclusive. This paragraph will apply save to the extent that the Parties decide to permit the level of production or consumption that is necessary to satisfy uses agreed by them to be essential. 4. Each Party shall ensure that for the twelve-month period commencing on 1 January 2007 and in each twelve-month period thereafter, its calculated level of production of the controlled substances in Group I of Annex B for the basic domestic needs of the Parties operating under paragraph 1 of Article 5 does not exceed fifteen per cent of the annual average of its production of those substances for basic domestic needs for the period 1998 to 2000 inclusive. 5. Each Party shall ensure that for the twelve-month period commencing on 1 January 2010 and in each twelve-month period thereafter, its calculated level of production of the controlled substances in Group I of Annex B for the basic domestic needs of the Parties operating under paragraph 1 of Article 5 does not exceed zero.

Article 2D: Carbon tetrachloride: 1. Each Party shall ensure that for the twelve-month period commencing on 1 January 1995, its calculated level of consumption of the controlled substance in Group II of Annex B does not exceed, annually, fifteen per cent of its calculated level of consumption in 1989. Each Party producing the substance shall, for the same period, ensure that its calculated level of production of the substance does not exceed, annually, fifteen per cent of its calculated level of production in 1989. However, in order to satisfy the basic domestic needs of the Parties operating under paragraph 1 of Article 5, its calculated level of production may exceed that limit by up to ten per cent of its calculated level of production in 1989. 2. Each Party shall ensure that for the twelve-month period commencing on 1 January 1996, and in each twelve-month period thereafter, its calculated level of consumption of the controlled substance in Group II of Annex B does not exceed zero. Each Party producing the substance shall, for the same periods, ensure that its calculated level of production of the substance does not exceed zero. However, in order to satisfy the basic domestic needs of the Parties operating under paragraph 1 of Article 5, its calculated level of production may exceed that limit by up to fifteen per cent of its calculated level of production in 1989. This paragraph will apply save to the extent that the Parties decide to permit the level of production or consumption that is necessary to satisfy uses agreed by them to be essential.

Article 2E: 1,1,1-Trichloroethane (Methylchloroform): 1. Each Party shall ensure that for the twelve-month period commencing on 1 January 1993, its calculated level of consumption of the controlled substance in Group III of Annex B does not exceed, annually, its calculated level of consumption in 1989. Each Party producing the substance shall, for the same period, ensure that its calculated level of production of the substance does not exceed, annually, its calculated level of production in 1989. However, in order to satisfy the basic domestic needs of the Parties operating under paragraph 1 of Article 5, its calculated level of production may exceed that limit by up to ten per cent of its calculated level of production in 1989. 2. Each Party shall ensure that for the twelve-month period commencing on 1 January 1994, and in each twelve-month period thereafter, its calculated level of consumption of the controlled substance in Group III of Annex B does not exceed, annually, fifty per cent of its calculated level of consumption in 1989. Each Party producing the substance shall, for the same periods, ensure that its calculated level of production of the substance does not exceed, annually, fifty per cent of its calculated level of production in 1989. However, in order to satisfy the basic domestic needs of the Parties operating under paragraph 1 of Article 5, its calculated level of production may exceed that limit by up to ten per cent of its calculated level of production in 1989. 3. Each Party shall ensure that for the twelve-month period commencing on 1 January 1996, and in each twelve-month period thereafter, its calculated level of consumption of the controlled substance in Group III of Annex B does not exceed zero. Each Party producing the substance shall, for the same periods, ensure that its calculated level of production of the substance does not exceed zero. However, in order to satisfy the basic domestic needs of the Parties operating under paragraph 1 of Article 5, its calculated level of production may exceed that limit by up to fifteen per cent of its calculated level of production for 1989. This paragraph will apply save to the extent that the Parties decide to permit the level of production or consumption that is necessary to satisfy uses agreed by them to be essential.

Article 2F: Hydrochlorofluorocarbons: 1. Each Party shall ensure that for the twelve-month period commencing on 1 January 1996, and in each twelve-month period thereafter, its calculated level of consumption of the controlled substances in Group I of Annex C does not exceed, annually, the sum of: (a) 2.8 per cent of its calculated level of consumption in 1989 of the controlled substances in Group I of Annex A; and (b) Its calculated level of consumption in 1989 of the controlled substances in Group I of Annex C. 2. Each Party shall ensure that for the twelve month period commencing on 1 January 2004, and in each twelve-month period thereafter, its calculated level of consumption of the controlled substances in Group I of Annex C does not exceed, annually, sixty-five per cent of the sum referred to in paragraph 1 of this Article.3.Each Party shall ensure that for the twelve-month period commencing on 1 January 2010, and in each twelve-month period thereafter, its calculated level of consumption of the controlled substances in Group I of Annex C does not exceed, annually, thirty-five per cent of the sum referred to in paragraph 1 of this Article. 4. Each Party shall ensure that for the twelve-month period commencing on 1 January 2015, and in each twelve-month period thereafter, its calculated level of consumption of the controlled substances in Group I of Annex C does not exceed, annually, ten per cent of the sum referred to in paragraph 1 of this Article. 5. Each Party shall ensure that for the twelve-month period commencing on 1 January 2020, and in each twelve-month period thereafter, its calculated level of consumption of the controlled substances in Group I of Annex C does not exceed, annually, zero point five per cent of the sum referred to in paragraph 1 of this Article. Such consumption shall, however, be restricted to the servicing of refrigeration and air conditioning equipment existing at that date. 6. Each Party shall ensure that for the twelve-month period commencing on 1 January 2030, and in each twelve-month period thereafter, its calculated level of consumption of the controlled substances in Group I of Annex C does not exceed zero. 7. As of 1 January 1996, each Party shall endeavour to ensure that: (a) The use of controlled substances in Group I of Annex C is limited to those applications where other more environmentally suitable alternative substances or technologies are not available; (b) The use of controlled substances in Group I of Annex C is not outside the areas of application currently met by controlled substances in Annexes A, B and C, except in rare cases for the protection of human life or human health; and (c) Controlled substances in Group I of Annex C are selected for use in a manner that minimizes ozone depletion, in addition to meeting other environmental, safety and economic considerations. 8. Each Party producing one or more of these substances shall ensure that for the twelve-month period commencing on 1 January 2004, and in each twelve-month period thereafter, its calculated level of production of the controlled substances in Group I of Annex C does not exceed, annually, the average of: (a) The sum of its calculated level of consumption in 1989 of the controlled substances in Group I of Annex C and 2.8 per cent of its calculated level of consumption in 1989 of the controlled substances in Group I of Annex A; and (b) The sum of its calculated level of production in 1989 of the controlled substances in Group I of Annex C and 2.8 per cent of its calculated level of production in 1989 of the controlled substances in Group I of Annex A. However, in order to satisfy the basic domestic needs of the Parties operating under paragraph 1 of Article 5, its calculated level of production may exceed that limit by up to fifteen per cent of its calculated level of production of the controlled substances in Group I of Annex C as defined above.

Article 2G: Hydrobromofluorocarbons: Each Party shall ensure that for the twelve-month period commencing on 1 January 1996, and in each twelve-month period thereafter, its calculated level of consumption of the controlled substances in Group II of Annex C does not exceed zero. Each Party producing the substances shall, for the same periods, ensure that its calculated level of production of the substances does not exceed zero. This paragraph will apply save to the extent that the Parties decide to permit the level of production or consumption that is necessary to satisfy uses agreed by them to be essential.

Article 2H: Methyl bromide: 1. Each Party shall ensure that for the twelve-month period commencing on 1 January 1995, and in each twelve-month period thereafter, its calculated level of consumption of the controlled substance in Annex E does not exceed, annually, its calculated level of consumption in 1991.

Each Party producing the substance shall, for the same period, ensure that its calculated level of production of the substance does not exceed, annually, its calculated level of production in 1991. However, in order to satisfy the basic domestic needs of the Parties operating under paragraph 1 of Article 5, its calculated level of production may exceed that limit by up to ten per cent of its calculated level of production in 1991. 2. Each Party shall ensure that for the twelve-month period commencing on 1 January 1999, and in the twelve-month period thereafter, its calculated level of consumption of the controlled substance in Annex E does not exceed, annually, seventy-five per cent of its calculated level of consumption in 1991. Each Party producing the substance shall, for the same periods, ensure that its calculated level of production of the substance does not exceed, annually, seventy-five per cent of its calculated level of production in 1991. However, in order to satisfy the basic domestic needs of the Parties operating under paragraph 1 of Article 5, its calculated level of production may exceed that limit by up to ten per cent of its calculated level of production in 1991. 3. Each Party shall ensure that for the twelve-month period commencing on 1 January 2001, and in the twelve-month period thereafter, its calculated level of consumption of the controlled substance in Annex E does not exceed, annually, fifty per cent of its calculated level of consumption in 1991. Each Party producing the substance shall, for the same periods, ensure that its calculated level of production of the substance does not exceed, annually, fifty per cent of its calculated level of production in 1991. However, in order to satisfy the basic domestic needs of the Parties operating under paragraph 1 of Article 5, its calculated level of production may exceed that limit by up to ten per cent of its calculated level of production in 1991. 4. Each Party shall ensure that for the twelve-month period commencing on 1 January 2003, and in the twelve-month period thereafter, its calculated level of consumption of the controlled substance in Annex E does not exceed, annually, thirty per cent of its calculated level of consumption in 1991. Each Party producing the substance shall, for the same periods, ensure that its calculated level of production of the substance does not exceed, annually, thirty per cent of its calculated level of production in 1991. However, in order to satisfy the basic domestic needs of the Parties operating under paragraph 1 of Article 5, its calculated level of production may exceed that limit by up to ten per cent of its calculated level of production in 1991. 5. Each Party shall ensure that for the twelve-month period commencing on 1 January 2005, and in each twelve-month period thereafter, its calculated level of consumption of the controlled substance in Annex E does not exceed zero. Each Party producing the substance shall, for the same periods, ensure that its calculated level of production of the substance does not exceed zero. However, in order to satisfy the basic domestic needs of the Parties operating under paragraph 1 of Article 5, its calculated level of production may, until 1 January 2002 exceed that limit by up to fifteen per cent of its calculated level of production in 1991; thereafter, it may exceed that limit by a quantity equal to the annual average of its production of the controlled substance in Annex E for basic domestic needs for the period 1995 to 1998 inclusive. This paragraph will apply save to the extent that the Parties decide to permit the level of production or consumption that is necessary to satisfy uses agreed by them to be critical uses.Each Party shall ensure that for the twelve-month period commencing on 1 January 2005 and in each twelve-month period thereafter, its calculated level of production of the controlled substance in Annex E for the basic domestic needs of the Parties operating under paragraph 1 of Article 5 does not exceed eighty per cent of the annual average of its production of the substance for basic domestic needs for the period 1995 to 1998 inclusive. 6. The calculated levels of consumption and production under this Article shall not include the amounts used by the Party for quarantine and pre-shipment applications.

Article 2I: Bromochloromethane: Each Party shall ensure that for the twelve-month period commencing on 1 January 2002, and in each twelve-month period thereafter, its calculated level of consumption and production of the controlled substance in Group III of Annex C does not exceed zero. This paragraph will apply save to the extent that the Parties decide to permit the level of production or consumption that is necessary to satisfy uses agreed by them to be essential.

Article 3: Calculation of control levels: For the purposes of Articles 2, 2A to 2I and 5, each Party shall, for each group of substances in Annex A, Annex B, Annex C or Annex E determine its calculated levels of: (a) Production by: (i) multiplying its annual production of each controlled substance by the ozone depleting potential specified in respect of it in Annex A, Annex B, Annex C or Annex E;and (ii) adding together, for each such Group, the resultingfigures; (b) Imports and exports, respectively, by following, *mutatis mutandis*, the procedure set out in subparagraph (a); andConsumption by adding together its calculated levels of production and imports and subtracting its calculated level of exports as determined in accordance with subparagraphs (a) and (b). However, beginning on 1 January 1993, any export of controlled substances to non-Parties shall not be subtracted in calculating the consumption level of the exporting Party.

Article 4: Control of trade with non-Parties: 1. As of 1 January 1990, each party shall ban the import of the controlled substances in Annex A from any State not party to this Protocol.Within one year of the date of the entry into force of this paragraph, each Party shall ban the import of the controlled substances in Annex B from any State not party to this Protocol. Within one year of the date of entry into force of this paragraph, each Party shall ban the import of any controlled substances in Group II of Annex C from any State not party to this Protocol.Within one year of the date of entry into force of this paragraph, each Party shall ban the import of the controlled substance in Annex E from any State not party to this Protocol.As of 1 January 2004, each Party shall ban the import of the controlled substances in Group I of Annex C from any State not party to this Protocol. Within one year of the date of entry into force of this paragraph, each Party shall ban the import of the controlled substance in Group III of Annex C from any State not party to this Protocol. 2. As of 1 January 1993, each Party shall ban the export of any controlled substances in Annex A to any State not party to this Protocol.Commencing one year after the date of entry into force of this paragraph, each Party shall ban the export of any controlled substances in Annex B to any State not party to this Protocol. Commencing one year after the date of entry into force of this paragraph, each Party shall ban the export of any controlled substances in Group II of Annex C to any State not party to this Protocol. Commencing one year of the date of entry into force of this paragraph, each Party shall ban the export of the controlled substance in Annex E to any State not party to this Protocol.As of 1 January 2004, each Party shall ban the export of the controlled substances in Group I of

Annex C to any State not party to this Protocol. Within one year of the date of entry into force of this paragraph, each Party shall ban the export of the controlled substance in Group III of Annex C to any State not party to this Protocol. 3. By 1 January 1992, the Parties shall, following the procedures in Article 10 of the Convention, elaborate in an annex a list of products containing controlled substances in Annex A. Parties that have not objected to the annex in accordance with those procedures shall ban, within one year of the annex having become effective, the import of those products from any State not party to this Protocol.Within three years of the date of the entry into force of this paragraph, the Parties shall, following the procedures in Article 10 of the Convention, elaborate in an annex a list of products containing controlled substances in Annex B. Parties that have not objected to the annex in accordance with those procedures shall ban, within one year of the annex having become effective, the import of those products from any State not party to this Protocol.Within three years of the date of entry into force of this paragraph, the Parties shall, following the procedures in Article 10 of the Convention, elaborate in an annex a list of products containing controlled substances in Group II of Annex C. Parties that have not objected to the annex in accordance with those procedures shall ban, within one year of the annex having become effective, the import of those products from any State not party to this Protocol. 4. By 1 January 1994, the Parties shall determine the feasibility of banning or restricting, from States not party to this Protocol, the import of products produced with, but not containing, controlled substances in Annex A. If determined feasible, the Parties shall, following the procedures in Article 10 of the Convention, elaborate in an annex a list of such products. Parties that have not objected to the annex in accordance with those procedures shall ban, within one year of the annex having become effective, the import of those products from any State not party to this Protocol. Within five years of the date of the entry into force of this paragraph, the Parties shall determine the feasibility of banning or restricting, from States not party to this Protocol, the import of products produced with, but not containing, controlled substances in Annex B. If determined feasible, the Parties shall, following the procedures in Article 10 of the Convention, elaborate in an annex a list of such products.

Parties that have not objected to the annex in accordance with those procedures shall ban or restrict, within one year of the annex having become effective, the import of those products from any State not party to this Protocol. Within five years of the date of entry into force of this paragraph, the Parties shall determine the feasibility of banning or restricting, from States not party to this Protocol, the import of products produced with, but not containing, controlled substances in Group II of Annex C. If determined feasible, the Parties shall, following the procedures in Article 10 of the Convention, elaborate in an annex a list of such products. Parties that have not objected to the annex in accordance with those procedures shall ban or restrict, within one year of the annex having become effective, the import of those products from any State not party to this Protocol.Each Party undertakes to the fullest practicable extent to discourage the export to any State not party to this Protocol of technology for producing and for utilising controlled substances in Annexes A, B, C and E. 6. Each Party shall refrain from providing new subsidies, aid, credits, guarantees or insurance programmes for the export to States not party to this Protocol of products, equipment, plants or technology that would facilitate the production of controlled substances in Annexes A, B, C and E. 7. Paragraphs 5 and 6 shall not apply to products, equipment, plants or technology that improve the containment, recovery, recycling or destruction of controlled substances, promote the development of alternative substances, or otherwise contribute to the reduction of emissions of controlled substances in Annexes A, B, C and E.8. Notwithstanding the provisions of this Article, imports and exports referred to in paragraphs 1 to 4 *ter* of this Article may be permitted from, or to, any State not party to this Protocol, if that State is determined, by a meeting of the Parties, to be in full compliance with Article 2, Articles 2A to 2I and this Article, and have submitted data to that effect as specified in Article 7.9. For the purposes of this Article, the term "State not party to this Protocol" shall include, with respect to a particular controlled substance, a State or regional economic integration organisation that has not agreed to be bound by the control measures in effect for that substance.10. By 1 January 1996, the Parties shall consider whether to amend this Protocol in order to extend the measures in this Article to trade in controlled substances in Group I of Annex C and in Annex E with States not party to the Protocol.

Article 4A: Control of trade with Parties: 1. Where, after the phase-out date applicable to it for a controlled substance, a Party is unable, despite having taken all practicable steps to comply with its obligation under the Protocol, to cease production of that substance for domestic consumption, other than for uses agreed by the Parties to be essential, it shall ban the export of used, recycled and reclaimed quantities of that substance, other than for the purpose of destruction. 2. Paragraph 1 of this Article shall apply without prejudice to the operation of Article 11 of the Convention and the non-compliance procedure developed under Article 8 of the Protocol.

Article 4B: Licensing: 1.Each Party shall, by 1 January 2000 or within three months of the date of entry into force of this Article for it, whichever is the later, establish and implement a system for licensing the import and export of new, used, recycled and reclaimed controlled substances in Annexes A, B, C and E. 2. Notwithstanding paragraph 1 of this Article, any Party operating under paragraph 1 of Article 5 which decides it is not in a position to establish and implement a system for licensing the import and export of controlled substances in Annexes C and E, may delay taking those actions until 1 January 2005 and 1 January 2002, respectively. 3. Each Party shall, within three months of the date of introducing its licensing system, report to the Secretariat on the establishment and operation of that system. 4. The Secretariat shall periodically prepare and circulate to all Parties a list of the Parties that have reported to it on their licensing systems and shall forward this information to the Implementation Committee for consideration and appropriate recommendations to the Parties.

Article 5: Special situation of developing countries: 1. Any Party that is a developing country and whose annual calculated level of consumption of the controlled substances in Annex A is less than 0.3 kilograms per capita on the date of the entry into force of the Protocol for it, or any time thereafter until 1 January 1999, shall, in order to meet its basic domestic needs, be entitled to delay for ten years its compliance with the control measures set out in Articles 2A to 2E, provided that any further amendments to the adjustments or Amendment adopted at the Second Meeting of the Parties in London, 29 June 1990, shall apply to the Parties operating under this paragraph after the review provided for in paragraph 8 of this Article has taken place and shall be based on the conclusions of that review. 2. However, any Party operating under paragraph 1 of this Article shall exceed neither an annual calculated level of consumption of the controlled substances in Annex A of 0.3 kilograms per capita nor an annual calculated level of consumption of controlled substances of Annex B of 0.2 kilograms per capita. 3. When implementing the control measures set out in Articles 2A to 2E, any Party operating under paragraph 1 of this Article shall be entitled to use: (a) For controlled substances under Annex A, either the average of its annual calculated level of consumption for the period 1995 to 1997 inclusive or a calculated level of consumption of 0.3 kilograms per capita, whichever is the lower, as the basis for determining its compliance with the control measures relating to consumption. (b) For controlled substances under Annex B, the average of its annual calculated level of consumption for the period 1998 to 2000 inclusive or a calculated level of consumption of 0.2 kilograms per capita, whichever is the lower, as the basis for determining its compliance with the control measures relating to consumption. (c) For controlled substances under Annex A, either the average of its annual calculated level of production for the period 1995 to 1997 inclusive or a calculated level of production of 0.3 kilograms per capita, whichever is the lower, as the basis for determining its compliance with the control measures relating to production. (d) For controlled substances under Annex B, either the average of its annual calculated level of production for the period 1998 to 2000 inclusive or a calculated level of production of 0.2 kilograms per capita, whichever is the lower, as the basis for determining its compliance with the control measures relating to production. 4. If a Party operating under paragraph 1 of this Article, at any time before the control measures obligations in Articles 2A to 2I become applicable to it, finds itself unable to obtain an adequate supply of controlled substances, it may notify this to the Secretariat. The Secretariat shall forthwith transmit a copy of such notification to the Parties, which shall consider the matter at their next Meeting, and decide upon appropriate action to be taken.

Article 6: Assessment and review of control measures: Beginning in 1990, and at least every four years thereafter, the Parties shall assess the control measures provided for in Article 2 and Articles 2A to 2I on the basis of available scientific, environmental, technical and economic information. At least one year before each assessment, the Parties shall convene appropriate panels of experts qualified in the fields mentioned and determine the composition and terms of reference of any such panels. Within one year of being convened, the panels will report their conclusions, through the Secretariat, to the Parties.

Article 7: Reporting of data: Each Party shall provide to the Secretariat, within three months of becoming a Party, statistical data on its production, imports and exports of each of the controlled substances in Annex A for the year 1986, or the best possible estimates of such data where actual data are not available.

Article 8: Non-compliance: The Parties, at their first meeting, shall consider and approve procedures and institutional mechanisms for determining non-compliance with the provisions of this Protocol and for treatment of Parties found to be in non-compliance.

Article 9: Research, development, public awareness and exchange of information: 1. The Parties shall co-operate, consistent with their national laws, regulations and practices and taking into account in particular the needs of developing countries, in promoting, directly or through competent international bodies, research, development and exchange of information on: (a) best technologies for improving the containment, recovery, recycling, or destruction of controlled substances or otherwise reducing their emissions; (b) possible alternatives to controlled substances, to products containing such substances, and to products manufactured with them; and (c) costs and benefits of relevant control strategies. 2. The Parties, individually, jointly or through competent international bodies, shall co-operate in promoting public awareness of the environmental effects of the emissions of controlled substances and other substances that deplete the ozone layer.3. Within two years of the entry into force of this Protocol and every two years thereafter, each Party shall submit to the Secretariat a summary of the activities it has conducted pursuant to this Article.

Article 10: Financial mechanism: 1. The Parties shall establish a mechanism for the purposes of providing financial and technical co-operation, including the transfer of technologies, to Parties operating under paragraph 1 of Article 5 of this Protocol to enable their compliance with the control measures set out in Articles 2A to 2E and Article 2I, and any control measures in Articles 2F to 2H that are decided pursuant to paragraph 1 *bis* of Article 5 of the Protocol. The mechanism, contributions to which shall be additional to other financial transfers to Parties operating under that paragraph, shall meet all agreed incremental costs of such Parties in order to enable their compliance with the control measures of the Protocol. An indicative list of the categories of incremental costs shall be decided by the meeting of the Parties.2. The mechanism established under paragraph 1 shall include a Multilateral Fund. It may also include other means of multilateral, regional and bilateral co-operation. 3. The Multilateral Fund shall: (a) Meet, on a grant or concessional basis as appropriate, and according to criteria to be decided upon by the Parties, the agreed incremental costs; (b) Finance clearing-house functions to: (i) Assist Parties operating under paragraph 1 of Article 5, through country specific studies and other technical co-operation, to identify their needs for co-operation; (ii) Facilitate technical co-operation to meet these identified needs; (iii) Distribute, as provided for in Article 9, information and relevant materials, and hold workshops, training sessions, and other related activities, for the benefit of Parties that are developing countries; and (iv) Facilitate and monitor other multilateral, regional and bilateral co-operation available to Parties that are developing countries; (c) Finance the secretarial services of the Multilateral Fund and related support costs. 4. The Multilateral Fund shall operate under the authority of the Parties who shall decide on its overall policies. 5. The Parties shall establish an Executive Committee to develop and monitor the implementation of specific operational policies, guidelines and administrative arrangements, including the disbursement of resources, for the purpose of achieving the objectives of the Multilateral Fund. The Executive Committee shall discharge its tasks and responsibilities, specified in its terms of reference as agreed by the Parties, with the co-operation and assistance of the International Bank for Reconstruction and Development (World Bank), the United Nations Environment Programme, the United Nations Development Programme or other appropriate agencies depending on their respective areas of expertise. The members of the Executive Committee, which shall be selected on the basis of a balanced representation of the Parties operating under paragraph 1 of Article 5 and of the Parties not so operating, shall be endorsed by the Parties. 6. The Multilateral Fund shall be financed by contributions from Parties not operating under paragraph 1 of Article 5 in convertible currency or, in certain circumstances, in kind and/or in national currency, on the basis of the United Nations scale of assessments. Contributions by other Parties shall be encouraged. Bilateral and, in particular cases agreed by a decision of the Parties, regional co-operation may, up to a percentage and consistent with any criteria to be specified by decision of the Parties, be considered as a contribution to the Multilateral Fund, provided that such co-operation, as a minimum: (a) Strictly relates to compliance with the provisions of this Protocol; (b) Provides additional resources; and (c) Meets agreed incremental costs. 7. The Parties shall decide upon the programme budget of the Multilateral Fund for each fiscal period and upon the percentage of contributions of the individual Parties thereto.8. Resources under the Multilateral Fund shall be disbursed with the concurrence of the beneficiary Party. 9. Decisions by the Parties under this Article shall be taken by consensus whenever possible. If all efforts at consensus have been exhausted and no agreement reached, decisions shall be adopted by a two-thirds majority vote of the Parties present and voting, representing a majority of the Parties operating under paragraph 1 of Article 5 present and voting and a majority of the Parties not so operating present and voting.10. The financial mechanism set out in this Article is without prejudice to any future arrangements that may be developed with respect to other environmental issues.

Article 10A: Transfer of technology: Each Party shall take every practicable step, consistent with the programmes supported by the financial mechanism, to ensure: (a) that the best available, environmentally safe substitutes and related technologies are expeditiously transferred to Parties operating under paragraph 1 of Article 5; and (b) that the transfers referred to in subparagraph (a) occur under fair and most favourable conditions.

Article 11: Meetings of the parties: 1. The Parties shall hold meetings at regular intervals. The Secretariat shall convene the first meeting of the Parties not later than one year after the date of the entry into force of this Protocol and in conjunction with a meeting of the Conference of the Parties to the Convention, if a meeting of the latter is scheduled within that period. 2. Subsequent ordinary meetings of the parties shall be held, unless the Parties otherwise decide, in conjunction with meetings of the Conference of the Parties to the Convention. Extraordinary meetings of the Parties shall be held at such other times as may be deemed necessary by a meeting of the Parties, or at the written request of any Party, provided that within six months of such a request being communicated to them by the Secretariat, it is supported by at least one-third of the Parties.

Article 13: Financial provisions: The funds required for the operation of this Protocol, including those for the functioning of the Secretariat related to this Protocol, shall be charged exclusively against contributions from the Parties. The Parties, at their first meeting, shall adopt by consensus financial rules for the operation of this Protocol.

Article 14: Relationship of this Protocolto the Convention: Except as otherwise provided in this Protocol, the provisions of the Convention relating to its protocols shall apply to this Protocol.

Article 15: Signature: This Protocol shall be open for signature by States and by regional economic integration organisations in Montreal on 16 September 1987, in Ottawa from 17 September 1987 to 16 January 1988, and at United Nations Headquarters in New York from 17 January 1988 to 15 September 1988.

Article 16: Entry into force: This Protocol shall enter into force on 1 January 1989, provided that at least eleven instruments of ratification, acceptance, approval of the Protocol or accession thereto have been deposited by States or regional economic integration organisations representing at least two-thirds of 1986 estimated global consumption of the controlled substances, and the provisions of paragraph 1 of Article 17 of the Convention have been fulfilled. In the event that these conditions have not been fulfilled by that date, the Protocol shall enter into force on the ninetieth day following the date on which the conditions have been fulfilled. 2. For the purposes of paragraph 1, any such instrument deposited by a regional economic integration organisation shall not be counted as additional to those deposited by member States of such organisation. 3. After the entry into force of this Protocol, any State or regional economic integration organisation shall become a Party to it on the ninetieth day following the date of deposit of its instrument of ratification, acceptance, approval or accession.

Article 17: Parties joining after entry into force: Subject to Article 5, any State or regional economic integration organisation which becomes a Party to this Protocol after the date of its entry into force, shall fulfil forthwith the sum of the obligations under Article 2, as well as under Articles 2A to 2I and Article 4, that apply at that date to the States and regional economic integration organisations that became Parties on the date the Protocol entered into force.

Article 18: Reservations: No reservations may be made to this Protocol.

Article 19: Withdrawal: Any Party may withdraw from this Protocol by giving written notification to the Depositary at any time after four years of assuming the obligations specified in paragraph 1 of Article 2A. Any such withdrawal shall take effect upon expiry of one year after the date of its receipt by the Depositary, or on such later date as may be specified in the notification of the withdrawal.

Article 20: Authentic texts: The original of this Protocol, of which the Arabic, Chinese, English, French, Russian and Spanish texts are equally authentic, shall be deposited with the Secretary-General of the United Nations.

Kyoto Protocol

According to wikipedia, the Kyoto Protocol is an international treaty, which extends the 1992 United Nations Framework Convention on Climate Change that commits State Parties to reduce greenhouse gases emissions, based on the premise that (a) global warming exists and (b) man-made CO_2 emissions have caused it. The Kyoto Protocol was adopted in Kyoto, Japan, on 11 December 1997 and entered into force on 16 February 2005. There are currently 192 Parties (Canada withdrew effective December 2012) to the Protocol. The main goal of the Kyoto Protocol is to control emissions of the main anthropogenic (i.e., human-emitted) greenhouse gases (GHGs) in ways that reflect underlying national differences in GHG emissions, wealth, and capacity to make the reductions.

The Kyoto Protocol is an international agreement linked to the United Nations Framework Convention on Climate Change, which commits its Parties by setting internationally binding emission reduction targets. Recognising that developed countries are principally responsible for the current high levels of GHG emissions in the atmosphere as a result of more than 150 years of industrial activity, the Protocol places a heavier burden on developed nations under the principle of "common but differentiated responsibilities."

The Kyoto Protocol's first round commitments are the first detailed step taken within the UN Framework Convention on Climate Change. The ultimate objective of the UNFCCC is the "stabilisation of greenhouse gas concentrations in the atmosphere at a level that would stop dangerous anthropogenic interference with the climate system." Under the Kyoto Protocol, 37 industrialised countries and the European Community commit themselves to binding targets for GHG emissions. The Protocol also reaffirms the principle that developed countries have to pay billions of dollars, and supply technology to other countries for climate-related studies and projects.

KP was structured on the principles of the Convention. It only binds developed countries because it recognises that they are largely responsible for the current high levels of GHG emissions in the atmosphere, which are the result of more than 150 years of industrial activity. KP places a heavier burden on developed nations under its central principle: that of "common but differentiated responsibility". In Doha, Qatar, on 8 December 2012, the Doha Amendment to the Kyoto Protocol was adopted. This launched a second commitment period, starting on 1 January 2013 until 2020.

Kyoto Protocol to the United Nations Framework Convention on Climate Change

Article 1: For the purposes of this Protocol, the definitions contained in Article 1 of the Convention shall apply. In addition: "Conference of the Parties" means the Conference of the Parties to the Convention. "Convention" means the United Nations Framework Convention on Climate Change, adopted in New York on 9 May 1992. "Intergovernmental Panel on Climate Change" means the Intergovernmental Panel on Climate Change established in 1988 jointly by the World Meteorological

Organisation and the United Nations Environment Programme. "Montreal Protocol" means the Montreal Protocol on Substances that Deplete the Ozone Layer, adopted in Montreal on 16 September 1987 and as subsequently adjusted and amended. "Parties present and voting" means Parties present and casting an affirmative or negative vote. "Party" means, unless the context otherwise indicates, a Party to this Protocol. "Party included in Annex I" means a Party included in Annex I to the Convention, as may be amended, or a Party which has made a notification under Article 4, paragraph 2 (g), of the Convention.

Article 2: 1. Each Party included in Annex I, in achieving its quantified emission limitation and reduction commitments under Article 3, in order to promote sustainable development, shall: (a) Implement and/or further elaborate policies and measures in accordance with its national circumstances, such as: (i) Enhancement of energy efficiency in relevant sectors of the national economy; (ii) Protection and enhancement of sinks and reservoirs of greenhouse gases not controlled by the Montreal Protocol, taking into account its commitments under relevant international environmental agreements; promotion of sustainable forest management practices, afforestation and reforestation; (iii) Promotion of sustainable forms of agriculture in light of climate change considerations; (iv) Research on, and promotion, development and increased use of, new and renewable forms of energy, of carbon dioxide sequestration technologies and of advanced and innovative environmentally sound technologies; (v) Progressive reduction or phasing out of market imperfections, fiscal incentives, tax and duty exemptions and subsidies in all greenhouse gas emitting sectors that run counter to the objective of the Convention and application of market instruments; (vi) Encouragement of appropriate reforms in relevant sectors aimed at promoting policies and measures which limit or reduce emissions of greenhouse gases not controlled by the Montreal Protocol; (vii) Measures to limit and/or reduce emissions of greenhouse gases not controlled by the Montreal Protocol in the transport sector; (viii) Limitation and/or reduction of methane emissions through recovery and use in waste management, as well as in the production, transport and distribution of energy. (b) Cooperate with other such Parties to enhance the individual and combined effectiveness of their policies and measures adopted under this Article, pursuant to Article 4, paragraph 2

(e) (i), of the Convention. To this end, these Parties shall take steps to share their experience and exchange information on such policies and measures, including developing ways of improving their comparability, transparency and effectiveness. The Conference of the Parties serving as the meeting of the Parties to this Protocol shall, at its first session or as soon as practicable thereafter, consider ways to facilitate such cooperation, taking into account all relevant information. 2. The Parties included in Annex I shall pursue limitation or reduction of emissions of greenhouse gases not controlled by the Montreal Protocol from aviation and marine bunker fuels, working through the International Civil Aviation Organisation and the International Maritime Organisation, respectively. 3. The Parties included in Annex I shall strive to implement policies and measures under this Article in such a way as to minimise adverse effects, including the adverse effects of climate change, effects on international trade, and social, environmental and economic impacts on other Parties, especially developing country Parties and in particular those identified in Article 4, paragraphs 8 and 9, of the Convention, taking into account Article 3 of the Convention. The Conference of the Parties serving as the meeting of the Parties to this Protocol may take further action, as appropriate, to promote the implementation of the provisions of this paragraph. 4. The Conference of the Parties serving as the meeting of the Parties to this Protocol, if it decides that it would be beneficial to coordinate any of the policies and measures in paragraph 1 (a) above, taking into account different national circumstances and potential effects, shall consider ways and means to elaborate the coordination of such policies and measures.

Article 3: 1. The Parties included in Annex I shall, individually or jointly, ensure that their aggregate anthropogenic carbon dioxide equivalent emissions of the greenhouse gases listed in Annex A do not exceed their assigned amounts, calculated pursuant to their quantified emission limitation and reduction commitments inscribed in Annex B and in accordance with the provisions of this Article, with a view to reducing their overall emissions of such gases by at least five per cent below 1990 levels in the commitment period 2008 to 2012. 2. Each Party included in Annex I shall, by 2005, have made demonstrable progress in achieving its commitments under this Protocol.3.

The net changes in greenhouse gas emissions by sources and removals by sinks resulting from direct human-induced land-use change and forestry activities, limited to afforestation, reforestation and deforestation since 1990, measured as verifiable changes in carbon stocks in each commitment period, shall be used to meet the commitments under this Article of each Party included in Annex I. The greenhouse gas emissions by sources and removals by sinks associated with those activities shall be reported in a transparent and verifiable manner and reviewed in accordance with Articles 7 and 8. 4. Prior to the first session of the Conference of the Parties serving as the meeting of the Parties to this Protocol, each Party included in Annex I shall provide, for consideration by the Subsidiary Body for Scientific and Technological Advice, data to establish its level of carbon stocks in 1990 and to enable an estimate to be made of its changes in carbon stocks in subsequent years. The Conference of the Parties serving as the meeting of the Parties to this Protocol shall, at its first session or as soon as practicable thereafter, decide upon modalities, rules and guidelines as to how, and which, additional human-induced activities related to changes in greenhouse gas emissions by sources and removals by sinks in the agricultural soils and the land-use change and forestry categories shall be added to, or subtracted from, the assigned amounts for Parties included in Annex I, taking into account uncertainties, transparency in reporting, verifiability, the methodological work of the Intergovernmental Panel on Climate Change, the advice provided by the Subsidiary Body for Scientific and Technological Advice in accordance with Article 5 and the decisions of the Conference of the Parties. Such a decision shall apply in the second and subsequent commitment periods. A Party may choose to apply such a decision on these additional human-induced activities for its first commitment period, provided that these activities have taken place since 1990.5. The Parties included in Annex I undergoing the process of transition to a market economy whose base year or period was established pursuant to decision 9/CP. 2 of the Conference of the Parties at its second session shall use that base year or period for the implementation of their commitments under this Article. Any other Party included in Annex I undergoing the process of transition to a market economy which has not yet submitted its first national communication under Article 12 of the Convention may also notify the Conference of the Parties serving as the meeting of the Parties to this Protocol that it intends to use an historical base year or period other than 1990 for the implementation of its commitments under this Article. The Conference of the Parties serving as the meeting of the Parties to this Protocol shall decide on the acceptance of such notification. 6. Taking into account Article 4, paragraph 6, of the Convention, in the implementation of their commitments under this Protocol other than those under this Article, a certain degree of flexibility shall be allowed by the Conference of the Parties serving as the meeting of the Parties to this Protocol to the Parties included in Annex I undergoing the process of transition to a market economy.7. In the first quantified emission limitation and reduction commitment period, from 2008 to 2012, the assigned amount for each Party included in Annex I shall be equal to the percentage inscribed for it in Annex B of its aggregate anthropogenic carbon dioxide equivalent emissions of the greenhouse gases listed in Annex A in 1990, or the base year or period determined in accordance with paragraph 5 above, multiplied by five. Those Parties included in Annex I for whom land-use change and forestry constituted a net source of greenhouse gas emissions in 1990 shall include in their 1990 emissions base year or period the aggregate anthropogenic carbon dioxide equivalent emissions by sources minus removals by sinks in 1990 from land-use change for the purposes of calculating their assigned amount.8. Any Party included in Annex I may use 1995 as its base year for hydrofluorocarbons, perfluorocarbons and sulphur hexafluoride, for the purposes of the calculation referred to in paragraph 7 above. 9. Commitments for subsequent periods for Parties included in Annex I shall be established in amendments to Annex B to this Protocol, which shall be adopted in accordance with the provisions of Article 21, paragraph 7. The Conference of the Parties serving as the meeting of the Parties to this Protocol shall initiate the consideration of such commitments at least seven years before the end of the first commitment period referred to in paragraph 1 above. 10. Any emission reduction units, or any part of an assigned amount, which a Party acquires from another Party in accordance with the provisions of Article 6 or of Article 17 shall be added to the assigned amount for the acquiring Party. 11. Any emission reduction units, or any part of an assigned amount, which a Party transfers to another Party in accordance with the provisions of Article 6 or of Article 17 shall be subtracted from the assigned amount for the transferring Party. 12. Any certified emission reductions which a Party acquires from another Party in accordance with the provisions of Article 12 shall be added to the assigned amount for the acquiring Party. 13. If the emissions of a Party included in Annex I in a commitment period are less than its assigned amount under this Article, this difference shall, on request of that Party, be added to the assigned amount for that Party for subsequent commitment periods. 14. Each Party included in Annex I shall strive to implement the commitments mentioned in paragraph 1 above in such a way as to minimise adverse social, environmental and economic impacts on developing country Parties, particularly those identified in Article 4, paragraphs 8 and 9, of the Convention. In line with relevant decisions of the Conference of the Parties on the implementation of those paragraphs, the Conference of the Parties serving as the meeting of the Parties to this Protocol shall, at its first session, consider what actions are necessary to minimise the adverse effects of climate change and/or the impacts of response measures on Parties referred to in those paragraphs. Among the issues to be considered shall be the establishment of funding, insurance and transfer of technology.

Article 4: 1. Any Parties included in Annex I that have reached an agreement to fulfil their commitments under Article 3 jointly, shall be deemed to have met those commitments provided that their total combined aggregate anthropogenic carbon dioxide equivalent emissions of the greenhouse gases listed in Annex A do not exceed their assigned amounts calculated pursuant to their quantified emission limitation and reduction commitments inscribed in Annex B and in accordance with the provisions of Article 3. The respective emission level allocated to each of the Parties to the agreement shall be set out in that agreement. 2. The Parties to any such agreement shall notify the secretariat of the terms of the agreement on the date of deposit of their instruments of ratification, acceptance or approval of this Protocol, or accession thereto. The secretariat shall in turn inform the Parties and signatories to the Convention of the terms of the agreement. 3. Any such agreement shall remain in operation for the duration of the commitment period specified in Article 3, paragraph 7. 4. If Parties acting jointly do so in the framework of, and together with, a regional economic integration organisation, any alteration in the composition of the organisation after adoption of this Protocol shall not affect existing commitments under this Protocol. Any alteration in the composition of the organisation shall only apply for the purposes of those commitments under Article 3 that are adopted subsequent to that alteration.5. In the event of failure by the Parties to such an agreement to achieve their total combined level of emission reductions, each Party to that agreement shall be responsible for its own level of emissions set out in the agreement.6. If Parties acting jointly do so in the framework of, and together with, a regional economic integration organisation which is itself a Party to this Protocol, each member State of that regional economic integration organisation individually, and together with the regional economic integration organisation acting in accordance with Article 24, shall, in the event of failure to achieve the total combined level of emission reductions, be responsible for its level of emissions as notified in accordance with this Article

Article 5: 1. Each Party included in Annex I shall have in place, no later than one year prior to the start of the first commitment period, a national system for the estimation of anthropogenic emissions by sources and removals by sinks of all greenhouse gases not controlled by the Montreal Protocol. Guidelines for such national systems, which shall incorporate the methodologies specified in paragraph 2 below, shall be decided upon by the Conference of the Parties serving as the meeting of the Parties to this Protocol at its first session. 2. Methodologies for estimating anthropogenic emissions by sources and removals by sinks of all greenhouse gases not controlled by the Montreal Protocol shall be those accepted by the Intergovernmental Panel on Climate Change and agreed upon by the Conference of the Parties at its third session. Where such methodologies are not used, appropriate adjustments shall be applied according to methodologies agreed upon by the Conference of the Parties serving as the meeting of the Parties to this Protocol at its first session. Based on the work of, *inter alia*, the Intergovernmental Panel on Climate Change and advice provided by the Subsidiary Body for Scientific and Technological Advice, the Conference of the Parties serving as the meeting of the Parties to this Protocol shall regularly review and, as appropriate, revise such methodologies and adjustments, taking fully into account any relevant decisions by the Conference of the Parties. Any revision to methodologies or adjustments shall be used only for the purposes of ascertaining compliance with commitments under Article 3 in respect of any commitment period adopted subsequent to that revision. 3. The global warming potentials used to calculate the carbon dioxide equivalence of Anthropogenic emissions by sources and removals by sinks of greenhouse gases listed in Annex A shall be those accepted by the Intergovernmental Panel on Climate Change and agreed upon by the Conference of the Parties at its third session. Based on the work of, *inter alia*, the Intergovernmental Panel on Climate Change and advice provided by the Subsidiary Body for Scientific and Technological Advice, the Conference of the Parties serving as the meeting of the Parties to this Protocol shall regularly review and, as appropriate, revise the global warming potential of each such greenhouse gas, taking fully into account any relevant decisions by the Conference of the Parties. Any revision to a global warming potential shall apply only to commitments under Article 3 in respect of any commitment period adopted subsequent to that revision.

Article 6: 1. For the purpose of meeting its commitments under Article 3, any Party included in Annex I may transfer to, or acquire from, any other such Party emission reduction units resulting from projects aimed at reducing anthropogenic emissions by sources or enhancing anthropogenic removals by sinks of greenhouse gases in any sector of the economy, provided that: (a) Any such project has the approval of the Parties involved; (b) Any such project provides a reduction in emissions by sources, or an enhancement of removals by sinks, that is additional to any that would otherwise occur; (c) It does not acquire any emission reduction units if it is not in compliance with its obligations under Articles 5 and 7; and (d) The acquisition of emission reduction units shall be supplemental to domestic actions for the purposes of meeting commitments under Article 3. 2. The Conference of the Parties serving as the meeting of the Parties to this Protocol may, at its first session or as soon as practicable thereafter, further elaborate guidelines for the implementation of this Article, including for verification and reporting. 3. A Party included in Annex I may authorise legal entities to participate, under its responsibility, in actions leading to the generation, transfer or acquisition under this Article of emission reduction units. 4. If a question of implementation by a Party included in Annex I of the requirements referred to in this Article is identified in accordance with the relevant provisions of Article 8, transfers and acquisitions of emission reduction units may continue to be made after the question has been identified, provided that any such units may not be used by a Party to meet its commitments under Article 3 until any issue of compliance is resolved.

Article 7: 1. Each Party included in Annex I shall incorporate in its annual inventory of anthropogenic emissions by sources and removals by sinks of greenhouse gases not controlled by the Montreal Protocol, submitted in accordance with the relevant decisions of the Conference of the Parties, the necessary supplementary information for the purposes of ensuring compliance with Article 3, to be determined in accordance with paragraph 4 below. 2. Each Party included in Annex I shall incorporate in its national communication, submitted under Article 12 of the Convention, the supplementary information necessary to demonstrate compliance with its commitments under this Protocol, to be determined in accordance with paragraph 4 below. 3. Each Party included in Annex I shall submit the information required under paragraph 1 above annually, beginning with the first inventory due under the Convention for the first year of the commitment period after this Protocol has entered into force for that Party. Each such Party shall submit the information required under paragraph 2 above as part of the first national communication due under the Convention after this Protocol has entered into force for it and after the adoption of guidelines as provided for in paragraph 4 below. The frequency of subsequent submission of information required under this Article shall be determined by the Conference of the Parties serving as the meeting of the Parties to this Protocol, taking into account any timetable for the submission of national communications decided upon by the Conference of the Parties.4.The Conference of the Parties serving as the meeting of the Parties to this Protocol shall adopt at its first session, and review periodically thereafter, guidelines for the preparation of the information required under this Article, taking into account guidelines for the preparation of national communications by Parties included in Annex I adopted by the Conference of the Parties. The Conference of the Parties serving as the meeting of the Parties to this Protocol shall also, prior to the first commitment period, decide upon modalities for the accounting of assigned amounts.

Article 8: 1. The information submitted under Article 7 by each Party included in Annex I shall be reviewed by expert review teams pursuant to the relevant decisions of the Conference of the Parties and in accordance with guidelines adopted for this purpose by the Conference of the Parties serving as the meeting of the Parties to this Protocol under paragraph 4 below. The information submitted under Article 7, paragraph 1, by each Party included in Annex I shall be reviewed as part of the annual compilation and accounting of emissions inventories and assigned amounts. Additionally, the information submitted under Article 7, paragraph 2, by each Party included in Annex I shall be reviewed as part of the review of communications. 2. Expert review teams shall be coordinated by the secretariat and shall be composed of experts selected from those nominated by Parties to the Convention and, as appropriate, by intergovernmental organisations, in accordance with guidance provided for this purpose by the Conference of the Parties. 3. The review process shall provide a thorough and comprehensive technical assessment of all aspects of the implementation by a Party of this Protocol. The expert review teams shall prepare a report to the Conference of the Parties serving as the meeting of the Parties to this Protocol, assessing the implementation of the commitments of the Party and identifying any potential problems in, and factors influencing, the fulfilment of commitments. Such reports shall be circulated by the secretariat to all Parties to the Convention. The secretariat shall list those questions of implementation indicated in such reports for further consideration by the Conference of the Parties serving as the meeting of the Parties to this Protocol. 4. The Conference of the Parties serving as the meeting of the Parties to this Protocol shall adopt at its first session, and review periodically thereafter, guidelines for the review of implementation of this Protocol by expert review teams taking into account the relevant decisions of the Conference of the Parties. 5. The Conference of the Parties serving as the meeting of the Parties to this Protocol shall, with the assistance of the Subsidiary Body for Implementation and, as appropriate, the Subsidiary Body for Scientific and Technological Advice, consider:

(a) The information submitted by Parties under Article 7 and the reports of the expert reviews thereon conducted under this Article; and (b) Those questions of implementation listed by the secretariat under paragraph 3 above, as well as any questions raised by Parties. 6. Pursuant to its consideration of the information referred to in paragraph 5 above, the Conference of the Parties serving as the meeting of the Parties to this Protocol shall take decisions on any matter required for the implementation of this Protocol.

Article 9: 1. The Conference of the Parties serving as the meeting of the Parties to this Protocol shall periodically review this Protocol in the light of the best available scientific information and assessments on climate change and its impacts, as well as relevant technical, social and economic information. Such reviews shall be coordinated with pertinent reviews under the Convention, in particular those required by Article 4, paragraph 2 (d), and Article 7, paragraph 2 (a), of the Convention. Based on these reviews, the Conference of the Parties serving as the meeting of the Parties to this Protocol shall take appropriate action.2. The first review shall take place at the second session of the Conference of the Parties serving as the meeting of the Parties to this Protocol. Further reviews shall take place at regular intervals and in a timely manner.

Article 10: All Parties, taking into account their common but differentiated responsibilities and their specific national and regional development priorities, objectives and circumstances, without introducing any new commitments for Parties not included in Annex I, but reaffirming existing commitments under Article 4, paragraph 1, of the Convention, and continuing to advance the implementation of these commitments in order to achieve sustainable development, taking into account Article 4, paragraphs 3, 5 and 7, of the Convention, shall: (a) Formulate, where relevant and to the extent possible, cost-effective national and, where appropriate, regional programme mes to improve the quality of local emission factors, activity data and/or models which reflect the socio-economic conditions of each Party for the preparation and periodic updating of national inventories of anthropogenic emissions by sources and removals by sinks of all greenhouse gases not controlled by the Montreal Protocol, using comparable methodologies to be agreed upon by the Conference of the Parties, and consistent with the guidelines for the preparation of national communications adopted by the Conference of the Parties; (b) Formulate, implement, publish and regularly update national and, where appropriate, regional programmes containing measures to mitigate climate change and measures to facilitate adequate adaptation to climate change: (i) Such programmes would, *inter alia*, concern the energy, transport and industry sectors as well as agriculture, forestry and waste management. Furthermore, adaptation technologies and methods for improving spatial planning would improve adaptation to climate change; and (ii) Parties included in Annex I shall submit information on action under this Protocol, including national programmes, in accordance with Article 7; and other Parties shall seek to include in their national communications, as appropriate, information on programmes which contain measures that the Party believes contribute to addressing climate change and its adverse impacts, including the abatement of increases in greenhouse gas emissions, and enhancement of and removals by sinks, capacity building and adaptation measures; (c) Cooperate in the promotion of effective modalities for the development, application and diffusion of, and take all practicable steps to promote, facilitate and finance, as appropriate, the transfer of, or access to, environmentally sound technologies, know-how, practices and processes pertinent to climate change, in particular to developing countries, including the formulation of policies and programmes for the effective transfer of environmentally sound technologies that are publicly owned or in the public domain and the creation of an enabling environment for the private sector, to promote and enhance the transfer of, and access to, environmentally sound technologies; (d) Cooperate in scientific and technical research and promote the maintenance and the development of systematic observation systems and development of data archives to reduce uncertainties related to the climate system, the adverse impacts of climate change and the economic and social consequences of various response strategies, and promote the development and strengthening of endogenous capacities and capabilities to participate in international and intergovernmental efforts, programmes and networks on research and systematic observation, taking into account Article 5 of the Convention; (e) Cooperate in and promote at the international level, and, where appropriate, using existing bodies, the development and implementation of education and training programmes, including the strengthening of national capacity building, in particular human and institutional capacities and the exchange or secondment of personnel to train experts in this field, in particular for developing countries, and facilitate at the national level public awareness of, and public access to information on, climate change. Suitable modalities should be developed to implement these activities through the relevant bodies of the Convention, taking into account Article 6 of the Convention; (f) Include in their national communications information on programmes and activities undertaken pursuant to this Article in accordance with relevant decisions of the Conference of the Parties; and (g) Give full consideration, in implementing the commitments under this Article, to Article 4, paragraph 8, of the Convention.

Article 11: 1.In the implementation of Article 10, Parties shall take into account the provisions ofArticle 4, paragraphs 4, 5, 7, 8 and 9, of the Convention. 2. In the context of the implementation of Article 4, paragraph 1, of the Convention, inaccordance with the provisions of Article 4, paragraph 3, and Article 11 of the Convention, and through the entity or entities entrusted with the operation of the financial mechanism of the Convention, the developed country Parties and other developed Parties included in Annex II to the Convention shall:Provide new and additional financial resources to meet the agreed full costs incurred by developing country Parties in advancing the implementation of existing commitments under Article 4, paragraph 1 (a), of the Convention that are covered in Article 10, subparagraph (a); and Also provide such financial resources, including for the transfer of technology, needed by the developing country Parties to meet the agreed full incremental costs of advancing the implementation of existing commitments under Article 4, paragraph 1, of the Convention that are covered by Article 10 and that are agreed between a developing country Party and the international entity or entities referred to in Article 11 of the Convention, in accordance with that Article. The implementation of these existing commitments shall take into account the need for adequacy and predictability in the flow of funds and the importance of appropriate burden sharing among developed country Parties. The guidance to the entity or entities entrusted with the operation of the financial mechanism of the Convention in relevant decisions of the Conference of the Parties, including those agreed before the adoption of this Protocol, shall apply mutatis mutandis to the provisions of this paragraph. 3. The developed country Parties and other developed Parties in Annex II to the Convention may also provide, and developing country Parties avail themselves of, financial resources for the implementation of Article 10, through bilateral, regional and other multilateral channels.

Article 12: 1. A clean development mechanism is hereby defined. 2. The purpose of the clean development mechanism shall be to assist Parties not included in Annex I in achieving sustainable development and in contributing to the ultimate objective of the Convention, and to assist Parties included in Annex I in achieving compliance with their quantified emission limitation and reduction commitments under Article 3. 3. Under the clean development mechanism: (a) Parties not included in Annex I will benefit from project activities resulting in certified emission reductions; and (b) Parties included in Annex I may use the certified emission reductions accruing from such project activities to contribute to compliance with part of their quantified emission limitation and reduction commitments under Article 3, as determined by the Conference of the Parties serving as the meeting of the Parties to this Protocol. 4. The clean development mechanism shall be subject to the authority and guidance of the Conference of the Parties serving as the meeting of the Parties to this Protocol and be supervised by an executive board of the clean development mechanism. 5. Emission reductions resulting from each project activity shall be certified by operational entities to be designated by the Conference of the Parties serving as the meeting of the Parties to this Protocol, on the basis of: (a) Voluntary participation approved by each Party involved; (b) Real, measurable, and long-term benefits related to the mitigation of climate change; and (c) Reductions in emissions that are additional to any that would occur in the absence of the certified project activity. 6. The clean development mechanism shall assist in arranging funding of certified project activities as necessary. 7. The Conference of the Parties serving as the meeting of the Parties to this Protocol shall, at its first session, elaborate modalities and procedures with the objective of ensuring transparency, efficiency and accountability through independent auditing and verification of project activities. 8. The Conference of the Parties serving as the meeting of the Parties to this

Protocol shall ensure that a share of the proceeds from certified project activities is used to cover administrative expenses as well as to assist developing country Parties that are particularly vulnerable to the adverse effects of climate change to meet the costs of adaptation. 9. Participation under the clean development mechanism, including in activities mentioned in paragraph 3 (a) above and in the acquisition of certified emission reductions, may involve private and/or public entities, and is to be subject to whatever guidance may be provided by the executive board of the clean development mechanism.10. Certified emission reductions obtained during the period from the year 2000 up to the beginning of the first commitment period can be used to assist in achieving compliance in the first commitment period.

Article 13: 1. The Conference of the Parties, the supreme body of the Convention, shall serve as the meeting of the Parties to this Protocol. 2. Parties to the Convention that are not Parties to this Protocol may participate as observers in the proceedings of any session of the Conference of the Parties serving as the meeting of the Parties to this Protocol. When the Conference of the Parties serves as the meeting of the Parties to this Protocol, decisions under this Protocol shall be taken only by those that are Parties to this Protocol.3. When the Conference of the Parties serves as the meeting of the Parties to this Protocol, any member of the Bureau of the Conference of the Parties representing a Party to the Convention but, at that time, not a Party to this Protocol, shall be replaced by an additional member to be elected by and from amongst the Parties to this Protocol. 4. The Conference of the Parties serving as the meeting of the Parties to this Protocol shall keep under regular review the implementation of this Protocol and shall make, within its mandate, the decisions necessary to promote its effective implementation. It shall perform the functions assigned to it by this Protocol and shall: (a) Assess, on the basis of all information made available to it in accordance with the provisions of this Protocol, the implementation of this Protocol by the Parties, the overall effects of the measures taken pursuant to this Protocol, in particular environmental, economic and social effects as well as their cumulative impacts and the extent to which progress towards the objective of the Convention is being achieved; (b) Periodically examine the obligations of the Parties under this Protocol, giving due consideration to any reviews required by

Article 4, paragraph 2 (d), and Article 7, paragraph 2, of the Convention, in the light of the objective of the Convention, the experience gained in its implementation and the evolution of scientific and technological knowledge, and in this respect consider and adopt regular reports on the implementation of this Protocol; (c) Promote and facilitate the exchange of information on measures adopted by the Parties to address climate change and its effects, taking into account the differing circumstances, responsibilities and capabilities of the Parties and their respective commitments under this Protocol; (d) Facilitate, at the request of two or more Parties, the coordination of measures adopted by them to address climate change and its effects, taking into account the differing circumstances, responsibilities and capabilities of the Parties and their respective commitments under this Protocol;(e) Promote and guide, in accordance with the objective of the Convention and the provisions of this Protocol, and taking fully into account the relevant decisions by the Conference of the Parties, the development and periodic refinement of comparable methodologies for the effective implementation of this Protocol, to be agreed on by the Conference of the Parties serving as the meeting of the Parties to this Protocol; (f) Make recommendations on any matters necessary for the implementation of this Protocol; (g) Seek to mobilise additional financial resources in accordance with Article 11, paragraph 2; (h) Establish such subsidiary bodies as are deemed necessary for the implementationof this Protocol; (i) Seek and utilise, where appropriate, the services and cooperation of, and information provided by, competent international organisations and intergovernmental and non-governmental bodies; and (j) Exercise such other functions as may be required for the implementation of this Protocol, and consider any assignment resulting from a decision by the Conference of the Parties.5.The rules of procedure of the Conference of the Parties and financial procedures applied under the Convention shall be applied *mutatis mutandis* under this Protocol, except as may be otherwise decided by consensus by the Conference of the Parties serving as the meeting of the Parties to this Protocol. 6. The first session of the Conference of the Parties serving as the meeting of the Parties to this Protocol shall be convened by the secretariat in conjunction with the first session of the Conference of the Parties that is scheduled after the date of the entry into force of this Protocol. Subsequent ordinary sessions of the Conference of the Parties serving as the meeting of the Parties to this Protocol shall be held every year and in conjunction with ordinary sessions of the Conference of the Parties, unless otherwise decided by the Conference of the Parties serving as the meeting of the Parties to this Protocol. 7. Extraordinary sessions of the Conference of the Parties serving as the meeting of the Parties to this Protocol shall be held at such other times as may be deemed necessary by the Conference of the Parties serving as the meeting of the Parties to this Protocol, or at the written request of any Party, provided that, within six months of the request being communicated to the Parties by the secretariat, it is supported by at least one third of the Parties.8.The United Nations, its specialised agencies and the International Atomic Energy Agency, as well as any State member thereof or observers thereto not party to the Convention, may be represented at sessions of the Conference of the Parties serving as the meeting of the Parties to this Protocol as observers. Any body or agency, whether national or international, governmental or non-governmental, which is qualified in matters covered by this Protocol and which has informed the secretariat of its wish to be represented at a session of the Conference of the Parties serving as the meeting of the Parties to this Protocol as an observer, may be so admitted unless at least one third of the Parties present object. The admission and participation of observers shall be subject to the rules of procedure, as referred to in paragraph 5 above.

Article 14: 1. The secretariat established by Article 8 of the Convention shall serve as the secretariat of this Protocol. 2. Article 8, paragraph 2, of the Convention on the functions of the secretariat, and Article 8, paragraph 3, of the Convention on arrangements made for the functioning of the secretariat, shall apply *mutatis mutandis* to this Protocol. The secretariat shall, in addition, exercise the functions assigned to it under this Protocol.

Article 15: 1. The Subsidiary Body for Scientific and Technological Advice and the Subsidiary Body for Implementation established by Articles 9 and 10 of the Convention shall serve as, respectively, the Subsidiary Body for Scientific and Technological Advice and the Subsidiary Body for Implementation of this Protocol. The provisions relating to the functioning of these two bodies under the Convention shall apply mutatis *mutandis* to this Protocol. Sessions of the meetings of the Subsidiary Body for Scientific and Technological Advice and the Subsidiary Body for Implementation of this Protocol shall be held in conjunction with the meetings of, respectively, the Subsidiary Body for Scientific and Technological Advice and the Subsidiary Body for Implementation of the Convention. 2. Parties to the Convention that are not Parties to this Protocol may participate as observers in the proceedings of any session of the subsidiary bodies. When the subsidiary bodies serve as the subsidiary bodies of this Protocol, decisions under this Protocol shall be taken only by those that are Parties to this Protocol. 3. When the subsidiary bodies established by Articles 9 and 10 of the Convention exercise their functions with regard to matters concerning this Protocol, any member of the Bureaux of those subsidiary bodies representing a Party to the Convention but, at that time, not a party to this Protocol, shall be replaced by an additional member to be elected by and from amongst the Parties to this Protocol.

Article 16: The Conference of the Parties serving as the meeting of the Parties to this Protocol shall, as soon as practicable, consider the application to this Protocol of, and modify as appropriate, the multilateral consultative process referred to in Article 13 of the Convention, in the light of any relevant decisions that may be taken by the Conference of the Parties. Any multilateral consultative process that may be applied to this Protocol shall operate without prejudice to the procedures and mechanisms established in accordance with Article 18.

Article 17: The Conference of the Parties shall define the relevant principles, modalities, rules and guidelines, in particular for verification, reporting and accountability for emissions trading. The Parties included in Annex B may participate in emissions trading for the purposes of fulfilling their commitments under Article 3. Any such trading shall be supplemental to domestic actions for the purpose of meeting quantified emission limitation and reduction commitments under thatArticle.

Article 18: The Conference of the Parties serving as the meeting of the Parties to this Protocol shall, at its first session, approve appropriate and effective procedures and mechanisms to determine and to address cases of non-compliance with the provisions of this Protocol, including through the development of an indicative list of consequences, taking into account the cause, type, degree and frequency of non-compliance. Any procedures and mechanisms under this Article entailing binding consequences shall be adopted by means of an amendment to this Protocol.

Article 19: The provisions of Article 14 of the Convention on settlement of disputes shall apply mutatis mutandis to this Protocol.

Article 20: 1. Any Party may propose amendments to this Protocol. 2. Amendments to this Protocol shall be adopted at an ordinary session of the Conference of the Parties serving as the meeting of the Parties to this Protocol. The text of any proposed amendment to this Protocol shall be communicated to the Parties by the secretariat at least six months before the meeting at which it is proposed for adoption. The secretariat shall also communicate the text of any proposed amendments to the Parties and signatories to the Convention and, for information, to the Depositary. 3. The Parties shall make every effort to reach agreement on any proposed amendment to this Protocol by consensus. If all efforts at consensus have been exhausted, and no agreement reached, the amendment shall as a last resort be adopted by a three-fourths majority vote of the Parties present and voting at the meeting. The adopted amendment shall be communicated by the secretariat to the Depositary, who shall circulate it to all Parties for their acceptance. 4. Instruments of acceptance in respect of an amendment shall be deposited with the Depositary. An amendment adopted in accordance with paragraph 3 above shall enter into force for those Parties having accepted it on the ninetieth day after the date of receipt by the Depositary of an instrument of acceptance by at least three-fourths of the Parties to this Protocol. 5. The amendment shall enter into force for any other Party on the ninetieth day after the date on which that Party deposits with the Depositary its instrument of acceptance of the said amendment.

Article 21: 1. Annexes to this Protocol shall form an integral part thereof and, unless otherwise expressly provided, a reference to this Protocol constitutes at the same time a reference to any annexes thereto. Any annexes adopted after the entry into force of this Protocol shall be restricted to lists, forms and any other material of a descriptive nature that is of a scientific, technical, procedural or administrative character. 2. Any Party may make proposals for an annex to this Protocol and may propose amendments to annexes to this Protocol. 3. Annexes to this Protocol and amendments to annexes to this Protocol shall be adopted at an ordinary session of the Conference of the Parties serving as the meeting of the Parties to this Protocol. The text of any proposed annex or amendment to an annex shall be communicated to the Parties by the secretariat at least six months before the meeting at which it is proposed for adoption. The secretariat shall also communicate the text of any proposed annex or amendment to an annex to the Parties and signatories to the Convention and, for information, to the Depositary. 4. The Parties shall make every effort to reach agreement on any proposed annex or amendment to an annex by consensus. If all efforts at consensus have been exhausted, and no agreement reached, the annex or amendment to an annex shall as a last resort be adopted by a three-fourths majority vote of the Parties present and voting at the meeting. The adopted annex or amendment to an annex shall be communicated by the secretariat to the Depositary, who shall circulate it to all Parties for their acceptance. 5. An annex, or amendment to an annex other than Annex A or B, that has been adopted in accordance with paragraphs 3 and 4 above shall enter into force for all Parties to this Protocol six months after the date of the communication by the Depositary to such Parties of the adoption of the annex or adoption of the amendment to the annex, except for those Parties that havenotified the Depositary, in writing, within that period of their non-acceptance of the annex or amendment to the annex. The annex or amendment to an annex shall enter into force for Parties which withdraw their notification of non-acceptance on the ninetieth day after the date on which withdrawal of such notification has been received by the Depositary. 6. If the adoption of an annex or an amendment to an annex involves an amendment to this Protocol, that annex or amendment to an annex shall not enter into force until such time as the amendment to this Protocol enters into force. 7. Amendments to Annexes A and B to this Protocol shall be adopted and enter into force in accordance with the procedure set out in Article 20, provided that any amendment to Annex B shall be adopted only with the written consent of the Party concerned.

Article 22: 1. Each Party shall have one vote, except as provided for in paragraph 2 below. 2. Regional economic integration organisations, in matters within their competence, shall exercise their right to vote with a number of votes equal to the number of their member States that are Parties to this Protocol. Such an organisation shall not exercise its right to vote if any of its member States exercises its right, and vice versa.

Article 23: The Secretary-General of the United Nations shall be the Depositary of this Protocol.

Article 24: 1. This Protocol shall be open for signature and subject to ratification, acceptance or approval by States and regional economic integration organisations which are Parties to the Convention. It shall be open for signature at United Nations Headquarters in New York from 16 March 1998 to 15 March 1999. This Protocol shall be open for accession from the day after the date on which it is closed for signature. Instruments of ratification, acceptance, approval or accession shall be deposited with the Depositary. 2. Any regional economic integration organisation which becomes a Party to this Protocol without any of its member States being a Party shall be bound by all the obligations under this Protocol. In the case of such organisations, one or more of whose member States is a Party to this Protocol, the organisation and its member States shall decide on their respective responsibilities for the performance of their obligations under this Protocol. In such cases, the organisation and the member States shall not be entitled to exercise rights under this Protocol concurrently.3. In their instruments of ratification, acceptance, approval or accession, regional economic integration organisations shall declare the extent of their competence with respect to the matters governed by this Protocol. These organisations shall also inform the Depositary, who shall in turn inform the Parties, of any substantial modification in the extent of their competence.

Article 25: 1. This Protocol shall enter into force on the ninetieth day after the date on which not less than 55 Parties to the Convention, incorporating Parties included in Annex I which accounted in total for at least 55 per cent of the total carbon dioxide emissions for 1990 of the Parties included in Annex I, have deposited their instruments of ratification, acceptance, approval or accession. 2. For the purposes of this Article, "the total carbon dioxide emissions for 1990 of the Parties included in Annex I" means the amount communicated on or before the date of adoption of this Protocol by the Parties included in Annex I in their first national communications submitted in accordance with Article 12 of the Convention. 3. For each State or regional economic integration organisation that ratifies, accepts or approves this Protocol or accedes thereto after the conditions set out in paragraph 1 above for entry into force have been fulfilled, this Protocol shall enter into force on the ninetieth day following the date of deposit of its instrument of ratification, acceptance, approval or accession. 4. For the purposes of this Article, any instrument deposited by a regional economic integration organisation shall not be counted as additional to those deposited by States members of the organisation.

Article 26: No reservations may be made to this Protocol.

Article 27: 1. At any time after three years from the date on which this Protocol has entered into force for a Party that Party may withdraw from this Protocol by giving written notification to the Depositary. 2. Any such withdrawal shall take effect upon expiry of one year from the date of receipt by the Depositary of the notification of withdrawal, or on such later date as may be specified in the notification of withdrawal. 3. Any Party that withdraws from the Convention shall be considered as also having withdrawn from this Protocol.

Article 28: The original of this Protocol, of which the Arabic, Chinese, English, French, Russian and Spanish texts are equally authentic, shall be deposited with the Secretary-General of the United Nations.

References

1. What is ozone layer (Available at http://www.conserve-energy-future.com/ozone-layer-and-causes-of-ozone-depletion.php)
2. The Process of Ozone Depletion (Available at http://www.epa.gov/ozone/science/process.html)
3. See http://www.britannica.com/science/ozone-depletion
4. See https://www.sdpi.org/publications/files/W10-Ozone% 20Layer%20Depletion.pdf
5. What is ozone layer (Available at http://www.conserve-energy-future.com/ozone-layer-and-causes-of-ozone-depletion.php)
6. Ozone depletion (Available at https://en.wikipedia.org/wiki/Ozone_depletion)
7. Ozone depletion: An introduction (Available at http://www.bcairquality.ca/101/ozone-depletion-intro.html)
8. See http://people.oregonstate.edu/~muirp/stratozo.htm

9. BC Air Quality (Available at http://www.bcairquality.ca/101/ozone-depletion-causes.html)
10. Protection of the ozone layer (Available at http://ec.europa.eu/clima/policies/ozone/faq_en.htm)
11. Ozone depletion (Available at https://en.wikipedia.org/wiki/Ozone_depletion)
12. What is the Ozone Hole? (Available at http://www.conserve-energy-future.com/causes-and-effects-of-ozone-hole.php)
13. Ozone depletion (Available at https://en.wikipedia.org/wiki/Ozone_depletion)
14. The impacts of Ozone depletion (http://www.bcairquality.ca/101/ozone-depletion-impacts.html)
15. Health and Environmental Effects of Ozone Layer Depletion (Available at http://www.epa.gov/spdpublc/science/effects/index.html)
16. Ozone Hole Consequences (http://www.theozonehole.com/consequences.htm)
17. Ozone Depletion Prevention (http://sciencehelp.blog.com/2013/03/04/ozone-depletion-prevention/)
18. Jane McGrath, How the Ozone Layer Works (Available at http://science.howstuffworks.com/environmental/green-science/ozone-layer4.htm)
19. See https://www.sdpi.org/publications/files/W10-Ozone% 20Layer% 20Depletion.pdf
20. What government are doing about Ozone depletion (Available at http://www.bcairquality.ca/101/government-ozone-depletion.html)
21. Solutions to Prevent Ozone Depletion (Available at http://www.buzzle.com/articles/solutions-to-prevent-ozone-depletion.html)
22. See https://www.sdpi.org/publications/files/W10-Ozone% 20Layer% 20Depletion.pdf

4

Global Warming

"If all mankind were to disappear, the world would regenerate back to the rich state of equilibrium that existed ten thousand years ago. If insects were to vanish, the environment would collapse into chaos."
-E.O. Wilson

Earth is the third planet from the Sun, the densest planet in the Solar System, the largest of the Solar System's four terrestrial planets, and the only astronomical object known to accommodate life. The earliest life on Earth arose at least 3.5 billion years ago. Earth's atmosphere and oceans formed by volcanic activity and out gassing that included water vapour. The origin of the world's oceans was condensation augmented by water and ice delivered by asteroids, protoplanets, and comets. The mechanically rigid outer layer of Earth, the lithosphere, is broken into pieces called tectonic plates. Earth's terrain varies greatly from place to place.

The abundance of water on Earth's surface is a unique feature that distinguishes the "Blue Planet" from other planets in the Solar System. Earth's hydrosphere consists chiefly of the oceans, but technically includes all water surfaces in the world; including inland seas, lakes, rivers, and underground waters down to a depth of 2,000 m. Earth's biosphere has significantly altered its atmosphere. Oxygenic photosynthesis evolved 2.7 Gya, forming the primarily nitrogen–oxygen atmosphere of today. Earth has resources that have been exploited by humans. Those termed non-renewable resources, such as fossil fuels, only renew over geological timescales. Large deposits of fossil fuels are obtained from Earth's crust, consisting of coal, petroleum, and natural gas. These deposits are used by humans both for energy production and as feedstock for chemical production.[1]

What is Global Warming?

Global warming and climate change are terms for the observed century-scale rise in the average temperature of the Earth's climate system and its related effects. The Intergovernmental Panel on Climate Change reported in 2014 that scientists were more than 95 per cent certain that most of global warming is caused by increasing concentrations of greenhouse gases and other human activities. Future climate change and associated impacts will differ from region to region around the globe.[2] It is the increase of Earth's average surface temperature due to effect of greenhouse gases, such as carbon dioxide emissions from burning fossil fuels or from deforestation, which trap heat that would otherwise escape from Earth. This is a type of greenhouse effect.[3]

Causes of Global Warming

For some years, global warming, the gradual heating of Earth's surface, oceans and atmosphere, was a topic of heated debate in the scientific community. Today, the overwhelming consensus of researchers is that global warming is real and is caused by human activity. A major report released Sept. 27, 2013, by the Intergovernmental Panel on Climate Change stated that scientists are more certain than ever of the link between human activities and global warming. More than 197 international scientific organisations agree that global warming is real and has been caused by human action. Greenhouse gases are the important factor before global warming. The primary greenhouse gases in Earth's atmosphere are water vapour, carbon dioxide, methane, nitrous oxide, and ozone.

Greenhouse Gases

Greenhouse gas is any gaseous compound in the atmosphere that is capable of absorbing infrared radiation, thereby trapping and holding heat in the atmosphere. By increasing the heat in the atmosphere, greenhouse gases are responsible for the greenhouse effect, which ultimately leads to global warming.

The primary greenhouse gases in Earth's atmosphere are water vapour, carbon dioxide, methane, nitrous oxide, and ozone. In the Solar System, the atmospheres of Venus, Mars and Titan also contain gases that cause a greenhouse effect. Human activities since the beginning of the Industrial Revolution have produced a 40 per cent increase in the atmospheric concentration of carbon dioxide, from 280 ppm in 1750 to 400 ppm in 2015.

Greenhouse gases are those that absorb and emit infrared radiation in the wavelength range emitted by Earth. Although contributing to many other physical and chemical reactions, the major atmospheric constituents, nitrogen, oxygen, and argon, are not greenhouse gases. Clouds also absorb and emit infrared radiation and thus have an effect on radiative properties of the greenhouse gases. Clouds are water droplets or ice crystals suspended in the atmosphere. Aside from purely human-produced synthetic halocarbons, most greenhouse gases have both natural and human-caused sources. During the pre-industrial Holocene, concentrations of existing gases were roughly constant. Water vapour accounts for the largest percentage of the greenhouse effect, between 36 per cent and 66 per cent for clear sky conditions and between 66 per cent and 85 per cent when including clouds.[4]

Deforestation and Climate Change

Deforestation is the second largest anthropogenic source of carbon dioxide to the atmosphere, after fossil fuel combustion. Forests are vital for life, home to millions of species, they protect soil from erosion, produce oxygen, store carbon dioxide, and help control climate. Forests play a huge role in the carbon cycle on our planet. Deforestation is an important factor in global climate change. It is estimated that more than 1.5 billion tonnes of carbon dioxide are released to the atmosphere due to deforestation, mainly the cutting and burning of forests, every year.[5]

Deforestation is the conversion of forest to another land use or the long-term reduction of the tree canopy cover. This includes conversion of natural forest to tree plantations, agriculture, pasture, water reservoirs and urban areas but excludes timber production areas managed to ensure the forest regenerates after logging. Forest degradation happens when changes within the forest negatively affect the structure or function of the stand or site, and thereby lower the capacity to supply products and/or ecosystem services. An estimated 13 million hectares of forests were lost each year between 2000 and 2010 due to deforestation.

Deforestation and forest degradation can cause wildlife to decline. Deforestation causes 15 per cent of global greenhouse gas emissions. Of these, carbon dioxide emissions represent up to one-third of total carbon dioxide emissions released because of human causes. As a result of deforestation, trees no longer evaporate groundwater, which can cause the local climate to be much drier. Deforestation continues to create severe social problems, sometimes leading to violent conflict.[6]

Warmer and drier conditions caused by deforestation could put agricultural productivity at risk, the study finds. Yields of soy in the Amazon, for example, are projected to drop by up to 60 per cent if more trees are cut down, and cattle production may not be viable in some areas as the quality of pasture declines. Adaptation measures might reduce the impact of these effects to some extent, of course. Deforestation can also cause longer dry seasons and delays to the start of the rainy season, the study suggests. Deforestation and land use change account for approximately 11 per cent of global carbon dioxide emissions. But the new research finds that cutting down trees doesn't only affect the carbon they lock up.[7]

Understanding the regional or global impacts of deforestation on climate, and ultimately on agriculture, requires modelling. General circulation models show that completely deforesting the tropics could result in global warming equivalent to that caused by burning of fossil fuels since 1850, with more warming and considerable drying in the tropics. More realistic scenarios of deforestation yield less warming and less drying, suggesting critical thresholds beyond which rainfall is substantially reduced.[8]

Effects of Global Warming

The effects of climate change on human systems, mostly due to warming or shifts in precipitation patterns, or both, have been detected worldwide. Production of wheat and maize globally has been impacted by climate change. There has been a shift from cold- to heat-related mortality in some regions as a result of warming. Livelihoods of indigenous peoples of the Arctic have been altered by climate change, and there is emerging evidence of climate change impacts on livelihoods of indigenous peoples in other region.[9]

The planet is warming, from North Pole to South Pole, and everywhere in between. Globally, the mercury is already up more than one degree Fahrenheit (0.8 degree Celsius), and even more in sensitive Polar Regions. The effects of rising temperatures aren't waiting for some far-flung future. Sea levels are expected to rise between 7 and 23 inches (18 and 59 centimeters) by the end of the century, and continued melting at the poles could add between 4 and 8 inches (10 to 20 centimeters). Floods and droughts will become more common. Rainfall in Ethiopia, where droughts are already common, could decline by 10 per cent over the next 50 years. Less fresh water will be available. If the Quelccaya ice cap in Peru continues to melt at its current rate, it will be gone by 2100, leaving thousands of people who rely on it for drinking water and electricity without a source of either.[10]

Extreme weather is an effect of global warming. Changes in climate can cause the jet stream to migrate south, bringing with it cold, Arctic air. Global warming may lead to extreme weather other than cold or heat extremes. For example, hurricane formations will change. Additionally, scientists are confident that hurricanes will become more intense due to climate change. This is because hurricanes get their energy from the temperature difference between the warm tropical ocean and the cold upper atmosphere. Global warming increases that temperature difference. Lightening is another weather feature that is being affected by global warming. Scientists project that extreme weather events, such as heat waves, droughts, blizzards and rainstorms will continue to occur more often and with greater intensity due to global warming.

As ice melts, the ocean levels rise. In 2014, the World Meteorological Organisation reported that sea level rise accelerated 0.12 inches (3 millimeters) per year on average worldwide. This is around double the average annual rise of .07 in (1.6 mm) in the twentieth century. Melting polar ice in the Arctic and Antarctic region, coupled with melting ice sheets and glaciers across Greenland, North America, South America, Europe and Asia, are expected to raise sea levels significantly.[11]

Global warming is already having significant and costly effects on our communities, our health, and our climate. Global warming is now accelerating the rate of sea level rise, increasing flooding risks to low-lying communities and high-risk coastal properties whose development has been encouraged by today's flood insurance system. Wildfires are increasing and wildfire season is getting longer as temperatures rise. Tens of millions of trees have died in the Rocky Mountains over the past 15 years, victims of a climate-driven triple assault of tree-killing insects, wildfires, and stress from heat and drought. Rising temperatures will likely lead to increased air pollution, a longer and more intense allergy season, the spread of insect-borne diseases, more frequent and dangerous heat waves, and heavier rainstorms and flooding.[12]

Researchers say extreme weather events that impact food production could be happening in seven years out of ten by the end of this century. The impacts are most likely to be felt across Africa and the Middle East. Poor harvests and low stocks of grains in 2008 combined with a host of other factors to produce a spectacular price rise in cereals, with a UN index of prices peaking at 2.8 times higher than it was at the turn of the millennium. In 2010-11, a heat wave in Russia led to the country's worst drought in 40 years, decimating the grain harvest and leading indirectly, to food riots in North African countries as prices of bread rose rapidly. The UN's Food and Agriculture Organisation says that increasing population will drive demand for food up by 60 per cent by 2050 in any case, so there is going to be significant pressure on food production.[13]

Intergovernmental Panel on Climate Change

The Intergovernmental Panel on Climate Change is a scientific intergovernmental body under the auspices of the United Nations, set up at the request of member governments. It was first established in 1988 by two United Nations organisations, the World Meteorological Organisation and the United Nations Environment Programme. The IPCC produces reports that support the United Nations Framework Convention on Climate Change (UNFCCC), which is the main international treaty on climate change. The IPCC bases its assessment on the published literature, which includes peer-reviewed and non-peer-reviewed sources. The IPCC has published five comprehensive assessment reports reviewing the latest climate science, as well as a number of special reports on particular topics. These reports are prepared by teams of relevant researchers selected by the Bureau from government nominations.

In addition to climate assessment reports, the IPCC is publishing Special Reports on specific topics. The preparation and approval process for all IPCC Special Reports follows the same procedures as for IPCC Assessment Reports. The IPCC concentrates its activities on the tasks allotted to it by the relevant WMO Executive Council and UNEP Governing Council resolutions and decisions as well as on actions in support of the UNFCCC process. In December 2007, the IPCC was awarded the Nobel Peace Prize "for their efforts to build up and disseminate greater knowledge about man-made climate change and to lay the foundations for the measures that are needed to counteract such change".[14]

The IPCC is a scientific body under the auspices of the United Nations. It reviews and assesses the most recent scientific, technical and socio-economic information produced worldwide relevant to the understanding of climate change. It does not conduct any research nor does it monitor climate related data or parameters. It is open to all member countries of the United Nations and WMO. Currently 195 countries are members of the IPCC. The IPCC has three working groups:

(a) Working Group I

(b) Working Group II: Impacts, Adaptation and Vulnerability

(c) Working Group III: Mitigation of Climate Change

(d) Task Force on Greenhouse Gas Inventories[15]

Preventive Measures

Global warming is an urgent problem facing our planet, but retailers are in a unique position to contribute to climate change prevention efforts. In addition to helping save the planet, there are a variety of reasons for retailers to help prevent climate change. As consumers' perspectives shift increasingly away from the idea that "going green" is just a trend to the understanding that sustainable practices are a necessity, retailers who follow suit are likely to see substantial spikes in business from environmentally minded shoppers.[16]

Climate change mitigation is the act of decreasing the factors that contribute to climate change. One of the most significant contributors to climate change is the rise in greenhouse gases. Other mitigation strategies include: (a) Improving the energy efficiency of buildings to reduce emissions from heating/cooling;

(b) Planting forests and tree to remove excess carbon dioxide from our atmosphere; and (c) Reducing fuel emissions associated with motor vehicles. Mitigation strategies like these can substantially reduce greenhouse gases and lessen the impacts of climate change.[17]

Scientists have concluded that human activity, primarily the burning of fossil fuels, is the major driving factor in global warming. Global warming can be slowed, and stopped, with practical actions that yield a cleaner, healthier atmosphere. The goal is to bring global warming under control by curtailing the release of carbon dioxide and other heat-trapping greenhouse gases into the atmosphere. The largest source of greenhouse gases is electric power generation. The average home actually contributes more to global warming than the average car.

To reduce the amount of electricity used in our homes: (a) Switch to energy-efficient lighting; (b) Improve the efficiency of home appliances; (c) Buy energy-efficient appliances when shopping for a new appliance; (d) Reduce energy needed for heating; and (e) Reduce energy needed for cooling. The second largest source of greenhouse gases is transportation. For improving vehicle fuel efficiency : (a) Practice fuel-efficient driving; (b) Buy a fuel-efficient car; and (c) Recycle air-conditioner coolant. Yard maintenance contributes significantly to greenhouse emissions. Per hour of operation, a power lawn mower emits 10-12 times as much hydrocarbon as a typical auto.[18]

Government Initiatives

The United States is leading global efforts to address the threat of climate change. Since 2005, the United States has reduced its total carbon pollution more than any other nation on Earth. Wind power has tripled, and energy from the sun has increased ten-fold. President Obama has taken a series of common-sense steps to curb carbon pollution and other greenhouse gases through initiatives that drive energy efficiency, promote clean energy, and put in place the first-ever carbon pollution standards for power plants. Since President Obama took office, the US has increased solar electricity generation by more than ten-fold, and tripled electricity production from wind power. When President Obama took office in 2009, there were zero renewable projects on public lands, and there was no process in place to move forward the hundreds of pending applications from American businesses that wanted to harness renewable energy to help power the US. Since President Obama took office, the Department of the Interior has approved over 50 wind, solar, and geothermal utility-scale projects on public or tribal lands. Together, these projects can support more than 20,000 US jobs and generate enough electricity to power 4.8 million homes[19].

The Environmental Protection Agency (EPA) has taken a common-sense approach to developing carbon pollution standards for both new and existing power plants. In September 2013, EPA announced proposed standards for new power plants and initiated outreach to a wide variety of stakeholders to help inform the development of emission guidelines for existing plants. The agency has approximately 15,193 full-time employees and engages many more people on a contractual basis. More than half of EPA human resources are engineers, scientists, and environmental protection specialists; other groups include legal, public affairs, financial, and information technologists. Each EPA regional office is responsible within its states for implementing the Agency's programmes, except those programmes that have been specifically delegated to states. The legislation here is general environmental protection legislation, and may also apply to other units of the government, including the Department of the Interior and the Department of Agriculture.[20]

The Government of Canada is committed to addressing greenhouse gas (GHG) emissions while keeping the Canadian economy strong. It are achieving success - from 2005 to 2012, Canadian GHG emissions have decreased by 5.1 per cent while the economy has grown by 10.6 per cent.[21] The Government of Canada is implementing a sector-by-sector regulatory approach to reduce GHG emissions that protects the environment and supports economic prosperity. The government has already taken action on two of Canada's largest sources of GHG emissions: transportation and electricity.

Canada boasts one of the cleanest electricity systems in the G7 and in the world, with 79 per cent of our electricity supply emitting no greenhouse gases. Canada's environmental efforts extend beyond actions to address climate change. For example, the National Conservation Plan will coordinate conservation efforts across the country with an emphasis on enabling Canadians to conserve and restore lands and waters in and around their communities, and making it easier for citizens living in cities to connect with nature. It complements significant efforts, including creating new parks, protecting ecologically sensitive lands, protecting species at risk and their habitat, and improving water quality.[22]

The Ministry of Environment, Forest and Climate Change is the nodal agency in the administrative structure of the Central Government for the planning, promotion, co-ordination and overseeing the implementation of India's environmental and forestry policies and programmes. The Ministry also serves as the nodal agency in the country for the United Nations Environment Programme, South Asia Co-operative Environment Programme, International Centre for Integrated Mountain Development and for the follow-up of the United Nations Conference on Environment and Development. The broad objectives of the Ministry are: Conservation and survey of flora, fauna, forests and wildlife; Prevention and control of pollution; Afforestation and regeneration of degraded areas; Protection of the environment and Ensuring the welfare of animals.[23]

National Action Plan on Climate Change[24]

The action plan outlines a number of steps to simultaneously advance India's development and climate change-related objectives. The National Action Plan on Climate Change (NAPCC) encompasses a range of measures. It focuses on eight missions, which are as follows:

(a) **National Solar Mission:** The NAPCC aims to promote the development and use of solar energy for power generation and other uses, with the ultimate objective of making solar competitive with fossil-based energy options. It also includes the establishment of a solar research centre, increased international collaboration on technology development, strengthening of domestic manufacturing capacity, and increased government funding and international support.

(b) **National Mission for Enhanced Energy Efficiency:** The NAPCC recommends mandating specific energy consumption decreases in large energy-consuming industries, with a system for companies to trade energy-saving certificates, financing for public–private partnerships to reduce energy consumption through demand-side management programmes in the municipal, buildings, and agricultural sectors, and energy incentives, including reduced taxes on energy-efficient appliances.

(c) **National Mission on Sustainable Habitat:** The NAPCC also aims at promoting energy efficiency as a core component of urban planning by extending the existing Energy Conservation Building Code, strengthening the enforcement of automotive fuel economy standards, and using pricing measures to encourage the purchase of efficient vehicles and incentives for the use of public transportation. The NAPCC also emphasises on waste management and recycling.

(d) **National Water Mission:** The NAPCC sets a goal of a 20 per cent improvement in water use efficiency through pricing and other measures to deal with water scarcity as a result of climate change.

(e) **National Mission for Sustaining the Himalayan Ecosystem:** This particular mission sets the goal to prevent melting of the Himalayan glaciers and to protect biodiversity in the Himalayan region.

(f) **Green India Mission:** The NAPCC also aims at afforestation of six million hectares of degraded forest lands and expanding forest cover from 23 to 33 per cent of India's territory.

(g) **National Mission for Sustainable Agriculture:** The NAPCC aims to support climate adaptation in agriculture through the development of climate-resilient crops, expansion of weather insurance mechanisms, and agricultural practices.

(h) **National Mission on Strategic Knowledge for Climate Change:** To gain a better understanding of climate science, impacts, and challenges, the plan envisions a new Climate Science Research Fund, improved climate modelling, and increased international collaboration. It also encourages private sector initiatives to develop adaptation and mitigation technologies through venture capital funds.

References

1. Earth (2015) (Available at https://en.wikipedia.org/wiki/Earth)
2. Global warming (Available at https://en.wikipedia.org/wiki/Global_warming)

3. Global warming FAQ (Available at http://www.nmsea.org/Curriculum/Primer/Global_Warming/fossil_fuels_and_global_warming.htm)
4. Greenhouse gas (Available at https://en.wikipedia.org/wiki/Greenhouse_gas)
5. See http://www.climateandweather.net/global-warming/deforestation.html
6. Deforestation (Available at http://wwf.panda.org/about_our_earth/deforestation/)
7. Robert McSweeney (2014), Deforestation in the tropics affects climate around the world, study finds (Available at http://www.carbonbrief.org/blog/2014/12/deforestation-in-the-tropics-affects-climate-around-the-world-study-finds/)
8. Deborah Lawrence and Karen Vandecar (2015), Effects of tropical deforestation on climate and agriculture (Available at http://www.nature.com/nclimate/journal/v5/n1/full/nclimate2430.html)
9. Global warming (Available at https://en.wikipedia.org/wiki/Global_warming)
10. Effects of global warming, From official website of National Geographic (Available at http://environment.national geographic. com/environment/global-warming/gw-effects/)
11. Alina Bradford (2014), Effects of Global Warming (Available at http://www.livescience.com/37057-global-warming-effects.html)
12. See http://www.ucsusa.org/our-work/global-warming/science-and-impacts/global-warming-impacts#.Vc6ktLJViko
13. Matt McGrath (2015), Global warming increases 'food shocks' threat (Available at http://www.bbc.com/news/science-environment-33910552)
14. Intergovernmental Panel on Climate Change (Available at https://en.wikipedia.org/wiki/Intergovernmental_ Panel_on_ Climate_Change)
15. See https://www.ipcc-wg2.gov/index.html
16. See https://www.retailpackaging.com/blog/2013/02/27-ways-to-prevent-climate-change-a-guide-for-independent-retailers/
17. Preventing and preparing for climate change (Available at http://www.ehib.org/page.jsp?page_key=692)
18. Global Warming / Climate Change: What we can do about it - See more at: http://learn.eartheasy.com/2009/03/global-warming-climate-change-what-we-can-do-about-it/#sthash.2DFk0i6B.dpuf
19. See https://www.whitehouse.gov/energy/climate-change
20. United States Environmental Protection Agency (Available at https://en.wikipedia.org/wiki/United_States_ Environmental_ Protection_Agency)
21. See http://climatechange.gc.ca/default.asp?lang=En&n= 4FE85A4C-1#X-201206200903271
22. Canada's action on climate change (Available at http://www.climatechange.gc.ca/default.asp?lang=En&n=72F16A84-1)
23. Official website of Ministry of Environment, Forest and Climate Change (Available at http://envfor.nic.in/about-ministry/about-ministry)
24. Harshal T. Pandve, India's National Action Plan on Climate Change, Indian J Occup Environ Med. 2009 Apr; 13(1): 17–19.

5

Disaster Management

"I have a very positive attitude to anyone who is protecting the environment, but it's inadmissible when people are using it as a means of promoting themselves, using it as a source of self-enrichment. I don't want to name any specific examples... but often, environmentalism is used to blackmail companies." **-Vladimir Putin**

Disaster is a serious disruption of the functioning of a community or a society involving widespread human, material, economic or environmental losses and impacts, which exceeds the ability of the affected community or society to cope using its own resources. Hazards are routinely divided into natural or human-made, although complex disasters, where there is no single root cause, are more common in developing countries. Natural hazard is a natural process or phenomenon that may cause loss of life, injury or other health impacts, property damage, loss of livelihoods and services, social and economic disruption, or environmental damage.

Various phenomena like earthquakes, landslides, volcanic eruptions, floods, hurricanes, tornadoes, blizzards, tsunamis, and cyclones are all natural hazards. Human-instigated disasters are the consequence of technological hazards. Examples include stampedes, fires, transport accidents, industrial accidents, oil spills and nuclear explosions/radiation. War and deliberate attacks may be put in this category.[1] The United Nations defines a disaster as a serious disruption of the functioning of a community or a society. Disasters involve widespread human, material, economic or environmental impacts, which exceed the ability of the affected community or society to cope using its own resources.[2] The term 'disaster', meaning 'bad star' in Latin, is defined as an impact of a natural or man-made hazard that causes human suffering or creates human needs that the victims cannot alleviate without assistance. Disasters occur when hazards strike in vulnerable areas.

What is Disaster Management?

It is the creation of plans through which communities reduce vulnerability to hazards and cope with disasters. It is known as emergency management. Disaster management does not avert or eliminate the threats; instead it focuses on creating plans to decrease the impact of disasters. Events covered by disaster management include acts of terrorism, industrial sabotage, fire, natural disasters (such as earthquakes, hurricanes, etc.), public disorder, industrial accidents, and communication failures.[3]

The Red Cross and Red Crescent societies define disaster management as the organisation and management of resources and responsibilities for dealing with all humanitarian aspects of emergencies, in particular preparedness, response and recovery in order to lessen the impact of disasters.[4] It can be defined as the organisation and management of resources and responsibilities for dealing with all humanitarian aspects of emergencies, in particular preparedness, response and recovery in order to lessen the impact of disasters.

Types of Disaster[5]

There is no country that is immune from disaster, though vulnerability to disaster varies. There are four main types of disaster.

- **Natural disasters:** Including floods, hurricanes, earthquakes and volcano eruptions that have immediate impacts on human health and secondary impacts causing further death and suffering from (for example) floods, landslides, fires, tsunamis.
- **Environmental emergencies:** Including technological or industrial accidents, usually involving the production, use or transportation of hazardous material, and occur where these materials are produced, used or transported, and forest fires caused by humans.
- **Complex emergencies:** Involving a break-down of authority, looting and attacks on strategic installations, including conflict situations and war.

- **Pandemic emergencies:** Involving a sudden onset of contagious disease that affects health, disrupts services and businesses, brings economic and social costs.

Significance of Disaster Management

Disasters are events that have a huge impact on humans and/or the environment. Disasters require government intervention. They are not always unpredictable. Disasters arise from both natural and human causes, and the responses needed could stretch community and government capacity to the limit. Disaster management aims to reduce the occurrence of disasters and to reduce the impact of those that cannot be prevented. The government White papers and Act on Disaster Management define the roles of Local Authorities as well as Provincial and National government in disaster management. The disaster management policy and legislation makes provision for government to declare disaster areas, and allow for resources to be allocated for immediate relief, as well as reconstruction. This includes things like food, blankets and medical supplies as relief and building materials for reconstruction.[6]

Disaster management personnel can undertake rescue operations effectively. Trained disaster management personnel can rescue people effectively at the time of floods, major fires, building collapses, and so on. Disaster management team is responsible to provide relief measures to the victims. They can help to reduce the trauma and tension before and after the disaster. They can help to protect and preserve the environment. They can help to minimise loss of life and property.[7]

Phases of Disaster Management[8]

Emergency management consists of five phases: prevention, mitigation, preparedness, response and recovery.

(a) **Prevention:** Prevention was recently added to the phases of emergency management. It focuses on preventing the human hazard, primarily from potential natural disasters or terrorist attacks. Preventive measures are taken on both the domestic and international levels, designed to provide permanent protection from disasters.

(b) **Mitigation:** Personal mitigation is a key to national preparedness. Individuals and families train to avoid unnecessary risks. Preventive or mitigation measures take different forms for different types of disasters. On a national level, governments might implement large scale mitigation measures.

(c) **Preparedness:** Preparedness focuses on preparing equipment and procedures for use when a disaster occurs. This equipment and these procedures can be used to reduce vulnerability to disaster, to mitigate the impacts of a disaster or to respond more efficiently in an emergency.

(d) **Response:** The response phase of an emergency may commence with Search and Rescue but in all cases the focus will quickly turn to fulfilling the basic humanitarian needs of the affected population. This assistance may be provided by national or international agencies and organisations. Medical considerations will vary greatly based on the type of disaster and secondary effects. Survivors may sustain a multitude of injuries to include lacerations, burns, near drowning, or crush syndrome.

(e) **Recovery:** The recovery phase starts after the immediate threat to human life has subsided. The immediate goal of the recovery phase is to bring the affected area back to normalcy as quickly as possible. During reconstruction it is recommended to consider the location or construction material of the property.

Disaster Management in Bangladesh

Bangladesh is a low-lying deltaic country in South Asia formed by the Ganges, the Brahmaputra and the Meghna rivers. It is a land of around 145 million people within its 147,570 sq. km territory. More than 230 waterways and tributaries have made this country a land of rivers. Historical data suggests that Bangladesh is one of the most disaster prone countries in the world. It is not that Bangladesh suffers from these events more than other countries; it is that the communities are more vulnerable to their impacts and therefore the consequences are more severe. The frequency of cyclones over the years has increased significantly. Major cyclones in 1970, 1991 and 1997 resulted in over 500,000 deaths. The Ministry of Food and Disaster Management has the mandate to co-ordinate all disaster management activities within the country.

The Ministry is located within the Secretariat Building and is supported by three operational elements: Disaster Management Bureau, Directorate of Relief and Rehabilitation and the Directorate of Food. The establishment of a National Framework for Action that integrates all programmes, priorities and resources of government, NGOs and the private sector into one risk reduction programme is a major priority. Mainstreaming risk reduction efforts within government, NGOs and private sector is viewed as being the key to achieving sustainable all hazards risk reduction interventions across the whole country. In Bangladesh mainstreaming is seen in much the same light as poverty reduction in that it is the outcome of many top down and bottom up interventions.

A Climate Change Cell has been established in the Department of Environment under the framework of the Comprehensive Disaster Management Programme. The Disaster Management Information Centre (DMIC) is an information sharing system that uses ICT to connect government agencies, NGOs, the private sector, regional and international agencies for cooperative action in risk reduction and emergency response. The DMIC is being established initially at the National and District levels but will be progressively expanded to provide a whole of country network. Bangladesh places great emphasises on the establishment of regional frameworks for disaster management. The Ministry of Food and Disaster Management is playing a lead role in supporting the introduction of regional frameworks to support the strengthening of disaster management within SAARC member countries.[9]

The National Plan for Disaster Management for 2010-2015 is a long desired document based on the global and regional commitment of the Government of Bangladesh and its vision on disaster management. The plan reflects the basic principles of the SAARC Framework on Disaster Management. The Disaster Management Vision of the Government of Bangladesh is to reduce the risk of people, especially the poor and the disadvantaged, from the effects of natural, environmental and human induced hazards, to a manageable and acceptable humanitarian level, and to have in place an efficient emergency response system capable of handling large scale disasters. The government, in coordination with NGOs and international organisations, has done a commendable job in responding to the cyclone emergency and assisting the affected population.

The Disaster Management and Relief Division (DM&RD), MoFDM of the Government of Bangladesh has the responsibility for coordinating national disaster management efforts across all agencies. In January 1997, the Ministry issued the Standing Orders on Disaster (SOD) to guide and monitor disaster management activities in Bangladesh. There is a District Disaster

Management Committee (DDMC) at the District level. The DDMC consists of the Deputy Commissioner of the District as the chairperson and members comprising all District level department heads, NGO leaders and civil society members. District Relief and Rehabilitation Officer (DRRO) acts as member secretary of the committee. There is an Upazila Disaster Management Committee (UzDMC) at the Upazila level. The UzDMC consists of the Upazila Nirbahi Officer as the chairperson and members comprising all Upazila level department heads, NGO leaders and civil society members. Pourashava is at the bottom of the urban administrative tier of Bangladesh. There is a Disaster Management Committee at the City Corporation/ Pourashava level. The Pourashava Chairman is the head of the committee. Every Ministry/Division of the Government of Bangladesh prepares their respective Sectoral Development Plans.[10]

Disaster Management in India

India is highly vulnerable to natural disasters, losing about two per cent of the GDP on an average to disasters. India has been traditionally vulnerable to natural disasters on account of its unique geo-climatic conditions. Floods, droughts, cyclones, earthquakes and landslides have been recurrent phenomena. Over the past couple of years, the Government of India has brought about a paradigm shift in the approach to disaster management. At the national level, the Ministry of Home Affairs is the nodal ministry for all matters concerning disaster management. The Central Relief Commissioner in the Ministry of Home Affairs is the nodal officer to coordinate relief operations for natural disasters. The CRC receives information relating to forecasting/warning of a natural calamity from India Meteorological Department) or from Central Water Commission of Ministry of Water Resources on a continuing basis.

Cabinet Secretary, who is the highest executive officer, heads the National Crisis Management Committee (NCMC). Secretaries of all the concerned Ministries /Departments as well as organisations are the members of the Committee. The NCMC gives direction to the Crisis Management Group as deemed necessary. The Central Relief Commissioner in the Ministry of Home Affairs is the Chairman of the CMG, consisting of senior officers from various concerned ministries. Each State Government has relief manuals/codes which identify that role of each officer in the State for managing the natural disasters. These are reviewed and updated periodically based on the experience of managing the disasters and the need of the State.

The Finance Commission makes recommendation regarding the division of tax and non-tax revenues between the Central and the State Governments and also regarding policy for provision of relief assistance and their share of expenditure thereon. A Calamity Relief Fund has been set up in each State as per the recommendations of the Eleventh Finance Commission. At the State level, as indicated in para disaster management was being handled by the Departments of Relief and Rehabilitation. The States have also been asked to set up Disaster Management Authorities under the Chief Minister with Ministers of relevant Departments as members. At the district level, the District Magistrate who is the chief coordinator will be the focal point for coordinating all activities relating to prevention, mitigation and preparedness apart from his existing responsibilities pertaining to response and relief. The States have been advised to enact Disaster Management Acts.

Indian Meteorological Department is mandated to monitor and give warnings regarding Tropical Cyclone. The goal of any warning system is to maximise the number of people who take appropriate and timely action for the safety of life and property. Cyclone warnings are communicated to Crisis Managers and other concerned organisations by high priority telegrams, telex, telephones and Police wireless. Cyclone warnings are provided by the IMD from the Area Cyclone Warning Centres at Calcutta, Chennai and Mumbai and Cyclone Warning Centres at Vishakhapatnam, Bhubaneswar and Ahmedabad.[11]

Technological innovations are vital for effective disaster management, the DST; Government of India is taking several measures to upgrade technological inputs. India Disaster Resource Network is a web enabled centralised data base which will ensure quick access to resources to minimise response time tune in emergencies. This database will be available at National, State and district level simultaneously. The GIS is an effective tool for emergency responders to access information in terms of crucial parameters for the disaster affected areas. This includes location of public facilities, communication links, transport network etc. The Central Government is now in the process of training and equipping specialist and rescue teams. Each team includes doctors, paramedics, structural engineers etc. These teams will be stationed in different parts of the country.[12]

National Disaster Management Authority[13]

It is an agency of the Ministry of Home Affairs whose primary purpose is to coordinate response to natural or man-made disasters and for capacity-building in disaster resiliency and crisis response. National Disaster Management Authority was established through the Disaster Management Act enacted by the Government of India in December 2005. The Prime Minister is the de facto chairperson of NDMA. The NDMA is governed by a nine member board chaired by the Prime Minister of India. The remainder of the board consists of members nominated based on their expertise in areas such as, planning, infrastructure management, communications, meteorology and natural sciences.

NDMA equips and trains other government officials, institutions and the community in mitigation for and response during a crisis situation or a disaster. NDMA also collaborates with the Lal Bahadur Shastri National Academy of Administration and Sardar Vallabhbhai Patel National Police Academy to impart training to administration and police officers in planning and incident response. NDMA runs various programmes for mitigation and responsiveness for specific situations.

International Organisation[14]

There are various international organisations working in disaster management. Some of them are:

(a) **The International Emergency Management Society:** It is an international non-profit NGO, registered in Belgium. It is a Global Forum for Education, Training, Certification and Policy in Emergency and Disaster Management. It provides a platform for stakeholders to meet, network and learn about new technical and operational methodologies. It focuses on cultural differences to be understood and included in the society's events, education and research programme.

(b) **International Association of Emergency Managers:** It is a non-profit dedicated to promoting the profession of emergency management by working with its membership to promote the goals of saving lives and protecting property during emergencies and disasters. IAEM promotes its Principles of Emergency Management, and also aims to provide information, networking and professional development for its members. IAEM administrates the following programmes on behalf of the profession: Certified Emergency Manager, Scholarship Programme and Awards Programme.[15]

(c) The International Recovery Platform: It was conceived at the World Conference on Disaster Reduction in Kobe, Hyogo, Japan in January 2005. The HFA is a global plan for disaster risk reduction adopted by 168 governments. The key role of IRP is to identify gaps in post disaster recovery and to serve as a catalyst for the development of tools and resources for recovery efforts.

(d) International Federation of Red Cross and Red Crescent Societies: It reaches 160 million people each year through its 189-member National Societies. It acts before, during and after disasters and health emergencies to meet the needs and improve the lives of vulnerable people. The seven Fundamental Principles that guide the work of the IFRC and its members are: humanity, impartiality, neutrality, independence, voluntary service, unity and universality. It persuades decision-makers to act in the interests of vulnerable people. It works to enable healthy and safe communities, reduce vulnerabilities, strengthen resilience and foster a culture of peace around the world. The IFRC coordinates between National Red Cross and Red Crescent Societies throughout the world.

(e) Baptist Global Response: It is a disaster relief and community development organisation. BGR and its partners respond globally to people with critical needs world-wide, whether those needs arise from chronic conditions or acute crises such as natural disasters.

(f) United Nations: The United Nations system rests with the Resident Coordinator within the affected country. However, in practice, the UN response will be coordinated by the UN Office for the Coordination of Humanitarian Affairs (UN Office for the Coordination of Humanitarian Affairs), by deploying a UN Disaster Assessment and Coordination (UNDAC) team, in response to a request by the affected country's government.

(g) World Bank: Since 1980, the World Bank has approved more than 500 projects related to disaster management, dealing with both disaster mitigation as well as reconstruction projects, amounting to more than US$40 billion. These projects have taken place all over the world, in countries such as Argentina, Bangladesh, Colombia, Haiti, India, Mexico, Turkey and Vietnam.

References

1. Disaster (Available at https://en.wikipedia.org/wiki/Disaster)
2. From official website of World Confederation for Physical Therapy (Available at http://www.wcpt.org/disaster-management/what-is-disaster-management)
3. Emergency management (Available at https://en.wikipedia.org/wiki/Emergency_management)
4. From official website of World Confederation for Physical Therapy (Available at http://www.wcpt.org/disaster-management/what-is-disaster-management)
5. From official website of World Confederation for Physical Therapy (Available at http://www.wcpt.org/disaster-management/what-is-disaster-management)
6. See http://www.etu.org.za/toolbox/docs/government/disaster.html
7. See http://www.omtexclasses.com/2010/02/needimportanceobjectiverolefunctionof_5134.html
8. Emergency management (Available at https://en.wikipedia.org/wiki/Emergency_management)
9. Comprehensive Disaster Management-Bangladesh Experience (Available at http://saarc-sdmc.nic.in/pdf/bangladesh/file4.pdf)
10. National Plan for Disaster Management 2010-2015 (Available at http://www.bd.undp.org/content/dam/bangladesh/docs/Publications/Nataional% 20Plan%20for%20Disaster%20(2010-2015)%20Final%20Version.pdf)
11. Disaster management in India (Available at http://www.unisdr.org/2005/mdgs-drr/national-reports/India-report.pdf)
12. Daya Kaul, Md. Ayaz, Lohitkumar S N, Disaster Management In India (Available at http://home.iitk.ac.in/~ayazmd/Projects/project.pdf)
13. National Disaster Management Authority (Available at https://en.wikipedia.org/wiki/National_ Disaster_ Management_Authority_(India))
14. Emergency management (Available at https://en.wikipedia.org/wiki/Emergency_management)
15. International Association of Emergency Managers (Available at https://en.wikipedia.org/wiki/International_ Association_ of_Emergency_ Managers)

Part II: Natural Calamities

6
Flood

"There is no single development, in either technology or management technique, which by itself promises even one order-of-magnitude improvement within a decade in productivity, in reliability, in simplicity."

-Fred Brooks

Flooding is a common natural disaster, and also very common in many places where rains fall. It is an overflow of water that submerges land which is usually dry. *It* can happen anywhere, at any time, and can be caused by more than just rain. The word "flood" comes from the Old English 'flod', a word common to Germanic languages. Floods can also occur in rivers when the flow rate exceeds the capacity of the river channel, particularly at bends or meanders in the waterway. Floods often cause damage to homes and businesses if they are in the natural flood plains of rivers.

Flood is a natural event that can have far reaching effects on people and the environment. Flood is a body of water that covers land which is normally dry. Floods are common natural disasters that can affect millions of people around the world. They destroy houses and buildings, and carry soil away from valuable farming land. Floods can contaminate drinking water and lead to diseases.[1] Flood is a temporary covering by water of land normally not covered by water. This shall include floods from rivers, mountain torrents, Mediterranean ephemeral water courses, and floods from the sea in coastal areas, and may exclude floods from sewerage systems. Floods are natural phenomena which cannot be prevented. Floods have the adverse impact on human health, the environment, cultural heritage and economic activity.[2]

Meaning

Flooding occurs in known floodplains when prolonged rainfall over several days, intense rainfall over a short period of time, or an ice or debris jam causes a river or stream to overflow and flood the surrounding area. Flash floods occur within six hours of a rain event, or after a dam or levee failure, or following a sudden release of water held by an ice or debris jam, and flash floods can catch people unprepared. Floods are among the most frequent and costly natural disasters in terms of human hardship and economic loss. As much as 90 per cent of the damage related to all natural disasters (excluding droughts) is caused by floods and associated debris flows.[3]

Types of Flood[4]

Floods are generally grouped into the following types:

1. **Riverine Flooding:** The dynamics of riverine flooding vary with terrain. In relatively flat areas, land may stay covered with shallow, slow-moving floodwater for days or even weeks. In hilly and mountainous areas, floods may come minutes after a heavy rain. The short notice, large depths, and high velocities of flash floods make these types of floods particularly dangerous. Riverine floodplains range from narrow, confined channels to wide, flat areas.

2. **Fluctuating Lake Levels:** Water levels in the nation's lakes can fluctuate of a short-term (e.g., seasonal) or long-term (e.g., yearly basis). Periods of heavy rainfall, for example, can cause high water levels for short periods of time and annual snowmelt can result in higher water levels in the spring. Long-term lake level fluctuations are a less-recognised phenomenon that can cause high water and subsequent flooding problems lasting for years or even decades.

3. **Coastal Flooding:** Coastal flooding and erosion are serious problems along much of the nation's coasts, although the frequency and magnitude of flooding and the severity of the erosion vary considerably. They result from storm surges and wave actions. Storm surge is the increase in water surface elevation above normal tide levels due primarily to low barometric pressure and the piling up of waters in coastal areas as a result of wind action over a long stretch of open water.
4. **Flash Flooding:** A flash flood is a fast-moving and unexpected flood. Flash flooding is usually due to heavy rain. While natural events may be responsible for most flash flooding, it may also arise if flood defences fail or drainage systems are insufficient. It is expected that flash flooding may become more frequent due to climate change and over-development in flood plains.
5. **Sewer Flooding:** It may result from a failure of the sewerage system. It may happen when the sewer system does not have enough capacity to take water entering the system from heavy rainfall or river or highway flooding. Sewage water flowing into a building is classified as internal flooding. When it floods a garden or other open space such as roads or public grounds it is considered as external flooding.
6. **Groundwater Flooding:** It can occur when water levels underneath the ground rise above normal levels approaching the surface. It is usually caused by prolonged periods of rainfall. Groundwater flooding can last for weeks and months. The UK Groundwater Forum estimates that groundwater flooding affects several hundred thousand properties in the UK.[5]
7. **Ice Jam Flooding:** In cold temperatures, bodies of water are often frozen. Heavy precipitation can cause chunks of ice to push together and create a dam in what is known as ice jam flooding. Behind the dam, water begins to pile up, spilling over to the plains nearby.

Causes of Flood

The amount, location, and timing of water reaching drainage channel from natural precipitation and controlled or uncontrolled reservoir releases determine the flow at downstream locations. The most important upslope factor in determining flood magnitude is the land area of the watershed upstream of the area of interest. Extreme flood events often result from coincidence such as unusually intense, warm rainfall melting heavy snow pack, producing channel obstructions from floating ice, and releasing small impoundments like beaver dams.[6]

Flooding occurs most commonly from heavy rainfall when natural watercourses do not have the capacity to convey excess water. Floods are not always caused by heavy rainfall. They can result from other phenomena, particularly in coastal areas where inundation can be caused by a storm surge associated with a tropical cyclone, a tsunami or a high tide coinciding with higher than normal river level.[7] Rains, water bodies, strong winds, hurricanes and tsunamis, dams and levees as well as snow melts are the most common *causes* of *flooding.*

Floods generally develop over a period of days, when there is too much rainwater to fit in the rivers and water spreads over the land next to it. They can happen very quickly when lots of heavy rain falls over a short period of time. These 'flash floods' occur with little or no warning and cause the biggest loss of human life than any other type of flooding. Coastal areas are also at risk from sea flooding, when storms and big waves bring seawater onto the land. The worst cases of flooding may occur if there is a combination of storms, 'spring tides' and low atmospheric pressure.

Indian Perspectives

Floods are the most common and widespread of all natural disasters. India is one of the highly flood prone countries in the world. Around 40 million hectares of land in India is prone to floods as per National Flood Commission report. Floods cause damage to houses, industries, public utilities and property resulting in huge economic losses, apart from loss of lives.[8] *India* is among the highly *flood* prone countries in the world and *flood* are most common and widespread of all other natural disasters.

Bihar is India's most flood-prone State, with 76 per cent of the population in the north Bihar living under the recurring threat of flood devastation. When heavy rains occur in the mountains of central and eastern Nepal the water flows into the major drainages of Narayani, Bagmati, and Koshi rivers. As these rivers cross into India they flow into the plains and lowlands of Bihar and break their banks.[9] In June 2013, a multi-day cloudburst centred on the North Indian state of Uttarakhand caused devastating floods and landslides becoming the country's worst natural disaster since the 2004 tsunami. Though some parts of Himachal Pradesh, Haryana, Delhi and Uttar Pradesh in India experienced the flood, some regions of Western Nepal, and some parts of Western Tibet also experienced heavy rainfall.[10]

Ever since independence, India has constantly witnessed some of the worst natural disasters most frequent among them were floods. Kosi, Bihar's sorrow, had wrecked havoc in 1987 and took lives of nearly 1,399 people and 5302 animals. Nearly 29 million people were affected across 30 districts in one of the deadliest floods in country's history. The 1998 Assam Floods is considered to be the most severe one since 1950. The Brahmaputra remained above the danger mark for almost three months at six major gauge sites on the river. Country witnessed yet another deadly flood in the year 2005 in Maharashtra. The 2005 Maharashtra flood was one of the most deadly floods in the region. At least 5,000 people died in this flood. Mumbai was the worst hit by the monsoon and even the maximum city came to a standstill.

A major cloudburst and heavy rainfall on the intervening night of August 6, 2010 triggered mudslides, flash floods and debris flow in Jammu and Kashmir's Ladakh. Seventy-one towns and villages in Leh were affected in the region and at least 255 people died. Assam once again faced the wrath of Brahmaputra due to significant monsoon rains in 2012. The unprecedented flood claimed human lives of 124 people. Worst hit area was Kaziranga National Park where 13 great India rhinos and around 500 animals died due to flooding.[11]

Effects of Flooding

The primary effects of flooding include loss of life, damage to buildings and other structures, including bridges, sewerage systems, roadways, and canals. Floods frequently damage power transmission and sometimes power generation, which then has knock-on effects caused by the loss of power. Damage to roads and transport infrastructure may make it difficult to mobilise aid to those affected or to provide emergency health treatment. Economic hardship due to a temporary decline in tourism, rebuilding costs, or food shortages leading to price increases is a common after-effect of severe flooding. Urban flooding can lead to chronically wet houses, which are linked to an increase in respiratory problems and other illnesses.

Floods can bring many benefits, such as recharging ground water, making soil more fertile and increasing nutrients in some soils. Flooding can spread nutrients to lakes and rivers, which can lead to increased biomass and improved fisheries for a few years. Periodic flooding was essential to the well-being of ancient communities along the Tigris-Euphrates Rivers, the Nile River, the Indus River, the Ganges and the Yellow River among others.[12]

Floodwater can seriously disrupt public and personal transport by cutting off roads and railway lines, as well as communication links when telephone lines are damaged. Floods disrupt normal drainage systems in cities, and sewage spills are common, which represents a serious health hazard, along with standing water and wet materials in the home. Floodwater can severely disrupt public and personal transport by cutting off roads and railway lines, as well as communication links when telephone lines are damaged. Floods can distribute large amounts of water and suspended sediment over vast areas, restocking valuable soil nutrients to agricultural lands.[13]

Flood Controlling

Flood control has been practiced since ancient times with methods such as reforestation, and the construction of levees, dams, reservoirs and channels diverting floodwater, called floodways. In many countries around the world, waterways prone to floods are often carefully managed. Defenses such as detention basins, levees, bunds, reservoirs, and weirs are used to prevent waterways from overflowing their banks. Planning for flood safety involves many aspects of analysis and engineering, including: (a) observation of previous and present flood heights and inundated areas, (b) statistical, hydrologic, and hydraulic model analyses; (c) mapping inundated areas and flood heights for future flood scenarios; (d) long-term land use planning and regulation; (e) engineering design and construction of structures to control or withstand flooding; (f) intermediate-term monitoring, forecasting, and emergency-response planning, and (g) short-term monitoring, warning, and response operations.

Flood control refers to all methods used to reduce or prevent the detrimental effects of flood waters. Flood relief refers to methods used to reduce the effects of flood waters or high water levels. Many dams and their associated reservoirs are

- Clean up spilled medicines, bleaches, gasoline, or other flammable liquids immediately. Avoid the hazard of a chemical emergency.
- Open closet and cabinet doors cautiously. Contents may have shifted during the shaking of an earthquake and could fall, creating further damage or injury.
- Inspect your home for damage. Get everyone out if your home is unsafe. Aftershocks following earthquakes can cause further damage to unstable buildings. If your home has experienced damage, get out before aftershocks happen.
- Help neighbours who may require special assistance.
- Listen to a portable, battery-operated radio (or television) for updated emergency information and instructions.
- Expect aftershocks. Each time you feel one, drop, cover, and hold on! Aftershocks frequently occur minutes, days, weeks, and even months following an earthquake.
- Watch out for fallen power lines or broken gas lines, and stay out of damaged areas. Hazards caused by earthquakes are often difficult to see, and you could be easily injured.
- Stay out of damaged buildings. If you are away from home, return only when authorities say it is safe. Damaged buildings may be destroyed by aftershocks following the main quake.
- Use battery-powered lanterns or flashlights to inspect your home. Kerosene lanterns, torches, candles, and matches may tip over or ignite flammables inside.
- Inspect the entire length of chimneys carefully for damage. Unnoticed damage could lead to fire or injury from falling debris during an aftershock.
- Take pictures of the damage, both to the house and its contents, for insurance claims.
- Avoid smoking inside buildings. Smoking in confined areas can cause fires.
- When entering buildings, use extreme caution.
- Check for gas leaks.
- Look for electrical system damage.
- Watch for loose plaster, dry wall, and ceilings that could fall.
- Watch animals closely.

References

1. Earthquake (Available at https://en.wikipedia.org/wiki/Earthquake)
2. Chapter 9 Earthquakes (Available at http://www.tclauset.org/20_ESbk/ch09.pdf)
3. Types of earthquakes (Available at http://www.scec.org/education/k12/learn/eq2.htm)
4. See http://www.universetoday.com/82164/types-of-earthquakes/
5. Why Do Earthquakes Happen? (Available at http://www.geo.mtu.edu/UPSeis/why.html)
6. See http://www.infoplease.com/encyclopedia/science/earthquake-causes-earthquakes.html
7. Ring of Fire (Available at https://en.wikipedia.org/wiki/Ring_of_Fire)
8. Earthquake (Available at https://en.wikipedia.org/wiki/Earthquake)
9. Robert Ferris (2015), the cities facing the greatest danger of a mega-earthquake (Available at http://www.cnbc.com/2015/04/29/the-cities-facing-the-greatest-danger-of-a-mega-earthquake.html)
10. Earthquakes in Japan (Available at https://en.wikipedia.org/wiki/Earthquakes_in_Japan)
11. Business Standard (April 27, 2015). At least 38 Indian cities in high-risk earthquake zones (Available at http://www.business-standard.com/article/specials/atleast-38-indian-cities-in-high-risk-earthquake-zones-115042700095_1.html)
12. See http://topyaps.com/7-indian-cities-earthquake-prone-zones
13. See http://saarc-sdmc.nic.in/pdf/earthquake.pdf
14. See http://indianexpress.com/article/india/fresh-tremors-in-delhi-and-ncr/
15. Earthquake Zones in India (Available at https://en.wikipedia.org/wiki/Earthquake_zones_of_India)
16. See http://saarc-sdmc.nic.in/pdf/earthquake.pdf
17. Earthquake (Available at https://en.wikipedia.org/wiki/Earthquake)
18. What Are Earthquake Hazards? (Available at http://www.geo.mtu.edu/UPSeis/hazards.html)
19. See http://www.geographylwc.org.uk/A/A2/A2tectonics/eqeffect.html
20. See http://www.mindfeeders.org/harmful-effects-of-earthquakes/
21. Earthquake (Available at https://en.wikipedia.org/wiki/Earthquake)
22. See http://www.ga.gov.au/scientific-topics/hazards/earthquake/basics/causes
23. See http://saarc-sdmc.nic.in/pdf/earthquake.pdf
24. See http://emergency.cdc.gov/disasters/earthquakes/prepared.asp
25. Precautions for Earthquakes (Available at http://www.pref.aichi.jp/global/en/living/prevention/)
26. See http://www.mcasiwakuni.marines.mil/UnitHome/NEO/EarthquakePrecautions.aspx
27. See http://www.mcasiwakuni.marines.mil/UnitHome/NEO/EarthquakePrecautions.aspx

8

Cyclone

> *"The development of civilisation and industry in general has always shown itself so active in the destruction of forests that everything that has been done for their conservation and production is completely insignificant in comparison."*
>
> **-Karl Marx**

There are a number of structural characteristics common to all cyclones. A cyclone is a low-pressure area. A cyclone's centre (often known in a mature tropical cyclone as the eye), is the area of lowest atmospheric pressure in the region. A cyclone is formed when a warm temperature of the sea reaches a threshold level and the wind structure is rising. The eye of the cyclone is the centre of the cyclone where the focus lies. The areas surrounding the eye will be most affected because of the strong wind. The cyclone is rising with a clockwise direction at the bottom and an anti-clockwise direction as it rises to the sky, forming a Tropical Cyclone.[1]

The terrifying word 'Cyclone' has been derived from the Greek word 'Cyclos' meaning coil of a snake. As tropical storms in the Indian seas resemble coiled serpents of the sea, these storms were named as Cyclones. Tropical cyclones are referred to as Hurricanes over Atlantic Ocean, Typhoons over Pacific Ocean, Willy-Willies over Australian Seas and Cyclones over north Indian Ocean.[2] The practice of naming storms (tropical cyclones) began years ago in order to help in the quick identification of storms in warning messages because names are presumed to be far easier to remember than the numbers and technical terms. Many agree that appending names to storms makes it easier for the media to report on tropical cyclones, heightens interest in warnings and increases community preparedness.[3]

When the winds in the rotating storm reach 39 mph, the storm is called a "tropical storm". And when the wind speeds reach 74 mph, the storm is officially a "tropical cyclone" or hurricane. Tropical cyclones usually weaken when they hit land, because they are no longer being "fed" by the energy from the warm ocean waters. However, they often move far inland, dumping many centimeters of rain and causing lots of wind damage before they die out completely. Cyclones are divided into categories depending on the strength of the winds produced. There are many different classification scales but one you may be familiar with is the Saffir-Simpson Hurricane Scale. This scale is used to desribe storms in Hollywood movies, e.g. "Twister" and "The Day after Tomorrow.[4]

The Indian Ocean tsunami of December 2004, which killed over 200,000 people and affected livelihoods and coastal resources in 14 Asian and African countries, highlighted the need for coastal protection against tsunamis and other hazards, including cyclones and storm surges. A number of countries have called for the restoration of coastal forests to improve protection of coastal areas.[5]

Meaning

Cyclone is an area of closed, circular fluid motion rotating in the same direction as the Earth. This is usually characterised by inward spiraling winds that rotate counterclockwise in the Northern Hemisphere and clockwise in the Southern Hemisphere of the Earth. Most large-scale cyclonic circulations are centred on areas of low atmospheric pressure. According to the National Hurricane Centre glossary, warm-core cyclones such as tropical cyclones and subtropical cyclones also lie within the synoptic scale.[6]

Cyclone is a swirling atmospheric disturbance in which strong winds blow in a circle, and rotate in the same direction as rotation of the earth. These comprise spiralling winds that are usually centred in areas that have low atmospheric pressures. At the same time, they are surrounded by high pressure.[7] It refers to any spinning storm that rotates around a low-pressure centre. The low-pressure centre is also referred to as the 'eye' of the storm, which is well known for being eerily calm compared with the areas under the spinning 'arms' of the storm.[8]

Types of Cyclone[9]

There are three main types' surface-based cyclones: Extratropical cyclones, Subtropical and Tropical cyclones.

1. **Extratropical cyclone** is an everyday phenomenon that is anticyclones drive the weather over much of the Earth. They are capable of producing anything from cloudiness and mild showers to heavy gales and thunderstorms. It form anywhere within the extratropical regions of the Earth (usually between 30° and 60° latitude from the equator), either through cyclogenesis or extratropical transition. There are two models of cyclone development and lifecycles in common use—the Norwegian model and the Shapiro-Keyser Model.
2. **Subtropical cyclone** is a weather system that has some characteristics of a tropical and an extratropical cyclone. It forms in a wide band of latitude, mainly south of the 50th parallel in the northern hemisphere. These storms can have maximum winds extending farther from the centre than in a purely tropical cyclone and have no weather fronts linking directly to the centre of circulation. The most common type of subtropical storm is an upper-level cold low with circulation extending to the surface layer and maximum sustained winds generally occurring at a radius of about 160 kilometers (99 mi) or more from the centre. second type of subtropical cyclone is a mesoscale low originating in or near a frontolysing zone of horizontal wind shear, also known as a dying frontal zone, with radius of maximum sustained winds generally less than 50 kilometers (31 mi).
3. **Tropical cyclone** is rapidly rotating storm system characterised by a low-pressure centre, strong winds, and a spiral arrangement of thunderstorms that produce heavy rain. Depending on its location and strength, tropical cyclone is referred to by names such as hurricane, typhoon

tropical storm, cyclonic storm, tropical depression, and simply cyclone. Tropical cyclones are areas of relatively low pressure in the troposphere, with the largest pressure perturbations occurring at low altitudes near the surface. The three-dimensional wind field in a tropical cyclone can be separated into two components: a primary circulation and a secondary circulation. The primary circulation is the rotational part of the flow; it is purely circular. The secondary circulation is the overturning part of the flow; it is in the radial and vertical directions.

Table 1: Cyclone Category Classification

Cyclone Category	*Description*	*Wind Speed (Km/h)*	*Characteristics*	*Effects*
1 TC	Strong Gale	Less than 125	High Waves, may affects visibility	Negligible property damages; minimal infrastructure and crop damages.
2. TC	Violent Strom	125-169	Air filled with form; high waves; visibility affects.	Minor property damages; significant infrastructure and crop damages; local power failure.
3. Severe TC	Very destructive winds (Hurricane)	170-224	Air filled with foam and spray, driving high waves; visibility affected.	Major property damages; significant infrastructure and crop damages.
4. Severe TC	Very destructive winds (Hurricane)	225-279	Air filled with foam and spray, driving high waves; visibility severally affected.	Major property damages; significant infrastructure and crop damages; widespread power failure; injuries and fatalities.
5. Severe TC	Very destructive winds (Hurricane)	More than 280	Air filled with foam and spray, driving high waves; visibility severally affected.	Major property damages; significant infrastructure and crop damages; widespread power failure; injuries and fatalities.

Causes of Cyclone

The main source of energy for tropical cyclones is the warm oceans in the tropical regions. To initiate a tropical cyclone the sea-surface temperature generally needs to be above 26.5°C. The development of a tropical cyclone also relies on favourable broad-scale wind regimes and can persist for several days with many following quite erratic paths.[10]

This heat from the ocean combines with the Earth's rotation to create the cyclone's spin and propulsion. As the cyclone moves across cooler waters, land or into unfavourable wind systems, it gradually begins to dissipate as it loses energy. There are a number of additional atmospheric conditions that must be present in order for a cyclone to form, including moisture layers in the mid-troposphere, approximately three miles above the Earth's surface, and low vertical wind shear between the Earth's surface and the upper troposphere. Cyclones also need to be at least 310 miles from the equator, where the deflective Coriolis force of the planet's rotation begins to take effect.[11]

Indian Perspectives

India has a coastline of about 7,516 km, 5,400 km along the mainland, 132 km in Lakshadweep and 1,900 km in the Andaman and Nicobar Islands. More cyclones form in the Bay of Bengal than in the Arabian Sea and the ratio is 4:1. It has been observed that between 1891 and 2006, 308 cyclones crossed the east coast, out of which 103 were severe. There are 13 coastal states and union territories (UTs) in the country, encompassing 84 coastal districts which are affected by tropical cyclones. Four states (Tamil Nadu, Andhra Pradesh, Odisha and West Bengal) and one UT (Pondicherry) on the east coast and one state (Gujarat) on the west coast are highly vulnerable to cyclone disasters.[12]

More cyclones form in the Bay of Bengal than in the Arabian Sea. As such, the eastern coast is more prone to cyclones and about 80 per cent of the total cyclones generated in the Indian Ocean strike the east coast of India. May, June, October and November are known for severe storms. The entire east coast from Odisha to Tamil Nadu is vulnerable to cyclones with varying frequency and intensity. Andhra Pradesh has a long coast line of 1,030 km from Srikakulam in the north to Nellore in the south along the east coast of India and bordering the Bay of Bengal. Nine coastal districts of Srikakulam, Vizianagaram, Visakhapatnam, East Godavari, West Godavari, Krishna, Guntur, Prakasam and Nellore are highly vulnerable to tropical cyclones.

This state has a very long history of cyclones and has experienced 71 cyclones from 1892 to 2004.

Like Andhra Pradesh, its neighbouring state Odisha is also vulnerable to tropical cyclones. The agriculturally rich districts of Khurda, Puri, Cuttack, Jagatsinghpur, Kendrapara were devastated due to storm while districts like Jajpur, Bhadrak, Keonjhar, Balasore and Mayurbhanj were severely affected by unprecedented flood. The state of Gujarat is the worst sufferer at the hands of cyclones on the west coast of India. According to vulnerability Altas of India, Kachchh, Jamnagar, Porbandar, Junagadh, Ameri and Bhavnagar districts lie in the Very High Damage zone for wind and cyclone hazards.[13]

Phailin was the strongest tropical cyclone that ever made landfall in India, behind only the Odisha Cyclone which ripped through the state in 1999. Phailin had lashed Gopalpur in Ganjam district of Odisha, with strong winds blowing at about 200-220 kmph at landfall. In its wake, Phailin brought torrential rains in Odisha and north coastal Andhra Pradesh, leaving behind a trail of destruction after making landfall on October 12, 2013. Prior to 2000, there was no practice of naming tropical storms. The 1999, cyclonic storm which ripped Odisha triggered the necessity of naming storms. The practice of naming helps in quick identification of storms because names are presumed to be far easier to remember than numbers and technical terms.[14]

Storm Thane was the strongest tropical cyclone of 2011 within the North Indian Ocean. Thane initially developed as a tropical disturbance within the monsoon trough to the west of Indonesia. Over the next couple of days the disturbance gradually developed further while moving towards the northwest, and was declared a Depression during December 25, 2011 before being declared Cyclonic Storm Thane during the next day. Seven hundred fishermen were reported to be stranded near the Nizampatnam Bay area due to the rough sea conditions near the coast due to the cyclone. Owners had asked the government as well as the National Coast Guard for the fishermen's search and rescue after they could not communicate with them. Fishing activities had come to a complete halt in the cities of Chennai, Tiruvallur and Kanchipuram in the wake of the storm after the warnings by the weather department were received. About 10,000 fishing boats were moved to safer locations in all fishing hamlets in these areas.[15]

Cyclone Nargis caused the worst natural disaster in the recorded history of Myanmar during early May 2008. The Labutta Township alone was reported to have 80,000 dead, with about 10,000 more deaths in Bogale. The first named storm of the 2008 North Indian Ocean cyclone season, Nargis developed on 27 April, 2008 in the central area of Bay of Bengal. On 27 and 28 April, the cyclone enhanced the South-West Monsoon over Sri Lanka which resulted in very heavy rain, flooding and landslides being reported within the Western, Sabaragamuwa and Southern provinces. Strong waves and gusty winds were expected along the Tamil Nadu and Andhra Pradesh coastline in India. Additionally, the influence of the cyclone lowered temperatures along the Indian coastline, which had been affected by a severe heat wave. Nargis was the deadliest tropical cyclone worldwide since the 1970 Bhola cyclone, which killed nearly 500,000 people.[16]

The 1970 Bhola cyclone was a devastating tropical cyclone in the history of south Asia. It was struck East Pakistan and India's West Bengal on 12 November 1970. This cyclone was the sixth cyclonic storm of the 1970 North Indian Ocean cyclone season, and also the season's strongest, reaching a strength equivalent to a strong Category 3 hurricane. The Indian government received many ship reports from the Bay of Bengal that were giving meteorological information on the cyclone, but as Indo-Pakistani relations were generally hostile, the information was not passed on to the Pakistani government. Following two previously destructive cyclones in October 1960 which killed at least 16,000 people in East Pakistan, the Pakistani government contacted the American government for assistance in developing a system to avert future disasters. The cyclone brought widespread rain to the Andaman and Nicobar Islands. There was also widespread rain in West Bengal and southern Assam. The rain caused damage to housing and crops in both Indian states, with the worst damage occurring in the southernmost districts.[17]

Cyclonic Storm Laila is the first cyclonic storm to affect southeastern India in May since the 1990 Andhra Pradesh cyclone. Laila is an Urdu/Arabic name, meaning Night. It is the worst storm to hit Andhra Pradesh over the last 14 years. Nine people were killed in rain related incidents in Tamil Nadu, as the cyclonic storm "Laila" battered the coastal areas in northern parts of Tamil Nadu, Chennai city and its suburbs. The fishermen of Pamban, Uchipuli and nearby areas who ventured into sea on May 17 nights in boats with outboard motors were missing. The cyclone caused heavy destruction in Prakasam, Krishna and Guntur districts and preliminary reports prepared by the State government put the loss at over Rs 500 crore.[18]

Extremely Severe Cyclonic Storm Hudhud was a strong tropical cyclone that caused extensive damage and loss of life in eastern India and Nepal during October 2014. Hudhud caused extensive damage to the city of Visakhapatnam and the neighbouring districts of Vizianagaram and Srikakulam of Andhra Pradesh. In light of the storm, the National Disaster Response Force mobilised 35 teams in Andhra Pradesh and Odisha. The East Coast Railway cancelled 38 trains on October 12 when the cyclone made landfall. An alert was sounded in nine out of thirteen districts of Andhra Pradesh where standing crops including paddy, groundnut, sugarcane, and pulses were yet to be harvested. Over 700,000 people, including 500,000 people in Andhra Pradesh, were evacuated and put up in relief camps. The Odisha government had placed 16 districts under high alert. On 14 October 2014, sudden weather changes from Cyclone Hudhud in Nepal reportedly caused an avalanche on Mount Dhaulagiri. The avalanche and heavy snowfall killed at least 43 hikers and guides in Nepal.[19]

Extremely Severe Cyclonic Storm Nilofar was the strongest tropical cyclone of 2014 within the North Indian Ocean and the strongest storm to form over the Arabian Sea since Phet in 2010. Nilofar originated from a low pressure area in the Arabian Sea that intensified into a depression on October 25. Over time the storm tracked northeastwards towards an area of high vertical wind shear, causing the storm to rapidly weaken. National Disaster Response Force deployed rescue and rehabilitation teams. The fishermen were warned to avoid the sea and the people from some coastal areas were evacuated.[20]

Tropical cyclones occur only rarely over the Arabian Sea—usually just one or two per year. The first to emerge in 2015 was on a collision course with Oman. The intensity of pre-monsoon storms over the Arabian Sea has increased in the past decade. Some researchers have attributed the increase to emissions of black carbon and other aerosols. According to that line of research, increasing aerosol emissions may be changing regional circulation patterns in ways that reduce wind shear over the Arabian Sea. The cyclonic storm Ashobaa has now weakened into a depression and has moved further away from the Indian coast. According to Skymet Meteorology Division in India, the weather system over east-central Arabian Sea has intensified further. Satellite images are showing cloud configuration, which is similar to that of a tropical cyclone.[21]

Cyclone Sidr was a tropical cyclone that resulted in one of the worst natural disasters in Bangladesh. The fourth named storm of the 2007 North Indian Ocean cyclone season, Sidr formed in the central Bay of Bengal. Save the Children estimated the number of deaths associated with the cyclone to be between 5,000 and 10,000, while the Red Crescent Society reported on November 18 that the number of deaths could be up to 10,000. Cyclone Sidr slammed the highly vulnerable low lying densely populated coastal areas of Bangladesh with heavy rain, winds of up to 120 miles/hr, and a storm surge. Coastal districts of Bangladesh faced heavy rainfall as an early impact of the cyclone. Dhaka and other parts of Bangladesh experienced drizzle and gusty winds. The damage in Bangladesh was extensive, including tin shacks flattened, houses and schools blown away and enormous tree damage. People of the cyclone affected area experienced severe health problems such as diseases like diarrhea, which spread due to shortage of drinking water.[22]

Effects of Cyclone

Severe tropical cyclones are responsible for large number of casualities and considerable damage to property and agricultural crop. Principal dangers from cyclones are: (i) very strong winds, (ii) torrential rain, and (iii) high storm tides. Most casualties are caused by coastal inundation by storm surge. Floods generated by cyclone rainfall are more destructive than winds. The collapse of buildings, falling trees, flying debris, electrocution, aircraft and ship accidents and disease from contaminated food and water in the post-cyclone period also contribute to loss of life and destruction of property.[23]

Cyclones are among the most dangerous and most destructive natural disasters that can occur. They have been responsible for about 1.9 million deaths worldwide over the last two centuries, and it is estimated that 10,000 people are killed each year by these storms. The strong winds of cyclones can cause damage over an area of 25 km in smaller systems and upto 500 km in larger systems. Winds have been known to destroy smaller buildings and knock out power for thousands of people. The thunderstorms produced in a cyclone system produce intense rainfall causing massive flooding, mudslides and landslides. This flooding tends to be more severe and destructive inland due to poor preparedness.[24]

The main effects of tropical cyclones include heavy rain, strong wind, large storm surges at landfall, and tornadoes. The destruction from a tropical cyclone depends mainly on its intensity, its size, and its location. After the cyclone has passed, devastation often continues. Standing water can cause the spread of disease, and transportation or communications infrastructure may have been destroyed, hampering clean-up and rescue efforts. Strong winds can damage or destroy vehicles, buildings, bridges, personal property and other outside objects, turning loose debris into deadly flying projectiles. The thunderstorm activity in a tropical cyclone produces intense rainfall, potentially resulting in flooding, mudslides, and landslides. Inland areas are particularly vulnerable to freshwater flooding, due to residents not preparing adequately. Tropical cyclones reshape the geology near the coast by eroding sand from the beach as well as offshore, rearranging coral, and changing dune configuration onshore. Severe tropical cyclones defoliate tropical forest canopy trees, remove vines and epiphytes from the trees, break tree crown stems, and cause tree falls.[25]

Primary effects of tropical storms include high winds, torrential rain and storm surges at landfall. There may also be localised tornadoes and waterspouts. These are all physical effects. Secondary effects of tropical storms are very wide-ranging. Effects of Cyclones and Hurricanes are:

1. Tropical cyclones cause heavy rainfall and landslides.
2. Agricultural land is severely affected, especially in terms of water supply and soil erosion.
3. It causes harm to human, plant and animal life.
4. Communication systems are badly affected due to cyclones.

5. They cause a lot of harm to towns and villages, causing severe damage to kuccha houses. Coastal businesses like shipyards and oil wells are destroyed.
6. They harm the ecosystem of the surrounding region.
7. Civic facilities are disturbed.[26]

Social effects of Tropical Storms[27]

1. There are likely to be food and water shortages.
2. As a result of extensive flooding, people may catch water-borne diseases. This may eventually lead to death.
3. Communities are displaced from their homes, and may be broken up if the area is not restored. Many people are made homeless.
4. People suffer from stress due to loss of possessions and housing.
5. There may be looting of properties - domestic and commercial.
6. People may lose their jobs if they work in an industry that has been badly affected.
7. If insurance premiums rise in the future, some people may not be able to afford them and will consequently not be financially protected against future storms.

Environmental Effects of Tropical Storms[28]

1. A huge amount of water is released in a tropical storm so there will be extensive flooding.
2. Flooding might led to sewer systems being flushed out and spreading disease.
3. There will be structural damage to buildings and they may have to be pulled down and rebuilt. This is very costly. Other buildings may have broken windows, chimneys etc.
4. Roads and other infrastructure such as railways may be destroyed. This can lead to communication problems.
5. Electricity lines might be blown down and, as a result, people could be without power supplies.
6. Sensitive ecosystems may be destroyed and plant and animal habitats lost.

7. Sea fish are often killed because of silting, and freshwater fish may be killed in storm surges.
8. Fishing boats and other craft may be damaged.
9. Crops and livestock may be damaged or destroyed.

Preparedness and Precautions

A better disaster management with minimum vulnerability is possible only by means of preparedness and mitigation measures. The first and probably the most complex task of mitigation is to map the hazard, risks and vulnerabilities, analyse and assess the levels of risks and monitor it continuously. Early warning of disasters and its dissemination to the community is an important preparatory measure to reduce the losses of life and property during disasters.[29]

Before the Cyclone[30]

1. Ensure that your house is in good condition and can withstand cyclone gusts.
2. Trim tree branches likely to cause damages to your house, telephone and electricity lines.
3. Clear your property of loose material that can cause injury and damage during extreme winds.
4. Identify secure places for your boat.
5. Be acquainted with the nearest cyclone refugee centres.
6. Prepare an emergency kit consisting of:
   a. Portable AM/FM radio and fresh batteries.
   b. Torch, lamps, candles, matches, etc.
   c. Water containers.
   d. Canned food, can opener, stove with sufficient gas.
   e. Rice, flour, biscuits, cheese, etc.
   f. First aid kit and essential medicines.
   g. Clothes secured in plastic bags.
   h. Tool kit for emergency repairs (hammer, nail, rope, etc.).

When the cyclone strikes[31]

1. Disconnect all electrical appliances. Listen to your battery radio for updates.

2. Stay inside and shelter {well clear of windows) in the strongest part of the building, i.e. cellar, internal hallway or bathroom. Keep evacuation and emergency kits with you.
3. If the building starts to break up, protect yourself with mattresses, rugs or blankets under a strong table or bench or hold onto a solid fixture, e.g. a water pipe.
4. Beware the calm 'eye'. If the wind drops, don't assume the cyclone is over; violent winds will soon resume from another direction. Wait for the official 'all clear'.
5. If driving, stop- but well away from the sea and clear of trees, power lines and streams. Stay in the vehicle.

After the cyclone[32]

1. Don't go outside until officially advised it is safe.
2. Check for gas leaks. Don't use electric appliances if wet.
3. Listen to local radio for official warnings and advice.
4. If you have to evacuate, or did so earlier, don't return until advised. Use a recommended route and don't rush.
5. Beware of damaged power lines, bridges, buildings, trees, and don't enter floodwaters.
6. Heed all warnings and don't go sightseeing. Check/help neighbours instead.
7. Don't make unnecessary telephone calls.

Reducing Vulnerability of Structures and Infrastructures[33]

- New buildings should be designed to be wind and water resistant. Design standards are usually contained in building codes;
- Communication and utility lines should be located away from the coastal area or installed underground;
- Improvement of building sites by raising the ground level to protect against flood and storm surges;
- Protective river embankments, levees and coastal dikes should be regularly inspected for breaches due to erosion and opportunities taken to plant mangroves to reduce breaking wave energy;

- Improved vegetation cover. This helps to reduce the impact of soil erosion and landslides and facilitates the absorption of rainfall to reduce flooding.

References

1. What is cyclone? (Available at http://www.sage.unsw.edu.au/currentstudents/ug/projects/Darmawan/Cyclone.html)
2. See http://www.skymetweather.com/content/weather-news-and-analysis/last-five-devastating-cyclones-in-india/
3. Names of Tropical Cyclones (Available at http://www.imd.gov.in/section/nhac/dynamic/cycname.pdf)
4. See https://sites.google.com/site/disasterportal/stroms_ cyclones/cyclone-formation
5. Hermann M. Fritz and Chris Blount, Protection from Cyclone, chapter 2 (Available at http://www.fao.org/forestry/13189-0eaa685d059973e879165d466dba43540.pdf)
6. Cyclone (Available at https://en.wikipedia.org/wiki/Cyclone)
7. Reena, J, 7 Harmful Effects of Cyclones and Hurricanes (Available at http://www.shareyouressays.com/110973/7-harmful-effects-of-cyclones-and-hurricanes)
8. See http://study.com/academy/lesson/what-are-cyclones-types-causes-effects.html
9. Cyclone (Available at https://en.wikipedia.org/wiki/Cyclone)
10. What causes cyclones? (Available at http://www.ga.gov.au/scientific-topics/hazards/cyclone/basics/causes)
11. See http://www.ask.com/science/causes-cyclone-fa980c 5ea1135f7b
12. Management of Cyclones (http://www.ndma.gov.in/images/guidelines/cyclones.pdf)
13. Negi Mohita, Tropical Cyclones in India: Notes on Tropical Cyclones in India (Available at http://www. yourarticlelibrary.com/cyclones/tropical-cyclones-in-india-notes-on-tropical-cyclones-in-india/13941/)
14. See http://www.skymetweather.com/content/weather-news-and-analysis/last-five-devastating-cyclones-in-india/
15. Cyclone Thane (Available at https://en.wikipedia.org/wiki/Cyclone_Thane)
16. Cyclone Nargis (Available at https://en.wikipedia.org/wiki/Cyclone_Nargis)
17. 1970 Bhola cyclone (Available at https://en.wikipedia.org/wiki/1970_Bhola_cyclone)
18. Cyclonic Storm Laila (Available at https://en.wikipedia.org/wiki/Cyclone_Laila)
19. Cyclone Hudhud (Available at https://en.wikipedia.org/wiki/Cyclone_Hudhud)
20. Cyclone Nilofar (Available at https://en.wikipedia.org/wiki/Cyclone_Nilofar)
21. See http://www.skymetweather.com/content/weather-news-and-analysis/low-pressure-area-in-arabian-sea-strengthens-into-depression/
22. Cyclone Sidr (Available at https://en.wikipedia.org/wiki/Cyclone_Sidr)
23. Nick Arya, What are the various effects of cyclone? (Available at http://www.preservearticles.com/201102173914/effects-of-cyclone.html)
24. Chad Stetson, Harmful Effects of Cyclones (Available at http://www.ehow.com/info_8489390_harmful-effects-cyclones.html)

designed completely or partially to aid in flood protection and control. Many large dams have flood-control reservations in which the level of a reservoir must be kept below a certain elevation before the onset of the rainy/summer melt season to allow a certain amount of space in which floodwaters can fill. Floods can be controlled by redirecting excess water to purpose-built canals or floodways, which in turn divert the water to temporary holding ponds or other bodies of water where there is a lower risk or impact to flooding.

The self-closing flood barrier/is a flood defence system designed to protect people and property from inland waterway floods caused by heavy rainfall, gales or rapid melting snow. Defences such as levees, bunds, reservoirs, and weirs are used to prevent rivers from bursting their banks. When these defences fail, emergency measures such as sandbags, hydrosacks or portable inflatable tubes are used. Tide gates are used in conjunction with dykes and culverts. They can be placed at the mouth of streams or small rivers, where an estuary begins or where tributary streams, or drainage ditches connect to sloughs.[14]

Anticipating floods before they occur allows for precautions to be taken and people to be warned so that they can be prepared in advance for flooding conditions.[15] There are a number of things you can do to prepare for a flood and minimise damage.

(a) Structures should not be built in a flood plain.

(b) Keep your furnace, water heater, and electric panel elevated, especially if you live in an area where flooding is likely.

(c) Put together an emergency kit and make plans with your family — something that is ideal for any emergency situation, not just flooding.

(d) If you find yourself under a flood warning, make sure to pay attention to radio or television warnings.

(e) If you have time prior to an evacuation, turn off utilities at the main switches and disconnect electrical appliances.

(f) Move furniture and important items to higher levels in your house and bring in any outdoor furniture.

(g) Avoid contact with flood water. It may contain oil, gasoline, raw sewage, or any number of undesirable materials.

(h) Wash your hands thoroughly with clean water before eating, and do not drink from contaminated sources.[16]

What to Do Before Flooding Occurs[17]

1. If it has been raining hard for several hours, or steadily raining for several days, be alert to the possibility of a flood. Floods happen as the ground becomes saturated.
2. Use a NOAA Weather Radio or a portable, battery-powered radio (or television) for updated emergency information. Local stations provide the best advice for your particular situation
3. When in or along stream channels, be aware of distant events, such as dam breaks or thunderstorms that may cause flash floods in the area.
4. If you are stopping your vehicle, camp or park away from streams and washes, particularly during threatening conditions. Flood waters can rise quickly and carry you or your belongings away.
5. Listen for distant thunder. In some types of terrain, runoff from a faraway thunderstorm could be headed your way.

How to Protect Your Property[18]

1. Keep insurance policies, documents, and other valuables in a safe-deposit box.
2. Avoid building in a floodplain unless you elevate and reinforce your home.
3. Contact your local emergency management office for more information on mitigation options to further reduce potential flood damage.
4. Consult with a construction professional for further information if these and other damage reduction measures can be taken.
5. Seal walls in basements with waterproofing compounds to avoid seepage through cracks.
6. Construct barriers such as levees, berms, and flood walls to stop flood water from entering the building.
7. Install check valves in building sewer traps to prevent flood water from backing up into the drains of your home.

What to Tell Children[19]

1. Stay away from flooded areas. Even if it seems safe, flood waters may still be rising.
2. Never try to walk, swim, drive, or play in flood water.

3. If you are in a vehicle and become surrounded by water, if you can get out safely, do so immediately and move to higher ground.
4. Watch out for snakes in areas that were flooded.
5. Stay away from creek and stream banks in flooded and recently flooded areas.
6. Never play around high water, storm drains, ditches, ravines, or culverts.
7. Throw away all food that has come into contact with flood waters.

References

1. See http://www.english-online.at/geography/floods/floods-and-flooding.htm
2. See http://www.svf.tuke.sk/erasmusip/Ganova.pdf
3. See http://www.disastercenter.com/guide/flood.pdf
4. Types of Floods and Floodplains, Chapter 2 (Available at http://training.fema.gov/hiedu/docs/fmc/chapter% 202%20-%20types%20of%20floods%20and%20 flood plains.pdf)
5. Types of flooding (Available at http://www. environmentlaw.org.uk/rte.asp?id=100)
6. Flood (Available at https://en.wikipedia.org/wiki/Flood)
7. What causes floods? (Available at http://www.ga.gov.au/scientific-topics/hazards/flood/basics/causes)
8. See http://agritech.tnau.ac.in/agriculture/agri_majorareas_ disastermgt_flood.html
9. Flood in Bihar (Available at https://en.wikipedia.org/wiki/Floods_in_Bihar)
10. See https://en.wikipedia.org/wiki/2013_North_ India_floods
11. Avinash Sharma, Read more at: http://www.oneindia. com/feature/have-a-look-at-9-deadliest-floods-in-indian-history-1517017.html
12. Flood (Available at https://en.wikipedia.org/wiki/Flood)
13. Flooding (Available at http://www.watersafetykids.co.uk/pdfs/Flooding.pdf)
14. Flood control (Available at https://en.wikipedia.org/wiki/Flood_control)
15. Flood (Available at https://en.wikipedia.org/wiki/Flood)
16. Nola Taylor Redd (2012), Flood Facts, Types of Flooding, Floods in History (Available at http://www.livescience. com/23913-flood-facts.html)
17. See http://www.disastercenter.com/guide/flood.pdf
18. *Ibid.*
19. *Ibid.*

7

Earthquake

"Almost half of the population of the world lives in rural regions and mostly in a state of poverty. Such inequalities in human development have been one of the primary reasons for unrest and, in some parts of the world, even violence."

-A.P.J. Abdul Kalam

Earthquake is the perceptible shaking of the surface of the Earth, which can be violent enough to destroy major buildings and kill thousands of people. The seismicity, seismism or seismic activity of an area refers to the frequency, type and size of earthquakes experienced over a period of time.[1] An earthquake is the movement of Earth's crust resulting from the release of built-up potential energy between two stuck lithospheric plates. The point below the surface where the rock breaks is called the earthquake focus. Earthquakes that result from movement in the crust are called shallow focus earthquakes because their focus is less than 50 kilometers below the surface. There are other kinds of earthquakes. Deep focus earthquakes occur at subduction zones when a subducting plate breaks. The focus of a breaking plate may be as deep as 700 kilometers below the surface.

An earthquake rapidly converts a large amount of built-up potential energy into the energy of motion. This energy of motion is spread by seismic waves. These waves start underground at the earthquake focus and radiate in all directions. People who record and interpret seismic waves are called seismologists. Seismic waves are recorded and measured by an instrument called a seismograph. Seismographs show the kinds of waves that occur, their strength, and the time that they arrive at the instrument. Today, seismologists use computers to determine the distance to an epicentre.[2]

Meaning

Earthquakes are one of the most destructive of natural hazards. Earthquake occurs due to sudden transient motion of the ground as a result of release of elastic energy in a matter of few seconds. The impact of the event is most traumatic because it affects large area, occurs all of a sudden and unpredictable. An Earthquake is a series of underground shock waves and movements on the earth's surface caused by natural processes within the earth's crust.

Types of Earthquake

There are many different types of earthquakes: tectonic, volcanic, and explosion. The type of earthquake depends on the region where it occurs and the geological make-up of that region. The most common are tectonic earthquakes. These occur when rocks in the earth's crust break due to geological forces created by movement of tectonic plates. Another type, volcanic earthquakes, occurs in conjunction with volcanic activity. Collapse earthquakes are small earthquakes in underground caverns and mines, and explosion earthquakes result from the explosion of nuclear and chemical devices.[3]

Earthquakes can come in three main forms, depending on the plate movements that occur beneath the earth's surface. They could occur on a Convergent Boundary, Divergent Boundary or a Transform Fault. There are two main types of earthquakes: natural and man-made. Naturally occurring (tectonic) earthquakes occur along tectonic plate lines (fault lines) while man-made earthquakes are always related to explosions detonated by man. Tectonic earthquakes will occur anywhere there is sufficient stored elastic strain energy to drive fracture propagation along a fault plane. The other type of earthquake is the artificial or man-made quake. This type of quake has been felt all over the world after the detonation of a nuclear weapon.[4]

Causes of Earthquake

Earthquakes are the vibrations caused by rocks breaking under stress. The underground surface along which the rock breaks and moves is called a fault plane. Earthquakes are usually caused when rock underground suddenly breaks along a fault. This sudden release of energy causes the seismic waves that make the ground shake. When two blocks of rock or two plates are rubbing against each other, they stick a little. They don't just slide smoothly; the rocks catch on each other.

The rocks are still pushing against each other, but not moving. After a while, the rocks break because of all the pressure that's built up.[5] Volcanic eruptions, rock falls, landslides, and explosions can also cause a quake, but most of these are of only local extent. Shock waves from a powerful earthquake can trigger smaller earthquakes in a distant location hundreds of miles away if the geologic conditions are favourable.[6]

Ring of Fire

It is an area in the basin of the Pacific Ocean where a large number of earthquakes and volcanic eruptions occur. In a 40,000 km (25,000 mi) horseshoe shape, it is associated with a nearly continuous series of oceanic trenches, volcanic arcs, and volcanic belts and/or plate movements. The Ring of Fire is a direct result of plate tectonics and the movement and collisions of lithospheric plates. About 90 per cent of the world's earthquakes and 81 per cent of the world's largest earthquakes occur along the Ring of Fire.[7]

Global Perspectives

It is estimated that around 500,000 earthquakes occur each year, detectable with current instrumentation. About 100,000 of these can be felt. The number of seismic stations has increased from about 350 in 1931 to many thousands today. Most of the world's earthquakes take place in the 40,000 km long, horseshoe-shaped zone called the circum-Pacific seismic belt, known as the Pacific Ring of Fire, which for the most part bounds the Pacific Plate. With the rapid growth of mega-cities such as Mexico City, Tokyo and Tehran, in areas of high seismic risk, some seismologists are warning that a single quake may claim the lives of up to 3 million people.[8]

Some of the most seismically active regions in the world also happen to have infrastructure that has not improved with their rapidly rising populations. In earthquake-prone cities, mushrooming populations are occupying buildings that are in many cases unable to withstand the effects of large quakes. The two deadliest earthquakes since 1980 were the 2010 quake in Haiti, which claimed more than 222,000 lives, and the 2004 Southeast Asian earthquake and tsunami that claimed 220,000 lives.[9]

Japan has had a long history of earthquakes and seismic activity. It is an area of high seismicity because it is located near major tectonic plate boundaries and is situated on the Pacific Ring of Fire. Over the years, the Japanese government has enforced measures to make buildings more resistant to earthquakes in known disaster zones. Frequent low intensity earth tremors and occasional volcanic activity are felt throughout the islands. Destructive earthquakes, often resulting in tsunamis, occur several times a century.[10] Iran is one of the most seismically active countries in the world, being crossed by several major fault lines that cover at least 90 per cent of the country. The Iranian plateau is subject to most types of tectonic activity, including active folding, faulting and volcanic eruptions. It is well known for its long history of disastrous earthquake activity.

Indian Perspectives

The Indian subcontinent has a history of earthquakes. The reason for the high frequency and intensity of earthquakes is the Indian plate driving into Asia at a rate of approximately 49 mm/year. At least 38 Indian cities lie in high-risk seismic zones; nearly 60 per cent of the sub-continental landmass is vulnerable to earthquakes and except for rare exceptions, such as the Delhi Metro, India's hastily-built cities are open to great damage from earthquakes. The earthquake that devastated the Kathmandu Valley in Nepal and jolted northern India, damaging buildings as far apart as Agra and Siliguri, was expected by geologists, who have warned of more Himalayan earthquakes, caused by the growing pressures of the subcontinent grinding into the Asian mainland. The Government of India today lists 38 cities in moderate to high-risk seismic zones. Typically, the majority of the constructions in these cities are not earthquake-resistant, notes a 2006 report written by the United Nations for the

Ministry of Home Affairs. The Himalayas and north India are on particularly shaky ground.[11]

Let us look at some of the Indian cities, which are regarded as high earthquake prone zones:[12]

1. **Guwahati:** Guwahati falls in zone five of the seismic zones in India, conducted by geologists. Apart from being the abode of the most frequent and dangerous earthquakes, Guwahati in Assam have seen the most devastating ones too. The place has a history of the deadliest earthquakes and till today small tremors are a usual affair.
2. **Delhi:** The capital of India falls in the zone four of the seismic zone divisions in India. Delhi faces risk of suffering earthquakes of very high intensity. They, in turn, have the power to cause a lot of damage to the city and surroundings.
3. **Srinagar:** Being very close to the Himalayas, Srinagar faces heavy risk of earthquakes, high as well as moderate. The friction between the Indian and the Eurasian plane causes earthquakes to occur on the areas close to the Himalayas.
4. **Kolkata:** Kolkata had recently felt the earthquake tremor, thanks to the epicentre being in the Bay of Bengal. Kolkata, being close to the coastal line, faces not only the dangers of earthquakes, but also of floods.
5. **Mumbai:** Like Kolkata, Mumbai too is located on the coastal line, hence increasing its risk of facing tsunami-like disasters. Mild to strong, earthquakes are very common in parts of Mumbai. It falls in the zone four of the seismic zone divisions which makes it quite vulnerable to damage.
6. **Shimla:** It is said that Himachal Pradesh is receiving very frequent earthquakes recently which hover around 5 or 6 on the Richter scale. Some consider Shimla to be one of the most disaster-prone cities in Northern India.

Strong and damaging earthquakes have been felt in all parts of the Indian Sub-continent. The most seismically active areas are those in the northern regions of the sub-continent and in the Andaman and Nicobar Islands. The deadliest earthquake in Indian history so far has been the M7.8 Kangra earthquake in Himachal Pradesh in 1905, which left 19,700 people dead. The largest earthquake recorded was an earthquake in Arunachal Pradesh in 1950. The Himalayas were formed by a head on collision of the Indian and Eurasian plates, and the Indian plate continues to push the Asian plate northward at the rate of about 2 cm per year. This means that in every 100 years India moves 200 cm north against the Asian plate and this colliding force builds up pressure continually for several years and is released in the form of earthquakes. Four great earthquakes of Himalaya i.e., Assam earthquake of 1897, Kangra earthquake of 1905, Nepal-Bihar earthquake of 1934 and Assam earthquake of 1950 rocked the Himalayan Kingdom of Nepal whose magnitude exceeds 8.0 Richter scale. The earthquake of 1833 with magnitude 7.8 occurring at a distance of 50 kms NE of Kathmandu also affected the Kathmandu Valley.[13]

The following is a list of major earthquakes affecting India.

Dates	*Time*	*Location*	*Deaths (Overall)*	*Comments*	*Magnitude*
June 28, 2015	06:35 IST	Dibrugarh, Assam	0	3 injured in Assam earthquake, tremors felt in West Bengal, Meghalaya and Bhutan	5.6
May 12, 2015	12:35 IST	Northern India North East India	121+	Epicentre 17 km S of Kodari, Nepal; Felt in Delhi, West Bengal, Bihar, U.P.; 44 killed in India	7.3
April 26, 2015	12:39 IST	Northern India North East India	Aftershock	Aftershock (Epicentre 17 km S of Kodari, Nepal)	6.7*
April 25, 2015	12:19 IST	Northern India	Aftershock	Aftershock (Epicentre 49 km east of Lamjung, Nepal)	6.6*
April 25, 2015	11:41 IST	Northern India North East India	8900+	Epicentre 34 km ESE of Lamjung, Nepal. Felt in eastern, northern, northeastern India and parts of Gujarat[4]	7.8
March 21, 2014	18:41 IST	Andaman and Nicobar Islands	0	Moderate earthquake in Andaman Islands	6.7
April 25, 2012	08:45 IST	Andaman and Nicobar Islands	0	Big earthquake in Andaman and Niocbar Islands	6.2

Dates	*Time*	*Location*	*Deaths (Overall)*	*Comments*	*Magnitude*
March 5, 2012	13:10 IST	New Delhi	1	Moderate earthquake in national capital, CBSE Physics board exam disrupted in Delhi	5.2
September 18, 2011	18:10 IST	Gangtok, Sikkim	118	Strong earthquake in NE India, tremors felt in Delhi, Kolkata, Lucknow and Jaipur	6.9
August 10, 2009	01:21 IST	Andaman Islands	26	Tsunami Warning issued	7.7
October 8, 2005	08:50 IST	Kashmir	130,000	95 km (59 mi) NE of Islamabad, Pakistan, 125 km (78 mi) WNW of Srinagar, Kangra, Jammu and Kashmir, India(pop 894,000)	7.6
December 26, 2004	09:28 IST	Off west coast northern Sumatra India Sri Lanka, Maldives	283,106	Third deadliest earthquake in the history of the world, the tsunami generated killed 15,000 people in India	9.1
January 26, 2001	08:50 IST	Gujarat	20,000	Indian Republic Day Gujarat earthquake, thousands killed	7.6/7.7
August 21, 1988	04:40 IST	Udayapur, Nepal	~1000	6,553 injured	6.3–6.7
August 15, 1950	19:22 IST	Arunachal Pradesh	1,526	Largest earthquake recorded in mainland India since Independence.	8.6
June 26, 1941	08:50 IST	Andaman Islands	7,000	Triggered a tsunami that affected eastern India and Sri Lanka	8.1
May 31, 1935	03:02 IST	Quetta, Baluchistan	30,000 / 60,000	Deadliest earthquake recorded in modern-day Pakistan.	7.7

Dates	*Time*	*Location*	*Deaths (Overall)*	*Comments*	*Magnitude*
January 15, 1934	14:13 IST	Nepal	>10,000	Epicenter lies 10 km south of Mt. Everest.	8.0
April 4, 1905	01:19 IST	Kangra	>20,000	It was a major earthquake that occurred in the Kangra Valley and the Kangra region of the Punjab Province (now Himachal Pradesh)	7.8
December 31, 1881	07:49 IST	Andaman Islands	0	Earliest earthquake for which rupture parameters have been estimated instrumentally (from tide gauges)	7.9
June 16, 1819	18:45 to 18:50 local time	Gujarat	>1,543	Formed the Allah Bund and Lake Sindri	8.2

Source: https://en.wikipedia.org/wiki/List_of_earthquakes_in_India
*https://en.wikipedia.org/wiki/List_of_earthquakes_in_India - cite_note-imd.gov.in-2

Earthquake Zones in India[15]

The Indian subcontinent has a history of devastating earthquakes. The earthquake zoning map of India divides India into four seismic zones (Zone 2, 3, 4 and 5) unlike its previous version which consisted of five or six zones for the country. According to the present zoning map, Zone 5 expects the highest level of seismicity whereas Zone 2 is associated with the lowest level of seismicity.

Table 1: Region falling in various zones of the country[16]

Zone	*Damage risk and Intensity*	*Region*
Zone V	(Earthquake Very high damage risk zone - areas may expect intensity maximum of MSK IX or more)	The entire North-east, including all the seven sister states, the Kutch district, parts of Himachal and Jammu & Kashmir, and the Andaman and Nicobar islands. These areas may experience.
Zone IV	(Earthquake High damage risk zone - areas may expect intensity maximum of MSK VIII)	Parts of the Northern belt starting from Jammu and Kashmir to Himachal Pradesh. Also including Delhi and parts of Haryana. The Koyna region of Maharashtra is also in this zone.
Zone III	(Earthquake Moderate damage risk zone - areas may expect intensity maximum of MSK VII)	A large part of the country stretching from the North including some parts of Rajasthan to the South through the Konkan coast, and also the Eastern parts of the country.
Zone II	(Earthquake Low damage risk zone - areas may experience intensity MSK VI)	These two zones are contiguous, covering parts of Karnataka, Andhra Pradesh, Orissa, Madhya Pradesh, and Rajasthan, known as low risk earthquake zones.

Effects of Earthquake

Shaking and ground rupture are the main effects created by earthquakes, principally resulting in more or less severe damage to buildings and other rigid structures. Specific local geological, geomorphological, and geostructural features can induce high levels of shaking on the ground surface even from low-intensity earthquakes. Earthquakes can cause fires by damaging electrical power or gas lines. Tsunamis are long-wavelength, long-period sea waves produced by the sudden or abrupt movement of large volumes of water. An earthquake may cause injury and loss of life, road and bridge damage, general property damage, and collapse or destabilisation of buildings. The aftermath may bring disease, lack of basic necessities, and higher insurance premiums.[17]

Earthquakes really pose little direct danger to a person. The first main earthquake hazard is the effect of ground shaking. Buildings can even sink into the ground if soil liquefaction occurs. Buildings can also be damaged by strong surface waves making the ground heave and lurch. The second main earthquake hazard is ground displacement along a fault. The third main hazard is flooding. An earthquake can rupture dams or levees along a river. The water from the river or the reservoir would then flood the area, damaging buildings and maybe sweeping away or drowning people. The fourth main earthquake hazard is fire. These fires can be started by broken gas lines and power lines, or tipped over wood or coal stoves.[18]

The destructive effects of an earthquake can be classified into primary and secondary effects. Primary effects are the immediate damage caused by the quake, such as collapsing buildings, roads and bridges, which may kill many people. Those lucky enough to survive can suffer badly from shock and panic. Secondary effects are the after-effects of the earthquake, such as fires, tsunami, landslides and disease.[19] Earthquakes cause great damage to human structures such as buildings, roads, rails, factories, dams, bridges etc, and thus cause heavy damage to human property. Strong seismic waves cause damage to dams thereby causing severe flash floods. Severe floods are also caused because of blocking of water flow of rivers due to rock blocks and debris produced by severe tremors in the hill slopes facing the river valleys. The seismic waves caused by earthquake travelling through sea water generate high sea waves and cause great loss of life and property.[20]

Measurement of Earthquake

Earthquakes can be recorded by seismometers up to great distances, because seismic waves travel through the whole Earth's interior. The absolute magnitude of a quake is conventionally reported by numbers on the moment magnitude scale (formerly Richter scale, magnitude 7 causing serious damage over large areas), whereas the felt magnitude is reported using the modified Mercalli intensity scale (intensity II–XII). Many methods have been developed for predicting the time and place in which earthquakes will occur. Despite considerable research efforts by seismologists, scientifically reproducible predictions cannot yet be made to a specific day or month. Earthquake warning systems have been developed that can provide regional notification of an earthquake in progress.[21]

The size or magnitude of earthquakes is determined by measuring the amplitude of the seismic waves recorded on a seismograph and the distance of the seismograph from the earthquake. These are put into a formula which converts them to a magnitude, which is a measure of the energy released by the earthquake. For every unit increase in magnitude, there is roughly a thirty-fold increase in the energy released. For instance, a magnitude 6.0 earthquake releases approximately 30 times more energy than a magnitude 5.0 earthquake, while a magnitude 7.0 earthquake releases approximately 900 times (30x30) more energy than a magnitude 5.0. Earthquake magnitude was traditionally measured on the Richter scale. It is often now calculated from seismic moment, which is proportional to the fault area multiplied by the average displacement on the fault.[22]

The Richter scale rates earthquakes according to the size of the seismic waves recorded on a seismograph. The Richter scale assumes that the measurements were taken near the earthquake epicentre. Both the Richter scale and the Moment Magnitude scale rate the energy of an earthquake. The Moment Magnitude scale rates the total energy released by an earthquake.

Table 2: The Richter scale

Level	Magnitude	Effects
Micro	Less than 2.0	Barely felt
Very minor	2.0 - 2.9	Recorded but not felt by most people
Minor	3.0 - 3.9	Little damage but felt by people
Light	4.0 - 4.9	No serious damage, objects shake
Moderate	5.0 - 5.9	Major damage to poorly-designed buildings
Strong	6.0 - 6.9	Serious damage over a 100-mile area or less
Major	7.0 - 7.9	Serious damage over a larger area
Great	8.0 - 8.9	Serious damage over several hundred miles
Rare great	9.0 or greater	Serious damage over several thousand miles

Source: http://www.tclauset.org/20_ESbk/ch09.pdf

The Mercalli Intensity scale has 12 descriptive categories. Each category is a rating of the damage suffered by buildings, the ground, and people. Because earthquake damage can be different from place to place, a single earthquake may have different Mercalli numbers in different locations.

Table 3: Mercalli Intensity Scale

Mercalli Intensity	*Characteristic Effects*	*Approximate Richter Magnitude*
I. Instrumental	Not felt	1
II. Just perceptible	Felt by only a few people, especially on upper floors of tall buildings	2.5
III. Slight	Felt by people lying down, seated on a hard surface, or in the upper stories of tall buildings	2
IV. Perceptible	Felt indoors by many, by few outside	3
V. Rather strong	Generally felt by everyone; sleeping people may be awakened	4
VI. Strong	Trees sway, chandeliers swing, bells ring, some damage from falling objects	5
VII. Very strong	General alarm; walls and plaster crack	5.5
VIII. Destructive	Felt in moving vehicles; chimneys collapse; poorly constructed buildings seriously damaged	6
IX. Ruinous	Some houses collapse; pipes break	6.5
X. Disastrous	Obvious ground cracks; railroad tracks bent; some landslides on steep hillsides	7
XI. Very disastrous	Few buildings survive; bridges damaged or destroyed; all services interrupted (electrical, water, sewage, railroad); severe landslides	7.5
XII. Catastrophic	Total destruction; objects thrown into the air; river courses and topography altered	8

Source: http://www.tclauset.org/20_ESbk/ch09.pdf

Preventive Measures

The immediate impact of an earthquake affects all sectors of the community and local authorities should initially emphasise search and rescue of victims. Secondly, emergency medical assistance must be provided especially during the first 72 hours. Third, a damage and needs assessment survey should be conducted to inform local and international agencies of needs. Fourth, the survivors will require relief assistance such as food, water and emergency shelter. Attention should be given to reopening roads, re-establishing communications, contacting remote areas and conducting disaster assessments. At the end of the emergency period, long-term recovery needs to take priority. The post-earthquake period presents an opportunity to minimise future risks through enactment or strengthening of land use and building codes as rebuilding takes place.[23]

By planning and practicing what to do if an earthquake strikes, you and your family can learn to react correctly and automatically when the shaking begins. During an earthquake, most deaths and injuries are caused by collapsing building materials and heavy falling objects, such as bookcases, cabinets, and heating units.[24] Here are some basic guidelines to follow in preparing for earthquakes and dealing with their aftermath.

1. **Improve your home's earthquake resilience**: Evaluate your home's earthquake resilience, and improve it through steps such as fastening down furniture and putting anti-shatter coatings on glass windows.
2. **Stockpile water and foodstuffs**: You should have at least three days' worth of drinking water and foodstuffs stockpiled. You should also have radios and flashlights prepared.
3. **Participate in disaster training**: Get to know the people in your community better by getting actively involved in community disaster training.
4. **Discuss disaster preparedness with your family**: Verify how you will get in touch with each other and where the relief shelters are.[25]

Precautions[26]

- If you are indoors during an earthquake, drop, cover, and hold on. Get under a desk, table or bench. Hold on to one of the legs and cover your eyes. If there's no table or desk nearby, sit down against an interior wall. An interior wall is less likely to collapse than a wall on the outside shell of the building.

- Pick a safe place where things will not fall on you, away from windows, bookcases, or tall, heavy furniture.
- It is dangerous to run outside when an earthquake happens because bricks, roofing, and other materials may fall from buildings during and immediately following earthquakes, injuring persons near the building.
- Wait in your safe place until the shaking stops, then check to see if you are hurt. You will be better able to help others if you take care of yourself first, then check the people around you.
- Move carefully and watch out for things that have fallen or broken, creating hazards. Be ready for additional earthquakes called "aftershocks."
- Be on the lookout for fires. Fire is the most common earthquake related hazard, due to broken gas lines, damaged electrical lines or appliances, and previously contained fires or sparks being released.
- If you must leave a building after the shaking stops, use the stairs, not the elevator. Earthquakes can cause fire alarms and fire sprinklers to go off. You will not be certain whether there is a real threat of fire. As a precaution, use the stairs.

What to do after an earthquake:[27]

- Protect yourself from further danger by putting on long pants, a long-sleeved shirt, sturdy shoes, and work gloves. This will protect you from further injury by broken objects.
- After you have taken care of yourself, help injured or trapped persons.
- Look for and extinguish small fires. Eliminate fire hazards. Putting out small fires quickly, using available resources, will prevent them from spreading.
- Leave the gas on at the main valve, unless you smell gas or think it's leaking.

25. Effects of tropical cyclone (Available at https://en.wikipedia.org/wiki/Effects_of_tropical_cyclones)
26. Reena J, 7 Harmful Effects of Cyclones and Hurricanes (Available at http://www.shareyouressays.com/110973/7-harmful-effects-of-cyclones-and-hurricanes)
27. K J Hutchinson, Causes and effects of tropical storms and responses to them (Available at http://worldlywise. pbworks.com/w/page/25349490/Unit%202% 20Section %20C%20-%20Causes%20and%20effects% 20of%20 tropical %20storms%20and% 20responses%20to%20them)
28. *Ibid.*
29. Prevention and mitigation measures (Available at http://www.kannur.nic.in/Prevention.pdf)
30. From official website of Mauritius Meteorological services (Available at http://metservice.intnet.mu/tropical-cyclone/precautions.php)
31. Surviving Cyclones: Preparation and Safety Procedures (Available at http://www.bom.gov.au/cyclone/about/tc-checklist.shtml)
32. Surviving Cyclones: Preparation and Safety Procedures (Available at http://www.bom.gov.au/cyclone/about/tc-checklist.shtml)
33. See http://www.weready.org/hurricane/index.php?option= com_content&view=article&id=36&Itemid=35

9

Tsunami

"I grew up in war and saw the United Nations help my country to recover and rebuild. That experience was a big part of what led me to pursue a career in public service. As Secretary-General, I am determined to see this organisation deliver tangible, meaningful results that advance peace, development and human rights." **-Ban Ki-moon**

The word tsunami comes from the Japanese language. The prefix 'tsu' means 'harbour' and the suffix 'nami' means 'wave.' It is a series of waves that may be dangerous and destructive. A tsunami, from the Japanese word for "harbour wave" is a series of giant, Long Ocean waves (10 or more) created by an underwater disturbance such as an earthquake, landslide, volcanic eruption, or meteorite.[1] Tsunamis has very long wavelengths. Crest to crest they measure between 10 and 500 km and they travel through the ocean at more than 700 km/h. Sometimes there appears to be just one wave but often there are multiple waves travelling a few minutes apart. Bays and harbours that are funnel shaped also suffer more from a tsunami because they concentrate the effects.[2]

Tsunamis are a series of large ocean waves generated by major earthquakes beneath the ocean floor or major landslides into the ocean. When the waves enter shallow water, they may rise to several feet or, in rare cases, tens of feet, striking the coast with devastating force.[3] The Indian Ocean tsunami of

December 2004 caused waves as high as 30 feet (9 meters) in some places, according to news reports.[4] One of the signs of a potential tsunami is the occurrence of a very large earthquake that lasts for more than 20 seconds. If an area has been shaken by a very large earthquake, one should be on alert that shorelines located within the radius of the earthquake's epicentre, may be hit by a tsunami. A more immediate and ominous sign of an approaching tsunami is a rapid and unexpected recession of water levels below the expected low tide. This can occur minutes before the shoreline is struck by a tsunami and can be the only sign along coastlines that are located too far from the earthquake epicentre to have felt the shaking.[5]

Meaning

Tsunami is a series of waves in a water body caused by the displacement of a large volume of water, generally in an ocean or a large lake. Tsunami waves do not resemble normal sea waves, because their wavelength is far longer. It sometimes referred to as tidal waves. Tsunami and tides both produce waves of water that move inland, but in the case of tsunami the inland movement of water may be much greater, giving the impression of an incredibly high and forceful tide.[6]

Causes of Tsunami

Earthquakes, volcanic eruptions and other underwater explosions, landslides, glacier calvings, meteorite impacts and other disturbances above or below water all have the potential to generate a tsunami. The principal generation mechanism of a tsunami is the displacement of a substantial volume of water or perturbation of the sea. This displacement of water is usually attributed to earthquakes, landslides, volcanic eruptions, glacier calvings or more rarely by meteorites and nuclear tests. Tsunami can be generated when the sea floor abruptly deforms and vertically displaces the overlying water. More specifically, a tsunami can be generated when thrust faults associated with convergent or destructive plate boundaries move abruptly, resulting in water displacement, owing to the vertical component of movement involved.[7]

The most common cause of a tsunami is an earthquake, which is a sudden shifting of the earth's crust, which releases energy. If an earthquake happens underwater, the seafloor lifts and then drops back down, causing the overlying water to be displaced and triggering waves of water. A tsunami wave that begins in the vast ocean has a very small wave height. For this reason, tsunamis in open ocean waters may go unnoticed.[8] Large underwater landslides off the flanks of volcanic islands or the continental slope, possibly triggered by earthquakes or volcanic eruptions, have also created destructive tsunamis. In 1998, a 20-foot-high tsunami produced by a submarine landslide struck the coast of Papua New Guinea. Explosive volcanic eruptions also generate tsunamis, as in 1883 when the Indonesian volcano called Krakatoa exploded.[9]

Effects of Tsunami

The effects of a tsunami on a coastline can range from unnoticeable to devastating. The effects of a tsunami depend on the characteristics of the seismic event that generated the tsunami, the distance from its point of origin, its size. Tsunamis have long periods and can overcome obstacles such as gulfs, bays and islands. However, when tsunami waves become extremely large in height, they savagely attack coastlines, causing devastating property damage and loss of life. Destruction is caused by two mechanisms: the smashing force of a wall of water travelling at high speed, and the destructive power of a large volume of water draining off the land and carrying all with it, even if the wave did not look large. Tsunami waves destroy boats, buildings, bridges, cars, trees, telephone lines, power lines - and just about anything else in their way.[10]

The effects of a tsunami include loss of human and animal life, devastating property damage, severe flooding and disease. There are also environmental effects such as contamination of soil and water, a permanent change to the landscape, solid waste and disaster debris, and hazardous materials and toxic substances. The central effect of large tsunamis is massive loss of human life. With no time to escape, tsunamis cause near instant death, usually by drowning, but also by collapsing buildings, electrocution and more. The severe flooding that occurs as a result of a tsunami also damages sewer systems, water supplies and soil. Stagnant and contaminated water leads to malaria and other diseases, causing illness, infection and death to spread rapidly. Soil becomes salinised from sea water and debris, effecting long-term yields of crops.

According to the Centres for Disease Control, the aftereffects for humans of a tsunami include lack of clean drinking water, loss of shelter and injury from remaining debris. Economically, areas affected by tsunamis struggle to amass funding to repair damaged structures. Those who survive tsunamis often suffer mentally and emotionally. Immediately after a tsunami, injured victims require access to prompt and effective medical care. This often leaves hospitals and medical staff overburdened. In many cases, outside help must be brought in from neighbouring cities and states, and this process is very expensive. Drinking water may become contaminated, leading to outbreaks of various bacterial diseases.[11]

Incidences of Tsunami

While Japan may have the longest recorded history of tsunamis, the sheer destruction caused by the 2004 Indian Ocean earthquake and tsunami event mark it as the most devastating of its kind in modern times, killing around 230,000 people. Tsunamis are an often underestimated hazard in the Mediterranean Sea region and Europe in general. On April 1, 1946, a magnitude-7.8 (Richter scale) earthquake occurred near the Aleutian Islands, Alaska. It generated a tsunami which inundated Hilo on the island of Hawaii with a 14-metre high surge. The 1960 Valdivia earthquake, 1964 Alaska earthquake, 2004 Indian Ocean earthquake, and 2011 Tokau earthquake are recent examples of powerful mega thrust earthquakes that generated tsunamis that can cross entire oceans.

The 1960 Valdivia earthquake of Sunday, 22 May 1960 was the most powerful earthquake ever recorded, rating a 9.5 on the moment magnitude scale. The resulting tsunami affected southern Chile, Hawaii, Japan, the Philippines, eastern New Zealand, southeast Australia, and the Aleutian Islands. The Chilean coast from Mocha Island (38°S) and to Aysén Region (45°S) was devastated by a tsunami. Across southern Chile the tsunami caused a huge loss of life, damage to port infrastructure and the loss of a large number of minor boats. It has been estimated that about 40 per cent of the houses in Valdivia were destroyed, leaving 20,000 people homeless. After the 1960 Valdivia earthquake, a committee was formed to solve problems caused by the earthquake. It continued to operate, to develop approaches for national emergencies.[12]

The 1964 Alaskan earthquake occurred on Good Friday, March 27. Lasting four minutes and thirty-eight seconds, it was the most powerful recorded mega thrust earthquake in US and North American history. The Alaska Earthquake was a subduction zone earthquake, caused by an oceanic plate sinking under a continental plate. Two types of tsunamis were produced by this subduction zone earthquake. There was a tectonic tsunami produced in addition to about 20 smaller and local tsunamis. Tsunami waves were noted in over 20 countries, including: Peru, New Zealand, Papua New Guinea, Japan, and Antarctica. The largest tsunami wave was recorded in Shoup Bay, Alaska, with a height of about 220 ft (67 m). Most coastal towns in the Prince William Sound, Kenai Peninsula, and Island areas, especially the major ports of Seward, Whittier and Kodiak were heavily damaged by a combination of seismic activity, subsidence, post-quake tsunamis and/or earthquake-caused fires.[13]

The 2004 Indian Ocean earthquake occurred at 00:58:53 UTC on 26 December with an epicentre off the west coast of Sumatra, Indonesia. The undersea mega thrust earthquake was caused when the Indian Plate was sub-ducted by the Burma Plate and triggered a series of devastating tsunamis along the coasts of most landmasses bordering the Indian Ocean, killing 230,000 people in 14 countries, and inundating coastal communities with waves up to 30 metres (100 ft) high. The sudden vertical rise of the seabed by several metres during the earthquake displaced massive volumes of water, resulting in a tsunami that struck the coasts of the Indian Ocean. There were no tsunami warning systems in the Indian Ocean to detect tsunamis or to warn the general populace living around the ocean. The tsunami caused serious damage and deaths as far as the east coast of Africa, with the farthest recorded death due to the tsunami occurring at Rooi Els in South Africa, 8,000 km (5,000 mi) away from the epicentre.[14]

The 2011 earthquake off the Pacific coast of Tokyo was under sea mega thrust earthquake off the coast of Japan that occurred on Friday, 11 March 2011. It was the most powerful earthquake ever recorded to have hit Japan, and the fourth most powerful earthquake in the world since modern record-keeping began in 1900. The tsunami caused nuclear accidents, primarily the level 7 meltdowns at three reactors in the Fukushima Daiichi Nuclear Power Plant complex, and the associated evacuation zones affecting hundreds of thousands of residents. Early estimates placed insured losses from the earthquake alone at US$14.5 to $34.6 billion.

An upthrust of 6 to 8 meters along a 180-km wide seabed at 60 km offshore from the east coast of Tokyo resulted in a major tsunami that brought destruction along the Pacific coastline of Japan's northern islands. Shortly after the earthquake, the Pacific Tsunami Warning Centre in Hawaii issued tsunami watches and announcements for locations in the Pacific. Japan's National Police Agency said on 3rd April 2011, that 45,700 buildings were destroyed and 144,300 were damaged by the quake and tsunami. All of Japan's ports were briefly shut down after the earthquake, though the ones in Tokyo and southwards soon re-opened. Japan declared a state of emergency following the failure of the cooling system at the Fukushima Daiichi Nuclear Power Plant, resulting in the evacuation of nearby residents. Japan's transport network suffered severe disruptions.[15]

Japan is one of the most earthquake-prone countries in the world, and has repeatedly suffered serious damage caused by earthquakes and tsunamis. The absence of information on areas that are at risk of tsunami strikes or subject to strong shaking would delay evacuation and emergency response by disaster prevention agencies, and may result in extensive damage. The Japan Meteorological Agency promptly issues warnings and information on earthquakes and tsunamis to mitigate disasters and protect life and property. Earthquake Early Warnings are warnings (or forecasts) of strong motion to be issued several seconds to several tens of seconds before its arrival. Tsunamis are one of damaging phenomena caused by earthquakes. If a tsunami strikes a coastal area, it can cause death or serious injury to people and damage to buildings.[16]

Preventive Measures

In some tsunami-prone countries earthquake engineering measures have been taken to reduce the damage caused onshore. Japan, where tsunami science and response measures first began following a disaster in 1896, has produced ever-more elaborate countermeasures and response plans. A tsunami cannot be precisely predicted, even if the magnitude and location of an earthquake is known. Regions with a high tsunami risk typically use tsunami warning systems to warn the population before the wave reaches land. On the west coast of the United States, which is prone to Pacific Ocean tsunami, warning signs indicate evacuation routes. The Pacific Tsunami Warning System is based in Honolulu, Hawaii. It monitors Pacific Ocean seismic activity. Computer models can predict tsunami arrival, usually within minutes of the arrival time. Some zoologists hypothesise that some animal species have ability to sense subsonic Rayleigh waves from an earthquake or a tsunami. Along the United States west coast, in addition to sirens, warnings are sent on television and radio via the National Weather Service, using the Emergency Alert System.[17]

Coastal areas in or near earthquake-prone regions should have warning systems in place to evacuate the area in the event of an incoming tsunami, and should make sure that citizens understand what the warning means and what to do when such a warning is given. Any buildings and the like that can cause wider damage should either be built elsewhere, or built so that even severe flooding damage will not render them unsafe. Various scientific tools should be used to watch for potential tsunamis, so that warnings can be given well in advance so people will have time to evacuate.[18]

Tsunami early warning systems exist for many countries around the Pacific Ocean, and in certain other tsunami-prone areas. These systems give the public advance warning of tsunami waves, enabling communities to take the appropriate precautions. Make sure that that early warning system warns all communities of coastal areas when there is the threat of a tsunami. Tsunami warnings should be disseminated at all levels (local, regional, national, international).[19]

References

1. Tsunami Fast Facts (Available at http://www. stopdisastersgame.org/en/pdf/Tsunami_fact-sheet.pdf)
2. http://www.gsa.org.au/resources/factites/factitesTsunami.pdf
3. http://www.redcross.org/images/MEDIA_CustomProduct Catalog/m4340167_Tsunami.pdf
4. http://news.nationalgeographic.com/news/2007/04/070402-tsunami_2.html
5. http://www.getprepared.gc.ca/cnt/hzd/tsnms-bfr-en.aspx
6. Tsunami (Available at https://en.wikipedia.org/wiki/Tsunami)
7. Tsunami (Available at https://en.wikipedia.org/wiki/Tsunami)
8. http://study.com/academy/lesson/the-causes-effects-of-a-tsunami.html

9. What are Tsunamis? - Causes, Effects and Facts (Available at http://study.com/academy/lesson/what-are-tsunamis-causes-effects-facts.html)
10. Tsunamis: the effects (Available at http://www.sms-tsunami-warning.com/pages/tsunami-effects#.VdIOMbJViko)
11. See http://www.ask.com/science/effects-tsunami-b27ba 6f6e7c2ddfe
12. 1960 Valdivia earthquake (Available at https://en.wikipedia.org/wiki/1960_Valdivia_earthquake)
13. 1964 Alaskan earthquake (Available at https://en.wikipedia.org/wiki/1964_Alaska_earthquake)
14. 2004 Indian Ocean earthquake and tsunami (Available at https://en.wikipedia.org/wiki/2004_Indian_ Ocean_earthquake_ and_tsunami)
15. Japan's transport network suffered severe disruptions (Available at https:// / en.wikipedia.org/wiki/2011_T%C5%8 Dhoku_ earthquake_ and_tsunami)
16. Earthquakes and Tsunamis (Available at http://www.jma.go.jp/jma/en/Activities/brochure_earthquake_and_tsunami.pdf)
17. Tsunami (Available at https://en.wikipedia.org/wiki/Tsunami)
18. See https://in.answers.yahoo.com/question/index?qid= 20120716081404 AAIPWuE
19. Tsunami Fast Facts (Available at http://www.stopd isastersgame.org/en/pdf/Tsunami_fact-sheet.pdf)

10

Landslide

"Some might complain that nuclear disarmament is little more than a dream. But that ignores the very tangible benefits disarmament would bring for all humankind. Its success would strengthen international peace and security. It would free up vast and much-needed resources for social and economic development. It would advance the rule of law."

-Ban Ki-moon

Land is the solid surface of the Earth that is not permanently covered by water. The vast majority of human activity occurs in land areas that support agriculture, habitat, and various natural resources. It includes oceans, lakes and rivers, mineral deposits, rainfall, water-power, fisheries, forests and numerous other things which nature provides and man uses. Land mass refers to the total surface area of the land of a geographical region or country. The land of the Earth interacts with and influences climate heavily since the surface of the land heats up and cools down faster than air or water. Earth's atmosphere and oceans were formed by volcanic activity and outgassing that included water vapour.[1]

Landslide is defined as a large mass of dirt and rock down a mountain or cliff. Landslide the exterior and downward movement of the natural rocks, every sort of soil and artificial filling in other words the movement of the masses on the slope slides.[2]

Land is central to macro-economic growth. Productive soil, fresh water, forests, clean air, animal life and other renewable resources underpin the survival and prosperity of people across the planet. Across many parts of the globe, land is losing its rich potential because of desertification and degradation. Often caused by human activities such as over-cultivation, deforestation and poorly planned irrigation systems, land degradation can be turned around.[3] Land as a factor of production is of immense importance. As has already been pointed out, everything that we use can be traced ultimately to land. Land may be rightly called the original source of all material wealth. The economic prosperity of a country is closely linked with the richness of her natural resources.[4]

The surface of the Earth, both on the continents and beneath the oceans is continually modified by internal forces and the forces of gravity; both, particularly the latter, produce landslides. The net morphologic effect of landslides is to reduce slopes to angles at which they possess long-term stability. The world's largest landslides are prehistoric, but their remains are displayed as significant morphologic features on the Earth's surface. Most very large landslides have been triggered by earthquakes or volcanic eruptions.[5]

Meaning

Landslide is a geological phenomenon that includes a wide range of ground movements. Rock falls, deep failure of slopes and shallow debris flows were common. It is a geological phenomenon which includes a wide range of ground movement, such as rock falls, deep failure of slopes and shallow debris flows, which can occur in offshore, coastal and onshore environments. Landslides frequently occur in mountainous areas and can cause serious damage. Roads, bridges, and houses may be destroyed and involve huge financial resources. The causes of landslides include heavy rainfall, snow melt, liquefaction, and seismic shaking.[6] The two major types of slides are rotational slides and translational slides:

(a) **Rotational slide:** This is a slide in which the surface of rupture is curved concavely upward and the slide movement is roughly rotational about an axis that is parallel to the ground surface and transverse across the slide.

(b) **Translational slide:** In this type of slide, the landslide mass moves along a roughly planar surface with little rotation or backward tilting. A block slide is a translational slide in which the moving mass consists of a single unit or a few closely related units that move down slope as a relatively coherent mass.[7]

According to research done by the Defence Terrain Research Laboratory, Landslides is rank third in terms of number of deaths due to natural disasters, while, Himalayan Landslides kill one person per 100km. The estimated average losses due to landslides in the Himalayas costs 200 lives and Rs 550 crore every year. Whereas, the hazard affects over 0.49 million km, over 15 per cent of our country's area. After the 1998 Malpa tragedy that killed 200 pilgrims of Kailash Mansarovar Yatra, widespread awareness of the problem was created. Even though we have the teams of National Disaster Response Force, the biggest challenge for the government is to ensure that landslide prone areas are evacuated and are not encroached again.

Causes of Landslide

Landslides can occur in offshore, coastal and onshore environments. Although the action of gravity is the primary driving force for a landslide to occur, there are other contributing factors affecting the original slope stability. Although the action of gravity is the primary driving force for a landslide to occur, there are other contributing factors affecting the original slope stability. Typically, pre-conditional factors build up specific sub-surface conditions that make the area/slope prone to failure, whereas the actual landslide often requires a trigger before being released.[8]

According to wikipedia, landslides occur when the stability of the slope changes from a stable to an unstable condition. A change in the stability of a slope can be caused by a number of factors, acting together or alone. Natural causes of landslides include:

(a) groundwater (pore water) pressure acting to destabilise the slope,

(b) loss or absence of vertical vegetative structure, soil nutrients, and soil structure,

(c) erosion of the toe of a slope by rivers or ocean waves,

(d) weakening of a slope through saturation by snow melt, glaciers melting, or heavy rains

(e) earthquakes adding loads to barely stable slope

(f) earthquake-caused liquefaction destabilising slopes

(g) volcanic eruptions.[9]

Human made causes of deforestation are:

(a) Interference with, or changes to, natural drainage,

(b) Leaking pipes such as water and sewer reticulation,

(c) Modification of slopes by construction of roads, railways, buildings,

(d) Overloading slopes,

(e) Mining and quarrying activities,

(f) Vibrations from heavy traffic, blasting, etc. and

(g) Excavation or displacement of rocks.

Earthquakes cause ground shaking which may directly lead to a landslide. Or, the ground shaking may cause the soil to loosen and become weak, leading to a landslide. To prevent earthquake induced landslides, the ideal solution is to design the geometry of the slope such that it has an adequate factor of safety even for seismic cases.[10]

Effects of Landslide

Landslides cause property damage, injury and death and adversely affect a variety of resources. For example, water supplies, fisheries, sewage disposal systems, forests, dams and roadways can be affected for years after a slide event. Large, infrequent landslides contribute less to personal and property losses than do the smaller, more frequent slides and debris torrents in populated areas. Water availability, quantity and quality can be affected by landslides. Geotechnical studies and engineering projects to assess and stabilise, potentially dangerous sites can be costly.[11]

The safety of a dam can be severely compromised by land sliding in the upstream area of the dam or on the slopes bordering the reservoir. Landslides and flooding are closely associated because both are related to intense rainfall, runoff and ground saturation. Landslides can result in death and injury of people and animals. The moving mass can bury people and animals under debris. Productive land area may be covered with debris or blocked from access. Due to the deaths of family members and the destruction of personal belongings, this may also have great sentimental value. Earth mass can effect water recourses in the area by blocking rivers, diverting water ways, blocking irrigation channels, reducing storage capacity of tanks, reservoirs, ponds, etc.[12]

Incidences of Landslide

The two regions in India most vulnerable to landslides are the Himalayas and the Western Ghats. The Himalayas mountain belt comprise of tectonically unstable younger geological formations subjected to severe seismic activity. The Western Ghats and Nilgiris are geologically stable but have uplifted plateau margins influenced by neo-tectonic activity.[13] Landslide, a frequently occurring natural hazard in the hilly terrains of India, shows preponderance of activity during the monsoon period from July to September and after the snow fall from January to March. The strong earthquakes also cause triggering of landslide, particularly in regions marked by critically disposed and unstable slopes.[14]

Landslide is a natural phenomenon which is caused majorly due to heavy rains, floods, earthquakes; construction etc.[15] According to Geological Survey of India, roughly 15 per cent of the country's landmass is prone to landslides. The National Disaster Management Authority lists the Himalayan states, Arakan-Yoma belt in the north east, Meghalaya plateau, Western Ghats and Nilgiri hills as landslide vulnerable areas. Overall, 22 states and parts of the UTs of Puducherry and Andaman and Nicobar Islands experience various types of landslides. A large majority of landslides take place during the monsoon. Compared to the Himalayan states, the Western Ghats and Nilgiri hills are located in a relatively stable region. The Western Ghats' vulnerability to landslides is largely attributed to the deposits of overburden materials on the steep hill slope. The Nilgiri hills are located at the convergence zone of the Eastern and Western Ghats. The loose overburden deposited on the slopes makes them vulnerable to landslides.[16]

Preventive Measures

Many methods are used to remedy landslide problems. The best solution, of course, is to avoid landslide-prone areas altogether. Before purchasing land or an existing structure or building a new structure, the buyer should consult an engineering geologist or a geotechnical engineer to evaluate the potential for landslides and other geology-related problems. Because water is a main factor in landslides, improving surface and subsurface drainage at the site can increase the stability of a landslide-prone slope. Removing the soil and rock at the head of the landslide decreases the driving pressure and can slow or stop a landslide. Piles are metal beams that are either driven into the soil or placed in drill holes. Properly placed piles should extend into a competent rock layer below the landslide.[17]

Maintaining the drainage system on private property is the owner's responsibility. Make sure drainage system directs water away from foundation and not on to neighbour's property. In general, trees and plants with strong root structures help prevent soil erosion but do not prevent landslides.[18] To prevent landslides triggered due to construction on top of the slope, a setback distance should be maintained between the top of slope and construction. The distance will depend on the type of construction and geology and geometry of the slope. Benching, constructing retaining walls, shotcreting, putting up steel nets, etc are some other methods of preventing or controlling landslides.[19]

Monitoring landslide movements provides useful information that can potentially prevent catastrophic loss of life and property, and assists in the development of guidelines for sustainable land use planning.[20] One of the quickest and easiest ways to prevent a landslide on a slope is to vegetate it. Building pathways to divert debris is another option to prevent landslides on your property. For temporary landslide prevention, sandbags can be used to divert water from uncontrolled spilling just as retaining walls or diverted pathways do.[21]

Preparedness measures for those living in landslide prone areas that should be observed during periods of heavy rain. These are general guidelines for those living in a landslide prone area:

(a) Listen to weather forecast on the radio, TV etc. about heavy rains.

(b) While evacuating, do not cross possible landslide paths.

(c) Listen for abnormal sounds of soil and rock movement or breaking of trees. They may be associated with landslide movements.

(d) When you see falling rocks, seek cover behind trees and other solid objects.

(e) Remain awake during nights of heavy continuous rain and be ready to move to a safer location.

(f) In case you have to evacuate, do so immediately. Do not try to collect belongings. Landslides can occur suddenly.[22]

References

1. Land, Available at https://en.wikipedia.org/wiki/Land
2. Landslides hazards zonation map of India, Available at http://chungthangsubdivision.nic.in/LANDSLIDES.pdf
3. The importance of sustainable land management, Available at http://global-mechanism.org/about-us/the-importance-of-sustainable-land-management
4. Tushar Seth, Land: Meaning, Importance and Other Details, Available at http://www.economicsdiscussion.net/articles/land-meaning-importance-and-other-details/1519
5. Robert L. Schuster and Lynn M. Highland, Impact of Landslides and Innovative Landslide-Mitigation Measures on the Natural Environment, Available at http://pubs.usgs.gov/op/HongKongJuly/HongKongJuly 21.pdf
6. Landslides - Causes, Effects, and Remedial Measures, Available at http://www.brighthubengineering.com/geotechnical-engineering/60082-landslides-causes-effects-and-remedial-measures/
7. See http://www.eoearth.org/view/article/154157/
8. Landslides: Causes, Types and Effects, Available at https://www.novapublishers.com/catalog/product_info. php? products_id=9657
9. Landslide, Available at https://en.wikipedia.org/wiki/Landslide, DNA News, http://www.dnaindia.com/india/report-india-s-worst-landslides-and-why-these-might-not-be-the-last-ones-2006836
10. Landslides- prevention, Available at https://kshitija. wordpress.com/2006/06/08/landslides-prevention/
11. How Do Landslides Affect Us?, Available at http://www.empr.gov.bc.ca/mining/geoscience/surficialgeology/landslides/pages/howdoland slidesaffectus.aspx
12. Learning to live with Landslides: Natural Hazards and Disasters, Available at http://www.preventionweb.net/files/3976_Landslides.english 18022007.pdf
13. See http://agritech.tnau.ac.in/agriculture/agri_majorareas_ disasterm gt_landslide.html
14. From official website of Geological Survey of India, Available at http://www.portal.gsi.gov.in/portal/page?_ pageid= 127,671641&_dad=portal&_schema=PORTAL
15. See http://indiatoday.intoday.in/education/story/landslides-india/1/452625.html
16. The Times of India (Aug. 4, 1914), Learning with the Times: Nearly 15% of landmass prone to landslides, Available at http://timesofindia.indiatimes.com/india/Learning-with-the-Times-Nearly-15-of-landmass-prone-to-landslides/articleshow/39582612.cms
17. Prevention and Remediation of Landslides, Available at http://www.kgs.ku.edu/Publications/pic13/pic13_5.html
18. See http://www.portlandoregon.gov/transportation/article/319810
19. Landslides-prevention, Available at https://kshitija. wordpress.com/2006/06/08/landslides-prevention/
20. See http://www.caee.utexas.edu/news/features/114-landslide
21. Landslide Prevention Methods, Available at http://www.ehow.com/info_8172849_landslide-prevention-methods.html
22. Learning to live with Landslides: Natural Hazards and Disasters, Available at http://www.preventionweb.net/files/3976_ Landslides.english 18022007.pdf

11

Drought

"The backbone of any improvement of governance, its development as well as its protection from any form of wastage or excessiveness, is a mechanism to place laws under the microscope of revision and modernisation until they resonate in tune with the methodological development and new administrative technologies."

-Khalifa bin Zayed Al Nahyan

Drought is a disaster which usually takes place slowly. It is difficult to decide the time of it started and its end. Its effects often build up slowly over a long period of time and may continue from months to years after the end of the event. Drought is a continuous period of dry weather due to lack of rain.[1] Annual dry seasons in the tropics significantly increase the chances of a drought developing and subsequent bush fires. Periods of heat can significantly worsen drought conditions by hastening evapouration of water vapour.[2] The period of unusual dryness is a normal feature of the climate and weather system in semi-arid and arid regions of the tropics, which covers more than one-third of the land surface and is vulnerable to drought and desertification. Rainfall, temperature, evapouration, vegetation health, soil moisture, stream flow, etc. are some of the critical parameters that are used in drought risk analysis.[3]

Drought can call to mind images of dry, cracked earth; low reservoir levels; and barren fields, yet these are actually examples of different types of drought, each of which is measured differently.[4] Rainfall is the ultimate source of water, affecting production of crops and other biomass by direct falling on the fields as well as supporting surface and ground water irrigation.[5] The farmers' crops dying would be the direct impact of drought. The dealer losing money and all of the other impacts would be the indirect impacts of drought.[6] Drought conditions result from a lack of precipitation and this has many effects on the surrounding land and weather conditions. Drought conditions can worsen after prolonged periods of no rainfall, especially in areas where the water supply is short.

Meaning

Drought is an extended period of deficient rainfall relative to the statistical multi-year average for a region.[7] It is an insidious hazard of nature. It is often referred to as a creeping phenomenon and its impacts vary from region to region. It can be difficult for people to understand. Conceptual definitions, formulated in general terms, help people understand the concept of drought. For example, *Drought is a protracted period of deficient precipitation resulting in extensive damage to crops, resulting in loss of yield.*[8]

Drought in Australia is defined by the Australian Bureau of Meteorology as rainfall over a three-month period being in the lowest decile of what has been recorded for that region in the past. This definition takes into account that drought is a relative term and rainfall deficiencies need to be compared to typical rainfall patterns including seasonal variations.[9]

Types of Drought[10]

According to wikipedia, People tend to define droughts in three main ways:

1. **Meteorological Drought:** It is brought about when there is a prolonged time with less than average precipitation. Meteorological drought usually precedes the other kinds of drought.
2. **Agricultural Drought:** It is drought that affects crop production or the ecology of the range. This condition can also arise independently from any change in precipitation levels when soil conditions and erosion

triggered by poorly planned agricultural endeavours cause a shortfall in water available to the crops.

3. **Hydrological Drought:** It is brought about when the water reserves available in sources such as aquifers, lakes and reservoirs fall below the statistical average. Hydrological drought tends to show up more slowly because it involves stored water that is used but not replenished.

Causes of Drought

Drought has many causes. It can be caused by not receiving rain or snow over a period of time. Changes in the wind patterns that move clouds and moisture through the atmosphere can cause a place to not receive its normal amount of rain or snow over a long period of time. People can play a big role in drought.[11] It is defined as a deficit in water supply; it can be caused by a number of factors. The most important one though relates to the amount of water vapour in the atmosphere as this is what creates precipitation. Deforestation for agriculture and/or building combined with the resultant erosion can cause drought to begin because as soil is moved away from an area it is less able to absorb moisture when it falls.[12]

Droughts in the Indian region are mainly due to various kinds of failures of rains from southwest monsoon. Also there seems to be some association between El Nino and La Nina events and weak monsoons. South-west monsoon over different parts of the country sets in at different times between May and September.[13]

Effects of Drought

Drought is responsible for many direct and indirect economic, social and environmental consequences throughout the world. Certain impacts are unavoidable but can be reduced significantly through planned interventions, whereas few other impacts can be mitigated by way of drought resistance.[14] Social and economic impact of a drought is more severe than the physical and agricultural impacts. Meteorological drought adversely affects the recharge of soil moisture, surface runoff and ground water table.[15]

Drought has greater impacts on poorer communities than on more prosperous communities who have better opportunities to bring in resources from other areas. When drought conditions persist with no relief, or not enough precipitation to lift the drought conditions, water restrictions are put into place by local or state governments. Water may become especially polluted during times of drought due to the lack of rain water to dilute industrial and agricultural chemicals. This toxic water can be harmful to plants and animals that use it and make it difficult to clean for drinking water. It is not only linked to increases in heat-related illness, waterborne illness and cardio respiratory illness, but also mental illness. It can have significant impacts on the economy. It can be reduced electrical generation.[16]

When a drought occurs, their food supply can shrink and their habitat can be damaged. Sometimes the damage is only temporary and their habitat and food supply return to normal when the drought is over. Social impacts include public safety, health, conflicts between people when there is not enough water to go around, and changes in lifestyle. Economic impacts are those impacts of drought that cost people money.[17]

The most immediate consequence of drought is a fall in crop production, due to inadequate and poorly distributed rainfall. Farmers are faced with harvests that are too small to both feed their families and fulfill their other commitments. Low rainfall causes poor pasture growth and may also lead to a decline in fodder supplies from crop residues. The overall effect of a fall in fodder and crop production is to reduce the draft capacity of the farming sector. Changes in the distribution of wealth usually accompany drought. Loss of livestock around the farming settlement also reduces the household's access to dung, a product of considerable importance both as a fuel where firewood is scarce and as a means to retain fertility on regularly cropped soils.[18]

Incidences of Drought

Drought is a common feature in many African countries. The Darfur conflict in Sudan affecting Chad was fueled by decades of drought; combination of drought, desertification and overpopulation are among the causes of the Darfur conflict. Approximately 2.4 billion people live in the drainage basin of the Himalàyan Rivers. Drought in India affecting the Ganges is of particular concern, as it provides drinking water and agricultural irrigation for more than 500 million people. By far the largest part of Australia is desert or semi-arid lands commonly known as the outback. Recurring droughts leading to desertification in East Africa have created grave ecological catastrophes, prompting food shortages in 1984–85, 2006 and 2011.[19]

Drought is common in Australia. The worst drought to affect the country occurred between the years 2003 to 2012. Nonetheless, many regions of Australia are still in widespread drought and rainfall records have showed a marked decrease in precipitation levels since 1994. During 1918 to 1920, a severe drought was experienced by Queensland, New South Wales, South Australia, Northern Territory, Western Australia, Victoria, and Tasmania. The drought in 1982–83 is regarded as the worst of the twentieth century for short-term rainfall deficiencies of up to one year and their over-all impact. A very severe drought occurred in the second half of 1991 which intensified in 1994 and 1995 to become the worst on record in Queensland. The Prime Minister at the time, John Howard, announced on 19 April 2007 that unless there was substantial rain in the next six weeks no water would be allocated to irrigators in the Murray-Darling basin for the coming year. The result of this would have directly affected the 50,000 farmers and the economy.[20] The 2000s drought in Australia, also known as the Millennium drought, is said by some to be the worst recorded since settlement.

Between July 2011 and mid-2012, a severe drought affected the entire East Africa region. The drought caused a severe food crisis across Somalia, Djibouti, Ethiopia and Kenya that threatened the livelihood of 9.5 million people. Other countries in East Africa, including Sudan, South Sudan and parts of Uganda, were also affected by a food crisis. On 20 July 2011, the UN declared a famine in the Lower Shabelle and Bakool, two regions of southern Somalia.

Famine was further declared in the Balcad and Cadale districts in Middle Shabelle as well as the IDP settlements in Mogadishu and Afgooye in response to data from the UN's food security and nutrition analysis unit. In addition, the Kenyan Red Cross warns of a looming humanitarian crisis in the northwestern Turkana region of Kenya, which borders South Sudan. Food shortages have also been reported in northern and eastern Uganda. The Karamoja region and the Bulambuli district, in particular, are among the worst hit areas, with an estimated

1.2 million Ugandans affected. By 15 September 2011, more than 920,000 refugees from Somalia had reportedly fled to neighbouring countries, particularly Kenya and Ethiopia. In July 2011, the head of United States Agency for International Development, Rajiv Shah, stated that the drought may worsen the security situation in the region. Fears of the Al-Shabaab insurgents, who control most of southern Somalia, continue to hinder humanitarian operations in the region. United Nations Secretary-General Ban Ki-moon called an urgent emergency meeting with the heads of UN agencies. He stated after the meeting that immediate action must be taken to prevent the crisis from deepening. According to Ban, "The human cost of this crisis is catastrophic. We cannot afford to wait."[21]

The worst droughts in the history of the United States occurred during the 1930s and 1950s, periods of time known as 'Dust Bowl' years in which droughts lead to significant economic damages and social changes. Certain regions within the United States are more susceptible to droughts than others. Droughts can be more damaging than tornadoes, tropical cyclones, winter storms and flooding combined. Unlike a hurricane, tornado or flooding, the onset of droughts happen gradually over a long period of time. The eighteenth century seems to have been a relatively wet century in North America, but there were apparently droughts in Iowa in 1721, 1736, and from 1771 to 1773. The 1870-1877 droughts brought with it a major swarm of Rocky Mountain Locusts, as droughts benefit locusts, making plants more nutritious and edible to locusts and reducing diseases that harm locusts.

Drought began in the Southwestern United States in 1944 and continued through the entire rest of the decade; one of the longest recorded droughts observed there. This drought continued into the 1950s. The Northeastern United States was hit with devastating drought which lasted almost four to five years in the 1960s. Short term droughts hit particular spots of the United States during 1976 and 1977. Droughts also affected the Northeast US, Corn Belt and Midwest States during 1980 and 1983. During 1993 the Southeastern United States experienced high temperatures and conditions of drought for extended periods. The Midwest and Rocky Mountain regions had a drought during 2002; the 2008-2011 California droughts continued through 2010 and did not end until March 2011. High wheat prices caused by the drought have discouraged farmers from investing in alternative drought-tolerant crops.[22]

Europe is poised to suffer more droughts as the twenty-first century progresses because of climate change. Many river basins, particularly in southern Europe, will probably become more prone to periods of reduced water supply as average global temperatures rise. Drought events in Europe in the past 30 years cost more than 100 billion Euros (US$136 billion).[23] It is a major natural disaster that can have considerable impacts on society, the environment and the economy. In Europe alone, the cost of drought over the past three decades has amounted to over 100 billion euros. The research shows that southern parts of Europe will be the most affected. Stream and river minimum flow levels may be lowered by up to 40 per cent and periods of water deficiency may increase up to 80 per cent due to climate change alone in the Iberian Peninsula, south of France, Italy and the Balkans.[24]

Drought in India

Drought in India has resulted in tens of millions of deaths over the course of the eighteenth, nineteenth, and twentieth centuries. In the past, droughts have periodically led to major Indian famines, including the Bengal famine of 1770, in which up to one-third of the population in affected areas died; the 1876–1877 famine, in which over five million people died; and the 1899 famine, in which over 4.5 million died.[25] The Bengal famine of 1770 was a catastrophic famine between 1769 and 1773 (1176 to 1180 in the Bengali calendar) that affected the lower Gangetic plain of India. The famine occurred in the territory which was called Bengal, then ruled by the British East India Company. This territory included modern West Bengal, Bangladesh, and parts of Assam, Odisha, Bihar, and Jharkhand. The famine occurred or was made more severe largely due to the British East India Company's policies in Bengal. By the time of the famine, monopolies in grain trading had been established by the Company and its agents. The Company had no plan for dealing with the grain shortage, and actions were only taken insofar as they affected the mercantile and trading classes.[26]

States affected by drought in India are Maharashtra, Karnataka, Andhra Pradesh, Odisha, Gujarat and Rajasthan,

Major population of these region depended on the rice crop of the winter season. Due to the failure of the monsoon, some parts of Bihar and Jharkhand along with Punjab and Haryana were also affected by drought. The Marathwada region of Maharashtra states is facing severe water scarcity. Drought affected region in Marathwada includes eight districts Aurangabad, Nanded, Latur, Jalna, Beed, Parbhani, Osmanabad, and Hingoli. Jalna is the most affected district among others in the region. The Chitradurga district of Karnataka state is among the talukas which are reeling under drought and North Karnataka is worst hit. Area of Bijapur, Dharwad, Hubli and Bagalkot are always the most affected when there is a drought in northern part of Karnataka. Bikaner and Jaisalmer districts are the major tourist attraction of great Thar Desert and known for its golden sand dunes and camel safari. They both fall in the drought prone area of Rajasthan along with Jodhpur, Nagaur and Barmer.

The Saurashtra region of Gujarat state is consists of seven districts is one of the drought-prone region, Kutch region being other. Kutch region is well famous as dead land and one of the hottest place in the country. The Mahbubnagar-Khammam district of Andhra Pradesh state was declared drought-hit in 2002. Poor and delayed monsoon affected its number of mandals which are declared as drought prone area. The Mayurbhanj-Balasore region of Odisha, 30 districts was identified as drought-hit due to the short rainfall. Mayurbhanj district was the worst-hit and Balasore has a worst history of Odisha famine of 1866.[27]

It has not washed away the fears of deficit rainfall, but the monsoon's satisfactory performance so far has sharply reduced the possibility of a second consecutive drought. In a drought year, average nationwide rainfall is at least 10 per cent below normal. A countrywide drought would occur only if rains are more than 14 per cent below average for the rest of the monsoon season. Given that overall meteorological conditions have been adverse for rains in India because of the El Nino factor, monsoon has so far been better than expected.[28]

Approximately 16 per cent of India's geographic area, mostly arid, semi-arid and sub-humid is drought-prone. Due to high temporal and spatial variability in rainfall and wide variations in physiographic and climatic conditions in the country, droughts are experienced in varying intensities almost every year irrespective of a good monsoon.[29] The drought-prone areas are confined mainly to the peninsular and western parts of the country, and there are only few pockets in the central, eastern, northern and southern parts. These regions suffer drought mostly due to the cumulative effects of changing precipitation pattern, excessive water utilisation and ecologically unsuitable agriculture practices.[30]

After independence droughts have received much more attention of policy makers than before. One observes an evolution in the drought policy over the past few decades. Famines have been eradicated and starvation deaths are rare if not nil. The government has adopted a three pronged strategy to face droughts: (1) providing relief to drought hit population under scarcity relief programmes, (2) designing special area development programme for drought prone areas and desert areas (DPAP – drought prone area programme and DDP – desert development programme) and (3) promoting dry farming agriculture as a part of agricultural policy.[31]

The governmental strategy generally focused on empirical measures of employment generation through relief works, cattle camps, fodder depots, animal healthcare, subsidised cattle feed for the milch cattle, drinking water arrangements, augmenting existing or creation of new sources, medical and health arrangements. The Central Government has permanent budgetary arrangements of Calamity Relief Fund and National Calamity Contingency Funds, for reducing the impact and severity of droughts. Some of the other sponsored programmes included: Rural Works Programme, Drought Prone Area Programme, Desert Development Programme, Food for Work Programme, Integrated Watershed Management Programmes etc. During 1979 drought, the Ministry of Agriculture set up a watch group consisting of representatives from the Department of Agriculture, India Meteorological Department, Indian Council of Agricultural Research, Ministry of Information and Broadcasting and others.[32]

Preventive Measures

Drought is causing certain difficulties for agricultural production. Sectors, localities and farmers have in recent times implemented many solutions to ensure sufficient water supplies for sowing the winter-spring rice crop. The prolonged drought is due to water shortages while many ponds and lakes have not been dredged, thus failing to prevent water from running to the sea.[33] It is very difficult to prevent droughts because it is a lack of rainfall and we can not control it. However, people can conserve water so that a little bit goes a long way. Make sure that conserve enough water for own and everyone. People can also reuse water by using the water you shower with to water your lawns.[34]

Water conservation and aforestation may be proper steps. Water conservation encompasses the policies, strategies and activities to manage fresh water as a sustainable resource, to protect the water environment, and to meet current and future human demand. Water conservation programmes involved in social solutions are typically initiated at the local level, by either municipal water utilities or regional governments. The goals of water conservation efforts include: (a) Ensuring availability of water for future generations. This requires that the withdrawal of fresh water from an ecosystem does not exceed its natural replacement rate; (b) Water pumping, delivery and waste water treatment facilities consume a significant amount of energy; and (c) Minimising human water use helps to preserve fresh fire habitats for local wildlife and migrating waterfowl, as well as reducing the need to build new dams and other water diversion infrastructures.[35]

Afforestation is the establishment of a forest or stand of trees in an area where there was no forest. Many governments and non-governmental organisations directly engage in programme of afforestation to create forests, increase carbon capture and sequestration, and help to anthropogenically improve biodiversity. Forests need help to reestablish themselves because of environmental factors.[36] It is the artificial establishment of forests by planting or seeding in an area of non-forest land. Trees are a beautiful, incredibly important part of our world and its various ecosystems. They clean our air, sequester carbon, and provide shade and natural resources in the form of fruit, bark, sap, timber and countless other commodities. Without them, our world would be uninhabitable.[37]

References

1. Drought, Available at https://simple.wikipedia.org/wiki/Drought
2. Drought, Available at https://en.wikipedia.org/wiki/Drought
3. Anil K. Gupta, Pallavee Tyagi and Vinay K. Sehgal, Drought disaster challenges and mitigation in India: strategic appraisal, Available at http:/

/www.nidm.gov.in/PDF/TrgReports/2011/September/temp/reading3.pdf

4. Causes of Drought: What's the Climate Connection?, Available at http://www.ucsusa.org/global_warming/science_and_ impacts/impacts/causes-of-drought-climate-change-connection.html#.VdfgnyVViko
5. Drought Management Strategies – 2009, National Rainfed Area Authority Ministry of Agriculture Government of India, New Delhi, Available at http://nrega.nic.in/DroughtStratDraft.pdf
6. From official website of National Drought Mitigation Centre, Available at http://drought.unl.edu/DroughtforKids/HowDoesDroughtAffectOurLives.aspx
7. 11 facts about drought, Available at https://www.dosomething.org/facts/11-facts-about-droughts
8. What is droughts, Available at http://drought.unl.edu/DroughtBasics/WhatisDrought.aspx
9. Droughts in Australia, Available at https://en.wikipedia.org/wiki/Drought_in_Australia
10. Drought, Available at https://en.wikipedia.org/wiki/Drought
11. From official website of National Drought Mitigation Centre, Available at http://drought.unl.edu/DroughtforKids/HowDoesDroughtAffectOurLives.aspx
12. http://geography.about.com/od/globalproblemsandissues/a/drought.htm
13. Effects of drought, Available at https://climate.ncsu.edu/edu/k12/.droughteffects
14. Anil K. Gupta, Pallavee Tyagi and Vinay K. Sehgal, Drought disaster challenges and mitigation in India: strategic appraisal, http://www.nidm.gov.in/PDF/TrgReports/2011/September/temp/reading3.pdf
15. Negi Mohita, Impact of Droughts in India: Physical; Agriculture and Economic Impact, Available at http://www.yourarticlelibrary.com/drought/impact-of-droughts-in-india-physical-agriculture-and-economic-impact/14066/
16. Effects of drought, Available at https://climate.ncsu.edu/edu/k12/.droughteffects
17. From official website of National Drought Mitigation Centre, Available at http://drought.unl.edu/droughtforkids/howdoesdroughtaffectourlives/typesofdroughtimpacts.aspx
18. Effects of drought on farm production and livestock holdings, Available at http://www.fao.org/wairdocs/ILRI/x5446E/x5446e02.htm
19. Drought, Available at https://en.wikipedia.org/wiki/Drought
20. Drought in Australia, Available at https://en.wikipedia.org/wiki/Drought_in_Australia
21. 2011 East Africa Droughts, Available at https://en.wikipedia.org/wiki/2011_East_Africa_drought
22. Drought in the United States, Available at https://en.wikipedia.org/wiki/Droughts_in_the_United_States
23. http://www.bloomberg.com/news/articles/2014-01-13/europe-seen-facing-more-droughts-this-century-on-climate-change
24. See http://www.egu.eu/news/97/europe-to-suffer-from-more-severe-and-persistent-droughts
25. Drought in India, Available at https://en.wikipedia.org/wiki/Drought_in_India
26. Bengal famine of 1770, Available at https://en.wikipedia.org/wiki/Bengal_famine_of_1770

27. Major drought prone regions of India, Available at http://www.walkthroughindia.com/location/major-drought-prone-regions-of-india/
28. The Times of India (July 13, 2015), India's drought concerns ease as monsoon beats the odds, Available at http://timesofindia.indiatimes.com/india/Indias-drought-concerns-ease-as-monsoon-beats-the-odds/articleshow/48046858.cms
29. Drought Conditions and Management Strategies in India, Available at http://www.moef.gov.in/sites/default/files/India_Country%20Report%20_Hanoi.pdf
30. Anil K. Gupta, Pallavee Tyagi and Vinay K. Sehgal, Drought disaster challenges and mitigation in India: strategic appraisal, Available at http://www.nidm.gov.in/PDF/TrgReports/2011/September/temp/reading3.pdf
31. Anil Kumar Roy and Indira Hirway, Multiple Impacts of Droughts and Assessment of Drought Policy in Major Drought Prone States in India, Available at http://planningcommission. gov.in/reports/sereport/ser/stdy_droght.pdf
32. Drought Management Strategies – 2009, National Rainfed Area Authority Ministry of Agriculture Government of India New Delhi, Available at http://nrega.nic.in/DroughtStratDraft.pdf
33. Drought prevention needs people's power, Available at http://english.vov.vn/Politics/World/Drought-prevention-needs-peoples-power/37924.vov
34. Prevention of droughts, Available at http://cassrose.wikispaces.com/prevention+of+droughts
35. Water conservation, Available at https://en.wikipedia.org/wiki/Water_conservation
36. Afforestation, Available at https://en.wikipedia.org/wiki/Afforestation
37. http://ourplanet.infocentral.state.gov/tag/aforestation/

12

Forest Fire

"The Millennium Development Goals were a pledge to uphold the principles of human dignity, equality and equity, and free the world from extreme poverty. The MDGs, with eight goals and a set of measurable time-bound targets, established a blueprint for tackling the most pressing development challenges of our time." **-Ban Ki-moon**

Fire is the rapid oxidation of a material in the exothermic chemical process of combustion, releasing heat, light, and various reaction products. In its most common form fire can result in conflagration, which has the potential to cause physical damage through burning. The ability to control fire was a dramatic change in the habits of early humans. Making fire to generate heat and light made it possible for people to cook food, increasing the variety and availability of nutrients. It has been used for centuries as a method of torture and execution, as evidenced by death by burning as well as torture devices such as the iron boot, which could be filled with water, oil, or even lead and then heated over an open fire to the agony of the wearer.[1] Forest fire also known as wildfire.

The most common hazard in forests is forests fire. Forests fires are as old as the forests themselves. They pose a threat not only to the forest wealth but also to the entire regime to fauna and flora seriously disturbing the bio-diversity and the ecology and environment of a region.[2] There are three conditions that need to be present in order for a wildfire to burn, which firefighters refer to as the fire triangle: fuel, oxygen, and a heat source. Fuel is any flammable material surrounding a fire, including trees, grasses, brush, even homes. The greater an areas fuel load, the more intense the fire. Air supplies the oxygen a fire needs to burn. Heat sources help spark the wildfire and bring fuel to temperatures hot enough to ignite.[3]

Forest fire are common in climates that are sufficiently moist to allow the growth of vegetation but feature extended dry, hot periods. Global warming may increase the intensity and frequency of droughts in many areas, creating more intense and frequent wildfires. The spread of wildfires varies based on the flammable material present and its vertical arrangement.

Meaning

Forest fire is an uncontrolled fire occurring in nature. Sometimes, it is so large that it takes a long time for the fire fighting crews to gain control over the situation. This could result in massive destruction. The number of forest fires varies from year to year, and quite a long time may elapse between forest fires that are considered to be large[4]. It is an uncontrolled fire in an area of combustible vegetation that occurs in the countryside area. Wildfires are characterised in terms of the cause of ignition, their physical properties such as speed of propagation, the combustible material present, and the effect of weather on the fire.

Causes of Forest Fire

Forest fire causes imbalances in nature and endangers biodiversity by reducing faunal and floral wealth. Traditional methods of fire prevention are not proving effective and it is now essential to raise public awareness on the matter, particularly among those people who live close to or in forested areas. The causes of forest fire have been increasing rapidly. The problem has been accentuated by the growing human and cattle population.[5] It occur when all of the necessary elements of a fire triangle come together in a susceptible area: an ignition source is brought into contact with a combustible material such as vegetation that is subjected to sufficient heat and has an adequate supply of oxygen from the ambient air. Heat waves, droughts, cyclical climate changes such as El Nino, and regional weather patterns such as high-pressure ridges can increase the risk and alter the behaviour of wildfires dramatically. Intensity also increases during daytime hours.[6]

Forest fires are caused by Natural causes as well as man-made causes:

(a) **Natural causes-** Many forest fires start from natural causes such as lightning which set trees on fire. However, rain extinguishes such fires without causing much damage. High atmospheric temperatures and dryness offer favourable circumstance for a fire to start.

(b) **Man-made causes:** Fire is caused when a source of fire like naked flame, cigarette or bidi, electric spark or any source of ignition comes into contact with inflammable material.[7]

Effects of Forest Fire

Inhalation of smoke from a forest fire can be a health hazard. Its smoke is primarily composed of carbon dioxide, water vapour, particulate matter, organic chemicals, nitrogen oxides and other compounds. Carbon monoxide is a colourless, odourless gas that can be found at the highest concentration at close proximity to a smoldering fire. The illnesses most commonly with exposure to fine particle from smoke are bronchitis, exacerbation of asthma, and pneumonia. Another important and somewhat less obvious health effect of wildfires is psychiatric diseases and disorders.

The most noticeable adverse effect of it is the destruction of property and biomass. People are exposed directly to smoke via the respiratory tract though inhalation of air pollutants. Indirectly, communities are exposed to wildfire debris that can contaminate soil and water supplies. It has continually been a threat to human populations. Human induced geographical and climatic changes are exposing populations more frequently to wildfires and increasing wildfire risk.[8]

Forest fires cause damages, killing some plants and occasionally animals. Firefighters have been injured or killed, and structures can be damaged or destroyed. The loss of plants can heighten the risk of significant erosion and landslides. Damages are almost certainly greater from stand replacement fires than from surface fires. It can have significant local economic effects, both short-term and long-term. Extensive fire damage to trees can significantly alter the timber supply; both through a short-term glut from timber salvage and a longer-term decline while the trees re-grow.[9]

Emissions from forest fires can travel large distances, affecting air quality and human health far from the originating fires. These emissions include: particulate matter; carbon monoxide; atmospheric mercury; ozone-forming chemicals; and volatile organic compounds.[10] It can exacerbate levels of carbon dioxide in the atmosphere, thereby strengthening the greenhouse effect that is already plaguing our earth. When the frequency of wildfires in a particular region is too much, it may have a devastating impact on the ecosystem.[11] Aside from deforestation and the increased release of carbon dioxide into the air, it can also affect the habitat of the environment (depending on the soil and the fire's intensity), the species population and distribution after the incident, and cause damage to some homes and buildings, as well as costly evacuations and even some human deaths.[12]

Forest fire has some positive effects. It can serve to clean up any dead or decaying matter strewn across forest, which, in turn, enables an increase in new plant growth. It is also useful in maintaining the balance within an ecosystem by removing any harmful insects and diseased plants.[13]

Incidences of Forest Fire

Fire is an integral part of western forests and all forest types throughout North America, Australia and elsewhere have evolved and adapted to fire.[14] On average, more than 100,000 wildfires, called wild land fires or forest fires, clear four million to five million acres (1.6 million to two million hectares) of land in the US every year. In recent years, wildfires have burned up to nine million acres (3.6 million hectares) of land.[15] Forest fires in Indonesia occur annually. When there is a weather pattern disturbance because of strong El Nino, the number and the distribution of forest fires in Indonesia increased significantly. When there is a weather pattern disturbance because of strong La Nina, the number and the distribution of forest fire in Indonesia decreased.

A large bushfire that has burned more than 800,000 hectares of forest and private land in Western Australia's southwest has been declared a national disaster in February, 2015. The state's premier, Colin Barnett, told a community meeting in Pemberton, about 30 km north of Northcliffe, that the fire had been declared a natural disaster, meaning the area would be eligible for state and federal assistance. The assistance will include personal hardship grants, financial assistance to local government, and interest rate subsidies for small businesses and primary producers who have been directly impacted by the fire.[16]

Major firestorms that result in severe loss of life are often named based on the day on which they occur, such as Ash Wednesday and Black Saturday. Bushfires in Australia, are generally defined as any uncontrolled, non-structural fire burning in a grass, scrub, bush, or forested area. The Ash Wednesday bushfires were a series of bushfires that occurred in south-eastern Australia on 16 February 1983, which was Ash Wednesday in the Christian calendar. The fires became the deadliest bushfire in Australian history, until the Black Saturday bushfires in 2009. Many of the Victorian fires were thought to have been caused by sparks between short-circuiting power lines, and tree branches connecting with power lines. Upto 8,000 people were evacuated in Victoria at the height of the crisis and a state of disaster was declared for the first time in South Australia's history.[17]

The Black Saturday bushfires were a series of bushfires that ignited or were burning across the Australian state of Victoria on and around Saturday, 7 February 2009 and were Australia's worst ever bush fire disasters. A total of 3,582 firefighting personnel, mainly from the Country Fire Authority and Department of Sustainability and Environment, were deployed across the state on the morning of 7 February in anticipation of the extreme conditions. Investigations began almost immediately following the fires to determine a wide variety of things including identification of victims, cause of ignition sources, and assessments of authority responses.[18]

During 2010, fires in five southern countries (Portugal, Spain, France, Italy, and Greece) burned a total area of 253,664 ha, which is less than the area burnt in 2009, and the fourth lowest value since 1980 (only 1996, 1999 and 2008 were lower). During

2010 Portugal was the worst affected country, recording half the fires and burnt area for the whole of the five southern Member States. Portugal developed a public awareness campaign for forest fires prevention under the slogan "Portugal without forest fires depends on all of us". The National Forest Authority kept its efforts in the forest fire planning at the local, municipal and regional (district) levels.

The Spanish Forest Fire Service is the administrative body responsible for providing state support to the Autonomous Communities to cover the forest fire under Article 7.2(c) of the Act 43/2003 on Forestry. In Italy forest fires occur in all regions. In winter they are located mostly in the Alpine regions; while in summer they are mostly concentrated in the Mediterranean regions. In Liguria fires occur both in summer and winter at about the same frequency. The phenomenon of forest fires is not generalised throughout the country, as about 50 out of the 110 provinces are the most affected and therefore these should receive special attention. In 2010, in the east and south of Austria there were several days with a high level of forest fire danger. During 2010 in Cyprus, 133 forest fires burnt a total area of 2000 ha. Most of these fires (55 per cent) were smaller than 1 ha.[19]

Fires are a widespread phenomenon in Indian forests. Most fires today are thought to be human-caused and are commonly considered to be a major cause of forest degradation.[20] A large fire was burning in India's Sri Venkateshwara National Park on March 24, 2014, when the Moderate Resolution Imaging Spectroradiometer on NASA's Aqua satellite acquired this image. The fires are outlined in red. The park consists of dry deciduous forest, and is home to a wide range of rare wildlife, including tigers and the golden gecko. According to local news reports, several forest fires have burned in national parks and wildlife reserves in the hills of Andhra Pradesh over the past week. The protected forested land is dark green in contrast to the surrounding tan landscape.[21]

Preventive Measures

Forest fire prevention refers to the preemptive methods of reducing the risk of fires as well as lessening its severity and spread. Effective prevention techniques allow supervising agencies to manage air quality, maintain ecological balances, protect resources, and to limit the effects of future uncontrolled fires. Forest fire prevention programmes around the world may employ techniques such as wild land fire use and prescribed or controlled burns. Using strategic cuts of trees, fuels may be removed by hand crews in order to clean and clear the forest, prevent fuel build-up, and create access into forested areas. Additionally, while fuel treatments are typically limited to smaller areas, effective fire management requires the administration of fuels across large landscapes in order to reduce future fire size and severity.[22]

Forest fires are mainly caused by human activities, due to negligence, accidents, or incendiary acts. Therefore, it is essential with regards to prevention, to create awareness that forest fire protection is the business of all. This awareness-building process builds on public education and sensitisation of people. The responsibility to inform, communicate, and train is in the hands of forest fires experts and decision-makers.[23] In order to fight a forest fire successfully, a thorough survey of the site is a must. The key focus areas are determined according to the following tactical priorities: (a) Protection of people; (b) Protection of animals; (c) Protection of structures (buildings, streets, utility lines); and (d) Protection of endangered or fast burning vegetation. Common fire fighting practice in Germany is a direct offensive attack on a fire front by means of fire fighting crews, fire engines and/or air tankers. If a direct attack is not possible, because the flames are too high to tackle or the surface is contaminated with ammunition, then these blazes are fought defensively. Establishing firebreaks is generally only sensible when intensive aerial fires are to be stopped. A large part of fighting forest fires is hard physical labour. Heavy equipment and helicopters are also used.[24]

Grass fires are a major concern for firefighters in early spring. They get quickly out of control and can cause serious damage in agricultural and forested lands. Forest fire officials encourage people not to light grass fires or burn debris.[25] Improperly doused or misplaced fires are one of the leading causes. Before starting a fire, make sure you check your area's forest fire alert system to make sure conditions are safe for an open flame. Every year inappropriately used fireworks cause forest fire. Before using any type of firework, make sure they are legal to use since fireworks laws vary greatly by state and county. Before burning any yard waste, it is important to check with your local municipality since many have regulations regarding yard waste. Never park any type of vehicle on dry vegetation; the heat from the exhaust can cause it to ignite.[26]

The followings are the important precautions against fire: (a) to keep the source of fire or source of ignition separated from combustible and inflammable material; (b) to keep the source of fire under watch and control; (c) not allow combustible or inflammable material to pile up unnecessarily and to stock the same as per procedure recommended for safe storage of such combustible or inflammable material; (d) To adopt safe practices in areas near forests viz. factories, coalmines, oil stores, chemical plants and even in household kitchens; (e) To incorporate fire reducing and fire fighting techniques and equipment while planning a building or coal mining operation; (f) In case of forest fires, the volunteer teams are essential not only for firefighting but also to keep watch on the start of forest and sound an alert; and (g) to arrange fire fighting drills frequently.[27]

References

1. Fire (2015), Available at https://en.wikipedia.org/wiki/Fire
2. Forest fire in India, Available at http://admis.hp.nic.in/himachal/home/HomeGuards/pdfs/forest%20Fires.pdf
3. http://environment.nationalgeographic.com/environment/natural-disasters/wildfires/
4. What is forest fire? Available at http://www.kriseinfo.no/en/Fire-and-explosions/Forest-fires/What-is-a-forest-fire/
5. Forest fire and its management, Available at http://agridr.in/forestry/forest_fire_index.html
6. Wildfire, Available at https://en.wikipedia.org/wiki/Wildfire
7. Forest fire, Available at http://agritech.tnau.ac.in/agriculture/agri_majorareas_disastermgt_forestfire.html
8. Wildfire, Available at https://en.wikipedia.org/wiki/Wildfire
9. Forest Fire/Wildfire Protection (2005), Available at http://www.coloradofirecamp.com/congressional_research/forest-fire-wildfire-effects.htm
10. How forest fire affects air quality, Available at http://www.bcairquality.ca/topics/forest-fires-air-quality.html
11. The Environmental Consequences of Forest Fires, Available at http://greenconduct.com/blog/2013/07/25/the-environmental-consequences-of-forest-fires/
12. Silvia Milanova (2011), Environmental Impact of Forest Fires, Available at http://www.ecoplum.com/greenliving/view/274?_dispatch=gcontents/view/274

13. The Environmental Consequences of Forest Fires, Available at http://greenconduct.com/blog/2013/07/25/the-environmental-consequences-of-forest-fires/
14. Three different types of forest fire, Available at https://drreese.wordpress.com/2013/05/08/three-different-types-of-forest-fires/
15. http://environment.nationalgeographic.com/environment/natural-disasters/wildfires/
16. http://www.theguardian.com/australia-news/2015/feb/06/western-australia-fire-declared-a-national-disaster
17. Ash Wednesday bushfires, Available at https://en.wikipedia.org/wiki/Ash_Wednesday_bushfires
18. Black Saturday bushfires, Available at https://en.wikipedia.org/wiki/Black_Saturday_bushfires
19. Forest Fires in Europe 2010, Available at http://forest.jrc.ec.europa.eu/media/cms_page_media/9/forest-fires-in-europe-2010.pdf
20. Forest fire in India, Available at http://www.forestfireindia.org/
21. See http://earthobservatory.nasa.gov/NaturalHazards/view.php?id=83402
22. Wildfire, Available at https://en.wikipedia.org/wiki/Wildfire
23. International Handbook on Forest Fire Protection, http://www.fao.org/forestry/27221-06293a5348df37 bc8b14e 24472df64810.pdf
24. Forest Fire Fighting, Available at http://www.waldwissen.net/waldwirtschaft/schaden/brand/fva_waldbrand_wb7_1/fva_waldbrand_wb7_summary_fire_fighting.pdf
25. See http://www.borealforest.org/world/innova/fire_ prevention.htm
26. Forest fire prevention, Available at http://www. cultureofsafety.com/wilderness/forest-fire-prevention/
27. Forest fire in India, Available at http://admis.hp.nic.in/himachal/home/HomeGuards/pdfs/forest%20Fires.pdf

13

Acid Rain

""Education is a human right with immense power to transform. On its foundation rest the cornerstones of freedom, democracy and sustainable human development."

–Kofi Annan

An acid is any chemical compound that, when dissolved in water, gives a solution with a pH less than 7.0. It is a chemical substance whose aqueous solutions are characterised by a sour taste, the ability to turn blue litmus red, and the ability to react with bases and certain metals to form salts. The Swedish chemist Svante Arrhenius attributed the properties of acidity to hydrogen ions or protons in 1884. In 1923, chemists Johannes Nicolaus Bronsted and Thomas Martin Lowry independently recognised that acid-base reactions involve the transfer of a proton. A third concept was proposed in 1923 by Gilbert N. Lewis which includes reactions with acid-base characteristics that do not involve a proton transfer.

There are numerous uses for acids. Acids are often used to remove rust and other corrosion from metals in a process known as pickling. They may be used as an electrolyte in a wet cell battery, such as sulphuric acid in a car battery. In the chemical industry, acids react in neutralisation reactions to produce salts. Strong acids, sulfuric acid in particular, are widely used in mineral processing. Tartaric acid is an important component of some commonly used foods like unripened mangoes and tamarind. The hydrochloric acid present in the stomach aids in digestion by breaking down large and complex food molecules.[1]

Meaning

Acid rain is a broad term referring to a mixture of wet and dries deposition from the atmosphere containing higher than normal amounts of nitric and sulfuric acids. It occurs when these gases react in the atmosphere with water, oxygen, and other chemicals to form various acidic compounds. The result is a mild solution of sulfuric acid and nitric acid. Wet deposition refers to acidic rain, fog, and snow. In areas where the weather is dry, the acid chemicals may become incorporated into dust or smoke and fall to the ground through dry deposition, sticking to the ground, buildings, homes, cars, and trees.[2]

Causes of Acid Rain

Acid rain is a rain or any other form of precipitation that is unusually acidic, meaning that it possesses elevated levels of hydrogen ions (low pH). Nitrogen oxides can be produced naturally by lightning strikes and sulphur dioxide is produced by volcanic eruptions. The chemicals in acid rain can cause paint to peel, corrosion of steel structures such as bridges, and erosion of stone statues. The most important gas which leads to acidification is sulphur dioxide. Emissions of nitrogen oxides which are oxidised to form nitric acid are of increasing importance due to stricter controls on emissions of sulphur containing compounds.[3]

The principal natural phenomena that contribute acid-producing gases to the atmosphere are emissions from volcanoes. The principal cause of acid rain is sulphur and nitrogen compounds from human sources, such as electricity generation, factories, and motor vehicles. Acid rain is measured using a scale called "pH".

Effects of Acid Rain

Acid rain has been shown to have adverse impacts on forests, freshwaters and soils, killing insect and aquatic life-forms as well as causing damage to buildings and having impacts on human health. At pH's lower than five most fish eggs will not hatch and lower pHs can kill adult fish. Soil biology and chemistry can be seriously damaged by acid rain. Some microbes are unable to tolerate changes to low pH and are killed. Adverse effects may be indirectly related to acid rain, like the acid's effects on soil or high concentration of gaseous precursors to acid rain. Acid rain can damage buildings, historic monuments, and statues, especially those made of rocks, such as limestone and marble, that contain large amounts of calcium carbonate.[4]

Acid rain causes acidification of lakes and streams and contributes to the damage of trees at high elevations and many sensitive forest soils.[5] Many species of fish are not able to survive in acidic water. Chronic acidification may reduce the levels of nutrients such as calcium, which, over time, may weaken the fish and other plants and animals in an aquatic ecosystem. Episodic acidification can cause sudden shifts in water chemistry. This may lead to high concentrations of substances such as aluminum, which may be toxic to fish.[6] Acid rain has the unsettling ability to erase and obliterate stone and metal, the most durable of materials. Old buildings, monuments and tombstones bear the smooth signs of acidic corrosion and deterioration. Since acid rain can kill aquatic animals, weaken trees and dissolve stone, it seems like it could also scald or burn humans.[7] Acidity affects the availability of nutrients that are essential for plant growth and increases leaching of aluminum and mercury, which are toxic to plants at high levels.[8]

Acids leach nutrients from the soil. They are carried deeper into the ground or into streams, depriving plants of essential elements calcium, potassium, magnesium and trace metals. The effect of acid rain on the environment depends greatly on the ability of soils to neutralise the acid. Limestone and other rocks and soils containing calcium carbonate are most effective. Acids react with calcium carbonate to produce neutral compounds and carbon dioxide.[9]

Incidences of Acid Rain

In 1852, Robert Angus Smith was the first to show the relationship between acid rain and atmospheric pollution in Manchester, England. The term "acid rain" was coined in 1872 by Robert Angus Smith.[10] Acid rain is a serious environmental problem that affects large parts of the United States and Canada. It is particularly damaging to lakes, streams, and forests and the plants and animals that live in these ecosystems.[11] It was a major problem in Europe and the USA in the last few decades of the twentieth century. Strong emission control laws have greatly reduced the problem in these areas. It continues to be a major problem in some developing countries, especially China. In the USA, many are located in the mid-west, and acid rain is common there and throughout the east coast. As power plant emissions are increasingly regulated, the amount of acid rainfall has decreased.[12]

The issue of acid rain emerged in the United States in the mid-1970s. At the time, little was known about the magnitude and distribution of acid rain or about its impacts on terrestrial and aquatic ecosystems. In October 1998, US Senator Daniel Patrick Moynihan testified before Congress on acid rain. A longtime champion of the issue, Moynihan stated that "As far back as the 1960s, fishermen in the Adirondacks began to complain about more than 'the big one that got away.' Fish, once abundant in the pristine, remote Adirondack lakes, were not just getting harder to catch. They were gone."[13]

Preventive Measures

In 1980, the US Congress passed an Acid Deposition Act. This Act established an 18-year assessment and research programme under the direction of the National Acidic Precipitation Assessment Programme (NAPAP). NAPAP looked at the entire problem from a scientific perspective. Many coal-firing power stations use flue-gas desulfurisation (FGD) to remove sulfur-containing gases from their stack gases. For a typical coal-fired power station, FGD will remove 95 per cent or more of the SO_2 in the flue gases. A number of international treaties on the long-range transport of atmospheric pollutants have been agreed for example, Sulphur Emissions Reduction Protocol under the Convention on Long-Range Transboundary Air Pollution. Canada and the US signed the Air Quality Agreement in 1991.[14]

Since the 1970s, various laws have reduced the emission of sulphur dioxides and nitrogen oxides from power plants, including the Clean Air Act of 1970 and the Canada-United States Air Quality Agreement of 1991. The longest continuous rain-chemistry monitoring station in North America, the Hubbard Brook Experimental Forrest in New Hampshire, found that hydrogen ion concentration decreased by roughly 60 per cent since the 1960s.[15]

References

1. Acid, Available at https://en.wikipedia.org/wiki/Acid
2. What is acid rain? Available at http://www.epa.gov/acidrain/what/
3. Acid rain, Available at https://en.wikipedia.org/wiki/Acid_rain
4. Acid rain, Available at https://en.wikipedia.org/wiki/Acid_rain
5. Effects of acid rain, Available at http://www.epa.gov/acidrain/effects/
6. Environmental Effects of Acid Rain, Available at http://www.epa.gov/region1/eco/acidrain/enveffects.html
7. How acid rain works, Available at http://science.howstuffworks.com/nature/climate-weather/atmospheric/acid-rain2.htm
8. What are the harmful Effect of Acid Rain? Available at http://www.preservearticles.com/2012011320782/what-are-the-harmful-effect-of-acid-rain.html
9. Acid Rain and Acid Deposition, Available at http://oceanworld.tamu.edu/resources/environment-book/acidrain.html
10. Acid rain, Available at https://en.wikipedia.org/wiki/Acid_rain
11. See http://www.epa.gov/acidrain/
12. Acid Rain and Acid Deposition, Available at http://oceanworld.tamu.edu/resources/environment-book/acidrain.html
13. See http://www.waterencyclopedia.com/A-Bi/Acid-Rain.html
14. https://en.wikipedia.org/wiki/Acid_rain
15. Negative Health Effects of Acid Rain on Humans, Available at http://science.opposingviews.com/negative-health-effects-acid-rain-humans-24007.html

Part III: Environmental Instruments

14

Joint Forest Management

"A lovely nook of forest scenery, or a grand rock, like a beautiful woman, depends for much of its attractiveness upon the attendance sense of freedom from whatever is low; upon a sense of purity and of romance." - **P.T. Barnum**

Forests in India are mostly state owned and cover an area of 67.71 million hectares, corresponding to 20.60 per cent of the total geographical area of the country. Nearly 100 million people reside in forests and another 275 million live on the periphery and earn their livelihood from forests. Forest resources are especially vulnerable to the "tragedy of commons", resulting from overexploitation of the resource by individual self-interest and the lack of effective institutions to govern the resource. Soon after India's independence from British colonial rule in 1947, state governments were urged by the Indian government to implement land reforms for providing poor and socially disadvantaged rural households the means of securing livelihoods and increasing agricultural productivity.

Although the redistributive outcomes of land reform were largely dismal in most states, the ceilings on land ownership set by legislation allowed many state governments to transfer large, privately owned forests to their forest departments following due compensation to owners. The National Planning Commission advised state forestry agencies to pursue afforestation strategies that centred on strict protection of existing forests undergoing natural regeneration, and extensive planting of fast-growing tree species in degraded public lands and other forest categories. In 1976, the Indian government responded by passing a constitutional amendment that made forestry a "concurrent subject."

Natural resources have always been an integral part of the Indian economy and culture and are held in high esteem. Ancient religious, political and literary writings are testament to the fact that people have historically been considered an integral part of nature and not superior to it. The British administration directed its forest policy towards commercial interests and the development of agriculture, which was a major source of revenue. These motives are explicitly documented in the National Forest Policy of 1894, the first formal forest policy in India. Likewise, the implementation of the Indian Forest Act, 1927 by the British Administration had an impact on those communities dependent on forests. The Indian Forest Act was drafted first in 1865, placing most forests under state ownership. It was further revised in 1878 and consolidated in 1927.

Joint Forest Management is in India for partnerships in forest movement involving both the state forest departments and local communities. The policies and objectives of Joint Forest Movement are detailed in the Indian comprehensive National Forest Policy of 1988 and the Joint Forest Movement Guidelines of 1990 of the Government of India. Employment opportunities in collection of minor forest produce; forest works as well as in agriculture are unable to support the tribal's throughout the year. This led on the one hand to the worsening of the state of forests and on the other in growing hardships inflicted upon the tribal's even for meeting their subsistence needs.

There are three types of products available to communities in JFM areas (i) immediate products like NTFPs, grass, fuel wood available almost immediately or after a time period depending upon the state of degradation of the forest that is being managed jointly, (ii) intermediate products from operations like thinning, other cultural operations, and (iii) final products like timber from fellings. Stabilising India's natural forests and watersheds is seen as a significant step in sustaining a rural environment that can support a still expanding population.

The fundamental premise of JFM is sustainable forest management through people's participation and a reinstatement of their subsistence rights over forests. At present, the National Ministry of Environment and Forests has limited capacity to guide the transition in public forest management systems. To shift the enduring injustices that characterise development interventions and civil society, forest reform processes and programmes require major political and legal reframe from the state custodial and industrial management models operational for almost a hundred and fifty years.

Meaning

Joint Forest Management is a concept of developing partnerships between fringe forest user groups and the Forest Department on the basis of mutual trust and jointly defined roles and responsibilities with regard to forest protection and development. It is slowly emerging into a form of sustainable forestry, which augments the forestry regime with processes for rapid adaptation to changes in what people need, want, and can do. The local village committees and the forest department enter into a MoU to manage the forest area jointly with forest department and are entitled to get usufructs benefits from the forest area managed under JFM.

Functioning of the JFM institution in an efficient manner requires the whole-hearted participation of the village households in the management and sustenance of forest resources. Involvement of the locals in regenerating the forest is governed by many socio-economic factors identified in the extent of their dependence on forest resources for subsistence. It is a concept of developing partnerships between fringe forest user groups and the Forest Department on the basis of mutual trust and jointly defined roles and responsibilities with regard to forest protection and development.

The JFM programme is a co-management regime for protection, regeneration and development of degraded forests where the role of NGOs was to act as a bridge between the State and the people dependent on forests. It has largely been implemented in a project mode as a major requirement of loans from the World Bank and other external donor agencies. The JFM provisions, under the JFM guidelines of 1990, are expected to promote peoples' involvement, collective decision-making, social fencing, empowerment of the village community, sharing of authority, focus on non-timber forest products and sustained harvest of usufructs. The *JFM* is based on the *principle* of 'Care and Share'.

Importance

Forests are vital for social, economic, ecological and environmental reasons. They play an important role in ecosystem processes, they provide habitat for wildlife and serve as sources of biodiversity, and they offer protection against soil erosion. Forests are also among the most effective systems for air pollution abatement and ground water recharge. In this era of global warming, forests help mitigate the effects of climate change, and maintain biodiversity and ecosystem functioning.

Forests are a crucial link in the ecosystem. In addition to the direct use values, forests resources protect the environment in different ways, such as watershed protection, nutrient cycling, pollution control, micro-climatic regulation, and carbon sequestration. Depletion and degradation of forest resources lead to serious wider environmental consequences, not only at the local and regional level but also as is increasingly apparent at global level. In earlier historical periods, people used forest resources with little intervention by the rulers, in different parts of the sub-continent. The commercialisation of forests during the colonial period resulted in large-scale degradation. The first Forest Policy of 1894 highlighted the intention of the state to recognise forestry as a land use distinctly different from agriculture, and earmarking areas for such land use had the major objective of timber production, ignoring the needs of the local people.

The primary objective of JFM is to provide a visible role to the local communities in planning, management and protection of forests and to give them a share in the benefits from these forests. On operational parameters, it is a concept of developing partnership between forest department and fringe forest user groups on the basis of jointly defined roles and responsibilities. Joint Forest Management in India, as the largest community forestry initiative globally, embraces the philosophy of sustaining the forests and improving the livelihoods. Accordingly, Forest Department makes strong claims about the contribution of JFM to both improvement of forests as well as livelihoods of people.

Poverty reduction and sustainable livelihood are the two main issues in JFM. The poverty reduction means to achieve the sustainable livelihood which is required to develop continue employment and income generation innovation for new economic choice, capacity building for livelihood goals and strategies.

Forest-user communities across the country, dependent on forests for fuel wood, fodder, small timber and NTFPs, have accessed forest products under different rights regimes. Under the JFM programme, residents of forest-fringe villages have been provided access to forest produce to meet their basic needs of fodder, fuel wood and NTFP. Fuel wood in the form of dry and fallen twigs and leaves from the forests is now available to participating communities. It generated from various silvicultural operations, also supplement fuel wood supply in different states. Most States did not allow any rights or share for people in from forest products like NTFP, timber and other intermediary products in the past, which has however changed with JFM.

JFM acted as a vehicle for process change in the forest department, which was widely perceived as a continuation of the British legacy and structure advocating exclusionary forestry. It has helped in reducing information asymmetry in natural resource management between the local people and forest department. It helped in the decentralisation of decision-making by empowering the Village Forest Committee politically and socioeconomically. It acted as an embodiment of the contemporary international and national paradigm in environmental governance favouring co-management of natural resources in India.

Joint Forest Management in India

Joint Forest Management has become the new catchphrase in forest management in India today, being regarded as a beacon of hope by the pro-people lobby and as a donor imposed fashion by many hardline foresters. The arguments for having jointness of either kind locally communal management or state-local cooperation are rooted in the interdependencies created by the nature of the forest ecosystem. In most third world countries such as India, forests were largely managed until recently, by the state, with a prime objective to produce timber. In the process, the forest dependent communities' rights were marginalised and, moreover, large degraded forest areas were converted for plantation purposes. Several attempts to conserve forests through state controlled programmes failed as they did not recognise the community's role in forest management.

National Forest Policy of 1988 envisioned the ecological, economic and social aspects of forest management. In India, there is an increased pressure on forest resources due to livelihood needs of millions of forest dwellers and people living around the forests. The forests have multi utility functions like providing direct livelihood to poor, biodiversity conservation, carbon storage and providing for future needs. To achieve all these objectives Sustainable Forest management is the option. Indian forest protection movement witnessed the emergence of three distinct types of community-based forest management. The first type of community-based forest management emerged out of local initiatives as a result of growing stress owing to rapid degradation of forest. Charismatic local leaders, enthusiastic youth groups, concerned outsiders like FD, and NGOs gave moral fillip to communities for consolidating their forest protection initiatives in an organised manner. The second type of community-based forest management was promoted by FD at different times. The third type of community-based forest management emerged with the active sponsorship of local government and NGOs.

Joint Forest Management originated in West Bengal accidentally at the Arabari Forest Range in West Midnapore, near Midnapore town in 1971. The major hardwood of Arabari is sal, a commercially profitable forest crop. As per the provisions of National Forest Policy 1988, the Government of India, vide letter No.6.21/89-PP dated 1st June, 1990, outlined and conveyed to State Governments a framework for creating massive people's movement through involvement of village committees for the protection, regeneration and development of degraded forest lands.

Government of India on June 1, 1990 issued guidelines to the state governments for involving local communities in the protection and development of the degraded forests. Based on this, the JFM programme has now been widely adopted in twenty two states of the country. These states are Andhra Pradesh, Arunachal Pradesh, Assam, Bihar, Gujarat, Himachal Pradesh, Haryana, Jammu and Kashmir, Karnataka, Kerala, Madhya

Pradesh, Maharashtra, Mizoram, Nagaland, Odisha, Punjab, Rajasthan, Sikkim, Tamil Nadu, Tripura, Uttar Pradesh and West Bengal.

India's forest management policies have been at the centre of an ongoing debate on the environment. Over the last several decades the human and cattle population has increased manifold. The holders of customary rights and concessions in forest areas should be motivated to identify themselves with the protection and development of forests from which they derive benefits. The rights and concessions from forests should primarily be for the bonafide use of the communities living within an around forest areas, specially the tribals.

After independence, the Constitution of India adopted a number of provisions from the Government of India Act of 1935 and retained forest as a state subject in the 7th schedule. The National Forest Policy Resolution adopted by the government in 1952 stressed that the forest policy shall be on national needs but not on commerce, industry and revenue. For the first time, the resolution was highlighted on the ecological and social aspects of forest management. But this remained as a pious declaration without any execution. The Ministry of Forest was initially a part of the Ministry of Agriculture which the National Commission on Agriculture treated it as such.

Table 1: State-wise forest cover and area under JFM in India

Sl. No.	*State*	*Recorded Forest Area (ha)*	*Area under JFM (ha)*	*Forest covered by JFM (per cent)*
1.	Jharkhand	2360500	1721700	72.94
2.	Bihar	647300	462333	71.42
3.	Madhya Pradesh	9468900	6687390	70.62
4.	Punjab	305800	178333	58.32
5.	Chhattisgarh	5977200	3319000	55.53
6.	West Bengal	1187900	646084	54.39
7.	Maharashtra	6193900	2403344	38.80
8.	Tripura	629400	241138	38.31
9.	Tamil Nadu	2287700	756446	33.07
10.	Haryana	155900	41188	26.42
11.	Rajasthan	3263900	858614	26.31
12.	Andhra Pradesh	6381400	1519000	23.80
13.	Gujarat	1892700	414151	21.88

Sl. No.	State	Recorded Forest Area (ha)	Area under JFM (ha)	Forest covered by JFM (%)
14.	Karnataka	3828400	808020	21.11
15.	Odisha	5813600	1148676	19.76
16.	Kerala	1126500	107404	18.41
17.	Uttarakhand	3465100	564221	16.28
18.	Sikkim	584100	88518	15.15
19.	Uttar Pradesh	1658300	183393	11.06
20.	Manipur	1741800	166767	9.57
21.	Goa	122400	10000	8.17
22.	Himachal Pradesh	3703300	205056	5.54
23.	Nagaland	922200	42929	4.66
24.	Mizoram	1671700	55990	3.33
25.	Assam	2683200	52499	1.96
26.	Arunachal Pradesh	5154000	100377	1.95
27.	Jammu and Kashmir	2023000	38736	1.91
28.	Meghalaya	949600	17245	1.82
29.	Andaman and Nicobar Islands	717100	262	0.04

Source: ICFRE, 2011.

The National Forest Policy of 1988 envisages people's involvement in the development and protection of forests. The requirement of fuel wood, fodder and small timber such as house-building material, of the tribals and other villagers living in and near the forests, are to be treated as first charge on forest produce. Government of India proposed that access to forest land and usufruct benefits should be provided to those who got organised into a village institution such as panchayat, cooperative of the village or village forest protection committee, specifically for forest regeneration and protection.

The involvement of people in forest management is started in some states like West Bengal much before 1988. Since 1970-71 the West Bengal Forest Department has been involving the people in forest protection and regeneration which demonstrated that if the rights are given to the communities they would effectively protect the forests. Government of Andhra Pradesh issued an order on JFM in 1992, becoming the eleventh state to do so, naming the forest protection committees as Vana Samrakshna Samithies for the protection and regeneration of forests.

The JFM provisions, under the JFM guidelines of 1990, are expected to promote peoples' involvement, collective decision-making, social fencing, empowerment of the village community, sharing of authority, focus on non-timber forest products and sustained harvest of usufructs. It is estimated that nearly 200,000 villages are found around the forests. Efforts at involving local people in management of forest resource have produced encouraging results with respect to conservation and regeneration in states such as West Bengal and Haryana. Haryana was among the early states to accept and implement a JFM programme based on guidelines issued by the central government in 1990. The state issued its JFM policy in 1990, and subsequently, in 1998 issued executive instructions to implement the programme. Despite having had an early start and gaining rich experiences, many issues still affect the JFM process in the state.

Forest Department, Government of Chhattisgarh has passed resolution in October 2001 and revised it in October 2002 to make Joint Forest Management as a basis of forest management. In Chhattisgarh Out of total 19720 villages in the State, there are 11,185 villages located within five kms periphery of forests. Thus, there was a paradigm shift from centralised, controlled and custodial forest management to democratic, devolving, participatory community-based natural resource management, resulting in orientation from revenue generation to resource development, single benefit to multiple benefits, mono-culture to multiple cropping and above all unilateral decision-making to participatory process.

Joint forest management, a centrally sponsored scheme meant to involve local people in forest management and development, will soon is a reality in Meghalaya. The joint forest management committees in fringe villages of Meghalaya have led to people's participation in conservation. There are approximately 4,000 forest fringe villages in the state and 285 joint forest management committees at the village/cluster level. Through such committees, an area of 261.4 square km has been brought under green cover and the aim is to increase such committees to 500 by 2017. In

2012-13, 79 biodiversity management committees have been formed while the location of 115 sacred groves in Meghalaya has been mapped through Geographical Information Systems.

The Joint Forest Management programme was initiated in Tripura in December, 1991 and since then there has been reasonable progress in involving the people living around the forests to protect and improve the forests and in their share the benefits there from. It was at first initiated in Melaghar, West Tripura District and resulted in turming the barren lands into verdant forests with protection made available by Forest Protection and Regeneration Committees. Several thousand villages in Odisha are involved in active protection and management of forests. Most started protecting on their own initiative as their response to forest degradation problem. Odisha has been struggling with the process of formalising these initiatives and bringing them to the 'Joint Forest Management' fold. The forest protecting villages find state promoted Joint Forest Management arrangement unacceptable and feel that this does not put the management powers and decision-making in the hands of local communities. Odisha is the pioneer state to take steps in the direction of adopting Joint Forest Management.

It was the first state to issue a resolution that seeks to involve local communities in protection of forests through a resolution in August 1988. This resolution was in response to pressure from below from thousands of forest protecting villages in Odisha. A large-scale post-card campaign was taken up in the State. Odisha also issued another resolution in 1996 that can be termed as "revolutionary" in some respects. This is the first resolution in the country that seeks to bring some changes in forest tenure. This resolution provides for declaration of forest patches being protected by villagers as Village Forests as per the provisions for Village Forests under the Odisha Forest Act.

While the primary objective of the JFM programme continues to be rehabilitation of degraded forestlands with peoples organisations (Village Forest Committees-VFCs), in the course of evolution, approaches like village resource development, micro watershed development have got integrated into JFM as most State governments are attempting to improve the socio-economic status of forest dependent communities in order to reduce pressure on forests. NGOs are increasingly getting involved with JFM. They have an important role to play in capacity building, information dissemination, monitoring and evaluation, policy-making and as facilitators in the programme implementation. There are three types of products available to communities in JFM areas (i) immediate products like NTFPs, grass, fuelwood available almost immediately or after a time period depending upon the state of degradation of the forest that is being managed jointly, (ii) intermediate products from operations like thinning, other cultural operations, and (iii) final products like timber from fellings.

References

1. Angana P. Chatterji, Community Forest Management-Odisha, Available at http://planningcommission.nic.in/reports/sereport/ser/seeds/seed_fortry.pdf
2. Anuradha Vemuri, Joint Forest Management in India: An Unavoidable and Conflicting Common Property Regime in Natural Resource Management, Available at http://www.maxwell.syr.edu/uploadedfiles/moynihan/dst/vemuri.pdf
3. Garima Tiwari, Joint Forest Management for Decline off Villagers Migration Problem: A Case Study of Three Villages of Central India, Available at http://www.ijsr.net/archive/v2i12/MDIwMTM1MjM=.pdf
4. Himadri Sinha, Forest and People: Understanding the Institutional Governance, Social Identity, and People's Participation in Indian Forest Management, Available at http://awsassets.wwfindia.org/downloads/social_identity_and_ people_s_participation_in_forest_management_1.pdf
5. http://shodhganga.inflibnet.ac.in/bitstream/10603/1876/11/12_chapter5.pdf
6. http://wgbis.ces.iisc.ernet.in/biodiversity/sahyadri_enews/newsletter/issue21/pdfs/Why,%20Who,%20and%20How%20of%20J ointness %20in%20 Joint%20Forest%20Management.pdf
7. http://www.cess.ac.in/cesshome/wp%5Cwp-62.pdf
8. http://www.ijpbs.net/cms/php/upload/3094_pdf.pdf
9. http://www.ijsf.org/dat/art/vol03/ijsf_vol3_no2_01_ datta_jfm_india.pdf
10. http://www.indiaenvironmentportal.org.in/content/150565/joint-forest-management-in-meghalaya/
11. http://www.streetdirectory.com/travel_guide/7628/recreation_and_sports/is_the_chipko_ movement_ towards_ forest_appraisal.html
12. http://www.teriuniversity.ac.in/mct/pdf/assignment/SS-KANDPAL.pdf
13. Indigenous Peoples and Forest Management: Comparative Analysis of Institutional Approaches in Australia and India, Available at http://www.uky.edu/~tmute2/geography_ methods/readingPDFs/rangan_forests. pdfParticipatory Forest Management in India An Analysis of Policy Trends amid 'Management Change', Available at http://pub.iges.or.jp/modules/envirolib/upload/371/attach/07_India.pdf
14. Institutional and benefit-sharing issues and strategies for Joint Forest Management in the state of Haryana: a policy brief, Available at http:/

/www.teriin.org/events/pdf/forestry_and_biodiversity/Policy_Brief_JFM_institutional_ and_benefit_sharing.pdf

15. Joint forest management programme, Available at http://agritech.tnau.ac.in/forestry/forest_jfm_index.html
16. Joint Forest Management, Available at http://www.naeb.nic.in/Reports%5Cjfm.pdf
17. Joint Forest Management, Available at https://en.wikipedia.org/wiki/Joint_Forest_Management
18. K.S. Murali, Joint forest management in India and its ecological impacts, Available at http://www.forest.jharkhand.gov.in/pdf/jfmassess2.pdf
19. K.S. Murali, R. Jagannatha Rao and N.H. Ravindranath, Evaluation studies of Joint Forest Management in India: a review of analytical processes, Available at http://www.geocities.ws/murali_kallur/jfmassess1.pdf
20. Neera M. Singh, Community Forest Management vs. Joint Forest Management in Odisha, Available at http://vasundharaodisha. org/download22/CFMVsjfm.pdf
21. P.N. Ray, Status of Joint Forest Management in Tripura, Available at http://www.indianforester.co.in/index.php/indianforester/article/view/3194/0
22. See http://www.fao.org/docrep/ARTICLE/WFC/XII/0676-C1.HTM
23. See http://www.moef.nic.in/sites/default/files/Document1_ 3.pdf
24. Study on Joint Forest Management conducted by TERI for Ministry of Environment and Forests, Available at http://www.moef.nic.in/sites/default/files/Document1_3.pdf
25. Study on Joint Forest Management conducted by TERI for Ministry of Environment and Forests, Available at http://www.moef.nic.in/sites/default/files/Document1_3.pdf
26. The Telegraph (May 30, 2013), More forest cover in Meghalaya's fringe villages, Available at http://www.telegraphindia.com/1130530/jsp/northeast/story_16950075.jsp#.VeZnZNJViko
27. Vijai Shanker Singh and Deep Narayan Pandey, What Makes Joint Forest Management Successful? Science-Based Policy Lessons on Sustainable Governance of Forests in India, Available at http://www.rpcb.rajasthan.gov.in/rpcbweb/Reports AndPaper/Joint_Forest_Management_Science-Based_Policy_Lessons.pdf

15

Pollution Control Instruments

"Unlike a drop of water which loses its identity when it joins the ocean, man does not lose his being in the society in which he lives. Man's life is independent. He is born not for the development of the society alone, but for the development of his self." - **B.R. Ambedkar**

Pollution is the introduction of contaminants into the natural environment that causes adverse change. It started from prehistoric times when man created the first fires. The burning of coal and wood, and the presence of many horses in concentrated areas made the cities the cesspools of pollution. It was the industrial revolution that gave birth to environmental pollution as we know it today. The major forms of pollution are listed below along with the particular contaminant relevant to each of them. A pollutant is a waste material that pollutes air, water or soil. Three factors determine the severity of a pollutant: its chemical nature, the concentration and the persistence.

Pollution has cost. Manufacturing activities that cause air pollution impose health and clean-up costs on the whole society, whereas the neighbours of an individual who chooses to fire-proof his home may benefit from a reduced risk of a fire spreading to their own houses.[1] One of the greatest problems that the world is facing today is that of environmental pollution, increasing with every passing year and causing grave and irreparable damage to the earth. Environmental pollution consists of five basic types of pollution, namely, air, water, soil, noise and light.[2] Pollution effects are indeed **many** and wide-ranging. All types of pollution – air, water and soil pollution have an impact on the living environment. The effects in living organisms may range from mild discomfort to serious diseases such as cancer to physical deformities; ex., extra or missing limbs in frogs.[3]

Air pollution is the most prominent and dangerous form of pollution. It occurs due to many reasons. Water pollution has taken toll of all the surviving species of the earth. Almost 60 per cent of the species live in water bodies. Soil pollution occurs due to incorporation of unwanted chemicals in the soil due to human activities. Noise pollution is caused when noise which is an unpleasant sound affects our ears and leads to psychological problems like stress, hypertension, hearing impairment, etc. Radioactive pollution is highly dangerous when it occurs. It can occur due to nuclear plant malfunctions, improper nuclear waste disposal, accidents, etc. Thermal/heat pollution is due to the excess heat in the environment creating unwanted changes over long time periods.[4]

Economists have long advocated the use of market-based policies to achieve environmental objectives. These policies include taxes on the waste emissions of firms, and programmes in which the government limits pollution by issuing emission permits that can be traded among firms. Tradable permits also raise firms' production costs and reduce economic activity. If a polluting firm increases production, it must either buy permits to cover the extra emissions or forgo sales of its own permits to other firms; either way, there is a financial penalty for producing polluting output. Policy-makers may be concerned about the effects of environmental policies on different household income groups.[5]

While command-and-control regulations have been a commonly used method of environmental regulation in the United States, EPA employs the three other approaches. Market-based incentives and hybrid approaches offer the regulated community an opportunity to meet standards with increased flexibility and lower costs compared to many command-and-control regulations, while voluntary initiatives may allow environmental improvements in areas not traditionally regulated by EPA.[6] For more than thirty years, environmental economists have been advocating emission taxes and cap and trade schemes as more flexible and cost-effective instruments for pollution control than the more traditional emission standards.[7] Economic evaluations of pollution control policies have traditionally focused on pure efficiency effects either a comparison of their economic costs and environmental benefits, or a comparison of their costs relative to those of alternative control policies.[8]

Traditional regulatory instruments applied to implement environmental policies, despite some successes, failed to address many environmental challenges and imposed high costs on the society to achieve environmental quality objectives.[9]

Command and Control Instruments

Command and control pattern of regulation set uniform targets for how much firms should emit, often by dictating the processes that should be used in their facilities. Two broad types of command and control regulations are discernible: technology-based and performance-based. The former specify the methods and equipment that firms must use to meet the target. Performance standards set an overall target for each firm, or plant, and give firms some discretion in how to meet the standard.[10] Command and control policies require firms to implement certain technologies and practices or reach certain levels of emission through either technology-based or performance-based standards. Technology-based standards specify either a certain technology that companies must use or specify that companies must employ the best available control technology. Performance-based standards set either a quantity of emissions that must be abated or a maximum level of emissions that can be released.[11]

Command and control regulations focus on preventing environmental problems by specifying how a company will manage a pollution-generating process. This approach generally relies on detailed regulations followed up by an ongoing inspection programme. Command and control regulations were popular in the early stages of American environmental regulation in the 1970's. The alternative to "command and control" regulation is "performance oriented" regulation, in which specific environmental performance goals.[12]

A CAC approach in policy is used for several reasons. It has been proposed that by imposing fixed standards with the force of law behind them, CAC can respond more quickly to activities which do not abide by the set standards. It also has benefits politically as the regulator is seen to be acting swiftly and decisively. In Environmental Policy, CAC is characterised by three different types of standards; the use of the standards is determined by various factors, including the nature of the environmental problem and the administrative capacities of the governing body. The 1987 Montreal Protocol is commonly cited as a CAC success story at international level. The aim of the agreement was to limit the release of Chlorofluorocarbons into the atmosphere and subsequently halt the depletion of Ozone (O_3) in the stratosphere.[14]

Command and control mechanisms normally operate through one of three means: ambient standards, source-specific emission limits, or technology requirements. In principle, ambient standards could be established with reference to incremental control costs and incremental pollution damage. Emission limits are applied to individual sources as a means of achieving health or environment-based ambient standards. Ambient standards specify a minimum level of environmental quality to be achieved through limits on sources, products, and other sources of pollution.[15]

The choice between alternative pollution control instruments typically centres on comparisons of transaction costs, and administrative and policy costs. Uncertainty can manifest itself to the individual firm's decision-makers and/or to the pollution control agency. Uncertainty at the level of the pollution control agency includes many of the same phenomena facing the firm, such as the uncertainty attached to the firm's marginal cost functions which in turn imparts uncertainty to the aggregate marginal control cost function facing the agency.[16]

Economic Instruments

Economists have long advocated the use of economic instruments as an alternative, or supplement, to direct regulation. Economic instruments allow for a more hands-off regulation and decentralised decision-making, giving greater freedom to firms and plants about how to comply. The underlying premise for economic instruments is to correct market failure by placing a cost on the release of pollutants. Placing a charge, or a fee, on every unit of effluent released into the river, transforms the manufacturer's decisions regarding how much he will produce, and how he will produce it. It can be applied to certain products which cause pollution in their production, use or disposal. Such products include fuel, fertilisers, pesticides, batteries etc.[17]

Many factors enter into the decision to favour either policy that lean more toward economic incentives and toward direct regulation, commonly referred to as command-and-control policy. Underlying determinants include a country's governmental and regulatory infrastructure, along with the nature of the environmental problem itself.[18]

(a) Market-based instruments

Market-based policies are regulations that "encourage behaviour through market signals rather than through explicit directives regarding pollution control levels or methods. Many market-based instruments function as follows: A polluting firm or consumer faces a potential penalty in the form of a tax or permit price per unit of emissions. Market-based policies give polluters more flexibility than most command-and-control policies.[19]

Market-based instruments are said to "harness market forces" so that they use market signals to affect behaviour (of both consumers and firms) towards pollution control. They are also called Economic Incentives for pollution control and include pollution charges or levies, taxes and tradable permits. This stresses the way in which MBIs achieve pollution control. They create an incentive for firms, by imposing an implicit or explicit price on emissions, so that it is beneficial to clean up more provided that a sufficiently low-cost method is available.[20]

Currently, the pollution control policies within the energy industry are focused on developing three main types of market based instruments, usually used separately as formalised trading schemes: green certificates, white certificates and black certificates. Tradable white certificates can be defined as market-based instruments used for promoting energy savings within economic activities. The scheme is less popular and more specific than tradable green certificates scheme. The main consequence of integrating market-based instruments for pollution control, within energy industry, is the development of a common market capable to assure the trading process for the entire commodities, facilitating the alignment between supply and demand in this particular sector.[21]

Tradable permits can be classified into three distinct forms – credit trading, averaging, and allowance trading and distinguished by their relation to a conventional environmental permit. Credit Trading is the form closest to the conventional permit. A facility that does more than required to meet the conditions of its permit may get credit for its extra effort and that credit can be transferred to another facility that is thereby excused from fulfilling the condition of its permit in like amount. Averaging constitutes a further step away from the underlying environmental permit in dispensing with certification. Allowance Trading is also known as cap-and-trade, so called because of the absolute cap on emissions and the ability to trade emissions under the cap. As the most evolved form of a tradable permit system, allowance trading has prerequisites that differ in important aspects from what conventional command-and-control systems require.[22]

Policymakers have paid increasing attention to market-based policy instruments over the last decades. Tradable emission permits have been at the centre of this discussion due to the theoretical promise of cost-effectiveness and because they have been used successfully in the United States to reduce sulphur dioxide and nitrogen oxides. Many donors and advisors have promoted the use of market-based instruments as the key to more effective environmental protection in the developing world. Although the efficiency properties of tradable permit programmes were discussed by some economists in the early 1970s, it was not until the early 1980s that they started to be promoted in academia. Apart from the European Union's Emission Trading Scheme, the world's first large-scale CO_2 emissions trading programme, few applications of tradable permits existed previously in Europe, since taxes and other instruments were used more frequently.[23]

Tradable permits are similar to charges and taxes except that they operate by fixing an aggregate quantity of emissions rather than charging a price for each unit of emissions. Instead of being charged for releases, one needs to hold a 'permit' to emit or discharge. By controlling the total number of permits, one is effectively controlling the aggregate pollution quantity.

Charge-Permit Hybrids is possible to blend the quantity-based permit approach with a price-based charge or tax approach to try to harness their different strengths while avoiding their weaknesses.[24] One common belief about tradable permit programmes is that their environmental effects are determined purely by the imposition of the aggregate limit, an act that is considered to lie outside the system. Hence, it is believed, the main purpose of the system is to protect the economic value of the resource, not the resource itself.[25]

Emissions trading are a market-based approach used to control pollution by providing economic incentives for achieving reductions in the emissions of pollutants. A central authority sets a limit or cap on the amount of a pollutant that may be emitted. The total number of permits cannot exceed the cap, limiting total emissions to that level. Firms that need to increase their volume of emissions must buy permits from those who require fewer permits. The buyer is paying a charge for polluting, while the seller gains a reward for having reduced emissions. Economists have urged the use of market-based instruments such as emissions trading to address environmental problems instead of prescriptive command and control regulation. Under an emissions trading system, emissions sources must meet a set of emissions target, but will have flexibility with regard to how they meet the target.[26]

Emissions trading are a market-based approach to controlling pollution. By creating tradable pollution permits it attempts to add the profit motive as an incentive for good performance, unlike traditional environmental regulation based solely on the threat of penalties. The main form of emissions trading is known as cap and trade: a cap on emissions is set and then permits are created up to the level of this cap. Emissions trading are a central element of the Kyoto protocol in the form of the Clean Development Mechanism and are the cornerstone policy of the EU, whose Emissions Trading System is the largest in the world.[27] Unlike a regulatory standard, a tradable permit system offers flexibility to the polluters on how to accomplish the environmental goal. If one polluter can overachieve at low cost, there is an incentive for them to do so. This can lead to the development of innovative solutions and minimises the costs to society of complying with the limits.[28]

The tradable permits policy for controlling pollution in the United States has evolved considerably since its inception in the mid 1970s. In an attempt to inject more flexibility into the manner in which the objectives of the Clean Air Act were met, during the last half of the 1970's the U.S. EPA created what has now become known as the Emissions Trading Programme. Following the path broken by the Emissions Trading Programme, the government began applying the transferable permit approach more widely in the mid-1980's. Under this programme a fixed amount of lead rights were allocated to the various refiners. The United States has chosen to use a transferable permit system to implement its responsibilities under the protocols. Another quite different version of the tradable permits concept was incorporated by the Clean Air Act Amendments of 1990 into the U. S. approach for achieving further reductions in those electric utility emissions contributing to acid rain. Due in part to the emission reductions achieved from stationary sources, in many regions of the United States mobile sources now account for a high percentage of the remaining pollution.[29]

A major advantage of the marketable permit approach is that it gives the environmental authority direct control over the quantity of emissions. Another advantage of the tradable permitover other instruments is their flexibility in relation to changes in economic general conditions.[30]

(b) Pollution Charge Systems

Pollution charge systems can be many kinds but their main defining feature is their reliance on markets and the price mechanism to internalise environmental externalities, thereby attempting to make polluters pay the full social costs of their activities. Pollution charges are best applied where property rights are not evident. Fiscal instruments (taxes) and financial instruments (subsidies) are the most widely used economic instruments. Fiscal instruments relate to a government tax or fiscal policy. Two types of tax have been used – the product charge (Pigouvian tax) and the emission charge. The product charge imposes a tax on products whose use or disposal causes pollution and an emissions charge assigns a price to emissions of pollution (e.g., $ per ton).

Pigovian tax is a tax applied to a market activity that is generating negative externalities. The tax is intended to correct an inefficient market outcome, and does so by being set equal to the social cost of the negative externalities. Pigovian taxes are named after economist Arthur Pigou who also developed the concept of economic externalities. William Baumol was instrumental in framing Pigou's work in modern economics. The Pigovian tax is a method commonly used by governments as it has relatively low transaction costs associated with implementation. Other methods such as command and control regulations or subsidies assume that the government has a complete knowledge of the market, which is almost never the case, and can often lead to inefficiencies and market failure though rent seeking behaviour by individuals and firms.[31]

Financial instruments primarily involve the use of subsidies, and less often investments, to accelerate the development of environmentally benign technologies. Subsidies, in the form of grants, tax credits, direct payments or low interest loans, essentially pay individuals, companies or industries not to pollute. The two main forms of subsidies are abatement equipment subsidies (Pogouvian subsidies) and per unit subsidies on pollution reduction (Coasian subsidies). Bonds and deposit-refund systems are both based on the principal of paying up front for the externality imposed and being able to recoup the cost, combining characteristics of taxes and subsidies.[32]

(c) Hybrid Instruments

Hybrid policies are: combining standards and pricing approaches, and the use of information as regulation. Pollution standards set specific emissions limits, and thereby reduce the chance of excessive health and environmental damages. Such standards, however, may impose large costs on polluters. Emissions taxes restrict costs by allowing polluters to pay a tax rather than undertake excessively expensive abatement. An instrument that has been used increasingly in industrialised countries as a method for regulation is the requirement that firms provide the government and public with information on pollution and abatement activities.[33]

Direct Regulatory Instruments

Compared with emissions taxes and tradable emissions allowances, direct regulations such as technology mandates and performance standards are at a disadvantage in meeting the conditions for cost-minimisation.[34] Economists have long argued that direct EI instruments are superior to CAC instruments in terms of static efficiency, dynamic efficiency, and flexibility—advantages that would appear to be especially attractive to developing countries given that financial and administrative resources are typically in short supply. The static efficiency advantages of direct economic incentive instruments stem in part from the fact that they leave firms free to choose abatement technologies that minimise costs given their individual circumstances. Although advocates of direct EI instruments generally focus on static efficiency arguments, the advantages of dynamic efficiency and flexibility may be of greater long-run importance.[35]

United Nations Environment Programme

The United Nations Environment Programme is the overall coordinating environmental organisation of the United Nations system. Its mission is to provide leadership and encourage partnerships in caring for the environment by inspiring, informing and enabling nations and people to improve their quality of life without compromising that of future generations. UNEP, which is headquartered in Nairobi, Kenya, marked its first 30 years of service in 2002.

In parallel, UNEP administers several multilateral environmental agreements including the Vienna Convention's Montreal Protocol on Substances that Deplete the Ozone Layer, the Convention on International Trade in Endangered Species of Wild Fauna and Flora, the Basel Convention on the Control of Transboundary Movements of Hazardous Wastes and their Disposal, the Convention on Prior Informed Consent Procedure for Certain Hazardous Chemicals and Pesticides in International Trade (Rotterdam Convention, PIC) and the Cartagena Protocol on Biosafety to the Convention on Biological Diversity as well as the Stockholm Convention on Persistent Organic Pollutants.[36]

References

1. Pollution, Available at https://en.wikipedia.org/wiki/Pollution
2. http://www.uccee.org/Environmental_Pollution.html
3. Pollution Effects on Humans, Animals, Plants and the Environment, Available at http://www.tropical-rainforest-animals.com/pollution-effects.html
4. http://www.conserve-energy-future.com/PollutionTypes.php

5. Ian W.H. Parry (2002), Are Tradable Emissions Permits a Good Idea?, Available at http://www.rff.org/files/sharepoint/WorkImages/Download/RFF-IB-02-33.pdf
6. Regulatory and Non-Regulatory Approaches to Pollution Control, Available at http://yosemite.epa.gov/ee/epa/eerm.nsf/vwAN/EE-0568-04.pdf/$file/EE-0568-04.pdf
7. http://www.bcu.gub.uy/Comunicaciones/Jornadas%20de%20Economa/iees03j3601010.pdf
8. Ian W.H. Parry, Hilary Sigman, Margaret Walls, and Roberton C. Williams, The Incidence of Pollution Control Policies, Available at http://www.rff.org/files/sharepoint/WorkImages /Download/RFF-DP-05-24.pdf
9. Task Force for the Implementation of the Environmental Action Programme for Central and Eastern Europe (EAP), Available at http://inece.org/oecdtmp/cd/en/docs/regional/use_economic_instruments_en.pdf
10. Duncan Austin, Economic Instruments for Pollution Control and Prevention – A Brief Overview, Available at http://pdf.wri.org/incentives_austin.pdf
11. http://www.bcu.gub.uy/Comunicaciones/Jornadas %20de%20Economa/iees03j3601010.pdf
12. Command and control regulation, Available at http://www.eoearth.org/view/article/151316/
13. Command and Control regulation, Available at http://www.env-econ.net/2006/11/command_and_con.html
14. http://yosemite.epa.gov/ee/epa/eed.nsf/fa6512c6e51c4a208525766200639df2/9b6ed 59f910a89ea85257746 000aff58!OpenDocument
15. Uncertainty and the Choice of Pollution Control Instruments, Available at http://citeseerx.ist.psu.edu/viewdoc/download? doi=10.1.1.335.6550&rep=rep1&type=pdf
16. Duncan Austin, Economic Instruments for Pollution Control and Prevention – A Brief Overview, Available at http://pdf.wri.org/incentives_austin.pdf
17. Winston Harrington and Richard D. Morgenstern, Economic Incentives versus Command and Control, Available at http://www.rff.org/files/sharepoint/WorkImages/Download/RFF_Resources_152_ecoincentives.pdf
18. 1 Sarah West and Ann Wolverton, Market-Based Policies for Pollution Control in Latin America, Available at http://yosemite.epa.gov/EE/epa/eed.nsf/54e92d0d1f202a 6885256e46007b104c/0a4498b6edb8f7 bd85256d0100601dfd/$FILE/2003-01.pdf
19. http://ageconsearch.umn.edu/bitstream/139637/2/DiFalco.pdf
20. Integrating Market Based Instruments for Pollution Control - Strategic Option for Enhancing Competitiveness within Energy Industry, Available at http://www.management.ase.ro/reveconomia/2011-2/12.pdf
21. A. Denny Ellrerman, A Note on Tradeable Permits, Environmental and Resource Economics (2005) 31: 123–131, see http://web.mit.edu/ceepr/www/publications/reprints/Reprint_175_WC.pdf
22. Jessica Coria and Thomas Sterner, Tradable Permits in Developing Countries: Evidence from Air Pollution in Santiago, Chile, Available at http://www.rff.org/files/sharepoint/WorkImages/Download/RFF-DP-08-51.pdf
23. Duncan Austin, Economic Instruments for Pollution Control and Prevention – A Brief Overview, Available at http://pdf.wri.org/incentives_austin.pdf
24. Tom Tietenberg, Tradable Permits in Principle and Practice, Available at http://web.mit.edu/ckolstad/www/TT_SBW.pdf

25. Emissions trading, Available at https://en.wikipedia.org/wiki/Emissions_trading
26. What is an emission trading? Available at http://www.theguardian.com/environment/2011/jul/05/what-is-emissions-trading
27. Tradable permit system, Available at http://fcm.sgrc.selkirk.ca/carbon-economy/tradable-permit-system/
28. Tom Tietenberg, Tradable Permits and the Control of Air Pollution in the United States, Available at http://personal.colby.edu/personal/t/thtieten/permits.pdf
29. Raquel, Jurado & A. Carina Garcia, Tradable Emission Permits, Available at http://www.ecosys.com/spec/ecosys/download/UNIFR%202010/rapports/TEPs_3.pdf
30. Pigovian tax, Available at https://en.wikipedia.org/wiki/Pigovian_tax
31. http://web.mit.edu/10.391J/www/proceedings/Pollution_ Roth2001.pdf
32. Sarah West and Ann Wolverton, Market-Based Policies for Pollution Control in Latin America, Available at http://yosemite. epa.gov/EE/epa/eed.nsf/54e92d0d1f202a6885256e 46007b104c/0a4498b6edb8f7bd85256d0100601dfd/$FILE/2003-01.pdf
33. Lawrence H. Goulder and Ian W.H. Parry, Instrument Choice in Environmental Policy, Available at http://web.stanford.edu/~goulder/Papers/Published%20Papers/Goulder-Parry%20Instrument%20Choice%20(REEP)%20Paper%20-%20Final.pdf
34. Allen Blackman and Winston Harrington (1999), The Use of Economic Incentives in Developing Countries: Lessons from International Experience with Industrial Air Pollution, Available at http://www.rff.org/files/sharepoint/WorkImages/Download/RFF-DP-99-39.pdf
35. http://www.unep.ch/etb/publication/EconInst/econInstruOppChnaFin.pdf

16

Environmental Laws and Regulations

"Smog is affecting larger parts of China, and environmental pollution has become a major problem, which is nature's red-light warning against the model of inefficient and blind development."

–Li Keqiang

Environmental law is a collective term describing the network of treaties, statutes, regulations, and common and customary laws addressing the effects of human activity on the natural environment. Environmental impact assessment is the formal process used to predict the environmental consequences (positive or negative) of a plan, policy, programme, or project prior to the decision to move forward with the proposed action. Air quality laws govern the emission of air pollutants into the atmosphere. Water quality laws govern the release of pollutants into water resources, including surface water, ground water, and stored drinking water. Waste management laws govern the transport, treatment, storage, and disposal of all manner of waste, including municipal solid waste, hazardous waste, and nuclear waste, among many other types.

Environmental cleanup laws govern the removal of pollution or contaminants from environmental media such as soil, sediment, surface water, or ground water. Chemical safety laws govern the use of chemicals in human activities, particularly man-made chemicals in modern industrial applications. Water resources laws govern the ownership and use of water resources, including surface water and ground water. Mineral resource laws cover several basic topics, including the ownership of the mineral resource and who can work them. Forestry laws govern activities in designated forest lands, most commonly with respect to forest management and timber harvesting. Wildlife laws govern the potential impact of human activity on wild animals, whether directly on individuals or populations, or indirectly via habitat degradation. Fish and game laws regulate the right to pursue and take or kill certain kinds of fish and wild animal. Environmental law has developed in response to emerging awareness of and concern over issues impacting the entire world (wikipedia).[1]

United States Environmental Law[2]

United States environmental law concerns legal standards to protect human health and improve the natural environment of the United States. The broad category of "environmental law" may be broken down into a number of more specific regulatory subjects. The United States Congress has enacted federal statutes intended to address pollution control and remediation, including for example the Clean Air Act (air pollution), the Clean Water Act (water pollution), and the Comprehensive Environmental Response, Compensation, and Liability Act. There are also federal laws governing natural resources use and biodiversity which are strongly influenced by environmental principles, including the Endangered Species Act, National Forest Management Act, and Coastal Zone Management Act.

The Clean Air Act is a United States federal law designed to control air pollution on a national level. It is one of the United States' first and most influential modern environmental laws, and one of the most comprehensive air quality laws in the world. The 1955 Air Pollution Control Act was the first US federal legislation that pertained to air pollution; it also provided funds for federal government research of air pollution. Major amendments to the law, requiring regulatory controls for air pollution, passed in 1970, 1977 and 1990. The 1990 amendments addressed acid rain, ozone depletion, and toxic air pollution, established a national permits programme for stationary sources, and increased enforcement authority. The Act authorised development of emission standards for stationary sources, but not mobile sources of air pollution.[3]

The Clean Water Act (CWA) is the primary federal law in the United States governing water pollution. The Clean Water Act does not directly address groundwater contamination. Groundwater protection provisions are included in the Safe Drinking Water Act, Resource Conservation and Recovery Act, and the Superfund act. The 1972 Act introduced the National Pollutant Discharge Elimination System (NPDES), which is a permit system for regulating point sources of pollution. Point sources may not discharge pollutants to surface waters without a permit from the National Pollutant Discharge Elimination System (NPDES). The 1972 CWA created a new requirement for technology-based standards for point source discharges. According to water quality standard regulations, states and Indian tribes are required to specify appropriate water uses. Water quality standards consist of an anti-degradation policy that requires states and tribes to establish a three-tiered anti-degradation programme. Agricultural storm water discharges and irrigation return flows were specifically exempted from permit requirements.[4]

Comprehensive Environmental Response, Compensation, and Liability Act of 1980 (CERCLA) is a United States federal law designed to clean up sites contaminated with hazardous substances as well as broadly defined "pollutants or contaminants". CERCLA's broad authority to clean up releases or threatened releases of hazardous substances that may endanger public health or welfare or the (natural) environment was given primarily to the Environmental Protection Agency (EPA) and to states. CERCLA was enacted by Congress in 1980 in response to the threat of hazardous waste sites, typified by the Love Canal disaster in New York, and the Valley of the Drums in Kentucky.[5]

The Endangered Species Act of 1973 is one of the few dozens of United States environmental laws passed in the 1970s. The ESA was signed into law by President Richard Nixon on December 28, 1973; it was designed to protect critically imperiled species from extinction as a "consequence of economic growth and development untempered by adequate concern and conservation." The ESA's primary goal is to prevent the extinction of imperiled plant and animal life, and secondly, to recover and maintain those populations by removing or lessening threats to their survival. The provision of the law in Section 4 that establishes critical habitat is a regulatory link between habitat protection and recovery goals, requiring the identification and protection of all lands, water and air necessary to recover endangered species. As habitat loss is the primary threat to most imperiled species, the Endangered Species Act of 1973 allowed the Fish and Wildlife Service (FWS) and National Marine Fisheries Service to designate specific areas as protected "critical habitat" zones. Section 6 of the Endangered Species Act provided funding for development of programmes for management of threatened and endangered species by state wildlife agencies.[6]

The National Forest Management Act (NFMA) of 1976 is a United States federal law that is the primary statute governing the administration of national forests. NFMA changed forest planning by obliging the Forest Service to use a systematic and interdisciplinary approach to resource management. It also provided for public involvement in preparing and revising forest plans. NFMA has spawned lawsuits regarding the degree of involvement required by both the forest service and the public.[7]

The Coastal Zone Management Act of 1972 is an Act of Congress passed in 1972 to encourage coastal states to develop and implement coastal zone management plans. It showed that the United States Congress "recognised the importance of meeting the challenge of continued growth in the coastal zone". The key goals of the National CZM programme include: "protecting natural resources, managing development in high hazard areas, giving development priority to coastal-dependent uses, providing public access for recreation, coordinating state and federal actions". The National Estuarine Research Reserve System is the second programmes established by the Coastal Zone Management Act of 1972 and is also administered by the National Oceanic and Atmospheric Administration.[8]

Environment Laws in India

Accordingly, Indian Parliament inserted two Articles, i.e., 48A and 51A in the Constitution of India in 1976, three Article 48A of the Constitution rightly directs that the State shall endeavour to protect and improve the environment and safeguard forests and wildlife of the country. Similarly, clause (g) of Article 51A imposes a duty on every citizen of India, to protect and improve the natural environment including forests, lakes, river, and wildlife and to have compassion for living creatures. The cumulative effect of Articles 48A and 51A (g) seems to be that the 'State' as well as the 'citizens' both are now under constitutional obligation to conserve, perceive, protect and improve the environment.[9] The different legislations enacted in India exclusively for environment protection are:

1. The Water (Prevention and Control of Pollution) Act, 1974

The Water (Prevention and Control of Pollution) Act was enacted in 1974 to provide for the prevention and control of water pollution, and for the maintaining or restoring of wholesomeness of water in the country. The Act was amended in 1988. The Water (Prevention and Control of Pollution) Cess Act was enacted in 1977, to provide for the levy and collection of a cess on water consumed by persons operating and carrying on certain types of industrial activities. This cess is collected with a view to augment the resources of the Central Board and the State Boards for the prevention and control of water pollution constituted under the Water (Prevention and Control of Pollution) Act, 1974. The Act was last amended in 2003.[10]

2. The Water (Prevention and Control of Pollution) Cess Act, 1977

The Water (Prevention and Control of Pollution) Cess Act, 1977 aims to provide levy and collection of a cess on water consumed by persons carrying certain industries and local authorities to augment the resources of the Central Board and the State Boards constituted for the prevention and control of water pollution. The object is to realise money from those whose activities lead to pollution and who must bear the expenses of the maintaining and running of such Boards.[11]

3. The Air (Prevention and Control of Pollution) Act, 1981

The Air (Prevention and Control of Pollution) Act, 1981 is an Act of the Parliament of India to control and prevent air pollution. It was amended in 1987. It is an Act to provide for the prevention, control and abatement of air pollution, for the establishment, with a view to carrying out the aforesaid purposes, of Boards, for conferring on and assigning to such Boards powers and functions relating thereto and for matters connecting therewith. The Air Act is implemented by the Central and State Governments and the Central and State Boards. Over the past few years, the implementing agencies have experienced some administrative and practical difficulties in effectively implementing the provisions of this Act and have brought these to the notice of Government.[12]

4. The Environment (Protection) Act, 1986

Environment Protection Act, 1986 is an Act of the Parliament of India. In the wake of the Bhopal Tragedy, the Government of India enacted the Environment Protection Act of 1986 under Article 253 of the Constitution. Passed in March 1986, it came into force on 19th November 1986. The purpose of the Act is to implement the decisions of the United Nations Conference on the Human Environments they relate to the protection and improvement of the human environment and the prevention of hazards to human beings, other living creatures, plants and property. The objectives of this Act are: (a) To co-ordinate the activities of the various regulatory agencies already in existence; (b) Creation of an authority or authorities with adequate powers for environmental protection; (c) Regulation of discharge of environmental pollutants and handling of hazardous substance; and (d) Speedy response in the event of accidents threatening environment and punishment to those who endanger human environment, safety and health.[13]

5. The Forest (Conservation) Act, 1980

The Parliament has enacted the Forest (Conservation) Act, 1980, to check further deforestation and conserve forests and to provide for matters connected therewith or ancillary or incidental thereto. The Act was enacted with the twin objectives under Section 2 of restricting the use of forest land for non--forest purposes, and preventing the de-reservation of forests that have been reserved under the Indian Forest Act, 1927. In 1988 the Act was further amended to include two new provisions under Section 2, where it sought to restrict leasing of forest land to private individuals, authority, corporations not owned by the government, and to prevent clear felling of naturally grown trees. The Act empowers the Central Government to constitute a committee to advise the government with a grant of approval under Section 2, as also on any other matter connected with the conservation of forest and referred to it by the Central Government. The Act provides for the punishment of imprisonment, extendable to fifteen days for the contravention of the provisions of the Act.[14]

6. The Wildlife Protection Act, 1972

The Wildlife Protection Act, 1972 is an Act of the Parliament of India enacted for protection of plants and animal species. The Act provides for the protection of wild animals, birds and plants; and for matters connected therewith or ancillary or incidental thereto. It extends to the whole of India, except the State of Jammu and Kashmir which has its own Wildlife Act.

7. The Public Liability Insurance Act, 1991

The Public Liability Act, 1991 was made effective from 01.04.1991 to provide through insurance, immediate relief, by you who control or handle hazardous chemicals, to persons affected due to accident due to handling of such hazardous substances on 'No Fault Liability' basis. The Policy covers your statutory liability arising out of accidents occurring during the currency of the Policy due to handling hazardous substances as provided in the Public Liability Insurance Act 1991 and the Rules framed thereunder.[15]

8. The National Environment Tribunal Act, 1995

National Environment Tribunal Act, 1995 consists of 31 Sections to fulfill the broad objectives laid under the Act. As the Act enacted with a broad objective to provide compensation to person who got injured, the owner has to pay compensation under Section 3, where there been damage caused to the environment and the death or injury has been resulted due to the accident. The person can make application with respect to claim for compensation to the Tribunal under provision as specified under Section 4(1), Tribunal while dealing with the application of compensation as specified in the provisions of Act shall exercise the same jurisdiction and authority as that of matters as specified in Public Liability Insurance Act, 1991.[16]

9. The National Environment Appellate Authority Act, 1997

The National Environment Appellate Authority was set up by the Ministry of Environment and Forests to address cases in which environment clearances are required in certain restricted areas. It was established by the National Environment Appellate

Authority Act 1997 to hear appeals with respect to restriction of areas in which any industries, operations or processes or class of industries, operations or processes shall or shall not be carried out, subject to certain safeguards under the Environment (Protection) Act, 1986. The Authority shall become defunct and the Act shall stand repealed upon the enactment of the National Green Tribunal Bill 2009 currently pending in Parliament.[17]

References

1. Environmental law, Available at https://en.wikipedia.org/wiki/Environmental_law
2. United States environmental law, Available at https://en.wikipedia.org/wiki/United_States_environmental_law
3. Clean Air Act (United States), Available at https://en.wikipedia.org/wiki/Clean_Air_Act_(United_States)
4. Clean Water Act, Available at https://en.wikipedia.org/wiki/Clean_Water_Act
5. Superfund, Available at https://en.wikipedia.org/wiki/Superfund
6. Endangered Species Act, Available at https://en.wikipedia.org/wiki/Endangered_Species_Act
7. National Forest Management Act (NFMA) of 1976, Available at https://en.wikipedia.org/wiki/National_Forest_ Management_ Act_of_1976.
8. Coastal Zone Management Act of 1972, Available at https://en.wikipedia.org/wiki/Coastal_Zone_Management_Act
9. V.K. Aggarwal, Environmental Laws in India: Challenges for Enforcement, Available at http://dl4a.org/uploads/pdf/environmental%20law.pdf
10. http://www.environmentallawsofindia.com/the-environment-definitions-and-acts.html
11. From official website of Ministry of Environment, Forest and Climate Change, Government of India, Available at http://envfor.nic.in/division/water-pollution
12. V.K. Aggarwal, Environmental Laws in India: Challenges for Enforcement, Available at http://dl4a.org/uploads/pdf/environmental%20law.pdf
13. http://nbaindia.org/uploaded/Biodiversityindia/Legal/23.%20Air%20(Prevention%20and%20control%20of%20Pollution)%20Act%201981.pdf
14. Environment Protection Act, 1986, Available at https://en.wikipedia.org/wiki/Environment_Protection_Act,_1986
15. http://www.vanashakti.in/resources_law2.html
16. Public Liability Act Policy, Available at http://www.rahejaqbe.com/Corporate/General-Liability/Public-Liability-Act-Policy/Insurance.html
17. The National Environment Tribunal Act, 1995, Detailed available at http://lawyerslaw.org/the-national-environment-tribunal-act-1995/
18. http://envfor.nic.in/rules-regulations/national-environment-appellate-authority

17

Sustainable Development

"Sustainable development is the pathway to the future we want for all. It offers a framework to generate economic growth, achieve social justice, exercise environmental stewardship and strengthen governance." **-Ban Ki-moon**

In the last half of the twentieth century, four key themes emerged from the collective concerns and aspirations of the world's peoples: peace, freedom, development, and environment. The peace that was thought to be secured in the post-world war of 1945 was immediately threatened by the nuclear arms race.[1] Components of a healthy environment, such as clean air and water, are considered public goods in that they are non-rivalrous and non-excludable. It is up to the public sector to maintain the provision of these goods and services. The precautionary principle establishes that "where there are threats of serious or irreversible damage; lack of full scientific certainty shall not be used as a reason for postponing cost-effective measure to prevent environmental degradation".[2]

Development involves a progressive transformation of economy and society. A development path that is sustainable in a physical sense could theoretically be pursued even in a rigid social and political setting. The satisfaction of human needs and aspirations are the major objective of development. Settled agriculture, the diversion of water courses, the extraction of minerals, the emission of heat and noxious gases into the atmosphere, commercial forests, and genetic manipulation are all examples of human intervention in natural systems during the course of development. Economic growth and development obviously involve changes in the physical ecosystem. Every ecosystem everywhere cannot be preserved intact.[3]

In November 1996, an international group of measurement practitioners and researchers from five continents came together at the Rockefeller Foundation's Study and Conference Centre in Bellagio, Italy to review progress to date and to synthesise insights from practical ongoing efforts.[4]

Meaning

Sustainable development has been defined in many ways, but the most frequently quoted definition is from *'Our Common Future'*, also known as the Brundtland Report:*"Sustainable development is development that meets the needs of the present without compromising the ability of future generations to meet their own needs. It contains within it two key concepts:* (a) *the concept of needs, in particular the essential needs of the world's poor, to which overriding priority should be given; and* (b) *the idea of limitations imposed by the state of technology and social organisation on the environment's ability to meet present and future needs."*[5] It is development that meets the needs of the present without compromising the ability of future generations to meet their own need.

Sustainable development is defined in the National Environmental Management Act as "the integration of social, economic and environmental factors into planning, implementation and decision-making so as to ensure that development serves present and future generations."[6] It constantly seeks to achieve social and economic progress in ways that will not exhaust the earth's finite natural resources. The needs of the world today are real and immediate, yet it's necessary to develop ways to meet these needs that do not disregard the future. Sustainable development promotes the idea that social, environmental, and economic progresses are all attainable within the limits of our earth's natural resources. Sustainable development approaches everything in the world as being connected through space, time and quality of life.[7]

Applied of Sustainability[8]

The Sustainable Development Goals are an intergovernmental set of aspiration Goals with 169 targets. The Goals are contained in paragraph 51 United Nations Resolution A/RES/70/1 of 25 September 2015. The history of the SDGs can be traced to 1972 when governments met under the auspices of the United Nations Human and Environment Conference, to consider the rights of the human family to a healthy and productive environment. People concerned about sustainable development suggest that meeting the needs of the future depends on how well we balance social, economic, and environmental objectives—or needs—when making decisions today.[9]

The Official Agenda for Sustainable Development adopted on 25 September 2015 has 92 paragraphs, with the main paragraph (51) outlining the 17 Sustainable Development Goals and its associated 169 targets. This included the following goals:

1. End poverty in all its forms every where (https://en.wikipedia.org/wiki/Sustainable_Development_Goals - cite_note-21)
2. End hunger, achieve food security and improved nutrition and promote sustainable agriculture.
3. Ensure healthy lives and promote well-being for all at all ages.
4. Ensure inclusive and equitable quality education and promote lifelong learning opportunities for all.
5. Achieve gender equality and empower all women and girls.
6. Ensure availability and sustainable management of water and sanitation for all (https://en.wikipedia.org/wiki/Sustainable_Development_Goals - cite_note-26)
7. Ensure access to affordable, reliable, sustainable and modern energy for all.
8. Promote sustained, inclusive and sustainable economic growth, full and productive employment and decent work for all.
9. Build resilient infrastructure, promote inclusive and sustainable industrialisation and foster innovation.
10. Reduce inequality within and among countries.

11. Make cities and human settlements inclusive, safe, resilient and sustainable.
12. Ensure sustainable consumption and production patterns.
13. Take urgent action to combat climate change and its impacts.
14. Conserve and sustainably use the oceans, seas and marine resources for sustainable development.
15. Protect, restore and promote sustainable use of terrestrial ecosystems, sustainably manage forests, combat desertification, and halt and reverse land degradation and halt biodiversity loss.
16. Promote peaceful and inclusive societies for sustainable development, provide access to justice for all and build effective, accountable and inclusive institutions at all levels.
17. Strengthen the means of implementation and revitalise the global partnership for sustainable development.

Importance

Sustainable development stands for meeting the needs of present generations without jeopardizing the ability of futures generations to meet their own needs – in other words, a better quality of life for everyone, now and for generations to come. It offers a vision of progress that integrates immediate and longer-term objectives, local and global action, and regards social, economic and environmental issues as inseparable and interdependent components of human progress.[10] It implies economic growth together with the protection of environmental quality, each reinforcing the other. Sustainable Development, thus, is maintaining a balance between the human need to improve lifestyles and feeling of well-being on one hand, and preserving natural resources and ecosystems, on which we and future generations depend.

Poverty and a degraded environment are closely inter-related, especially where people depend for their livelihoods primarily on the natural resource base of their immediate environment. While conventional economic development leads to the elimination of several traditional occupations, the process of sustainable development, guided by the need to protect and conserve the environment, leads to the creation of new jobs and of opportunities for the reorientation of traditional skills to new occupations.[11] Economists have used the term sustainable development in an attempt to clarify the balance between economic growths on the one hand and conservation and protection of environment on the other.[12]

A local sustainable development process must enable a community to meet the needs of the present without compromising the ability of future generations to meet their own needs. Although the success of a sustainable development process depends, above all, on the quality of the process by which it is realised, its content is even more important.

Dimensions

Sustainable development does not focus solely on environmental issues. More broadly, it encompasses the three general policy areas namely, economy, environment and society. Achieving SD requires more effective, open, and productive association among the people themselves. Models help us gather, share, and analyse information; they help coordinating work; and educate and train professionals, policy-makers, and the public in general. Triangle of environmental (conservation), economic (growth), and social (equity) dimensions is modelled as three pillars.[13]

There has generally been recognition of three aspects of sustainable development:

- **Economic:** An economically sustainable system must be able to produce goods and services on a continuing basis, to maintain manageable levels of government and external debt, and to avoid extreme sectoral imbalances which damage agricultural or industrial production.
- **Environmental:** An environmentally sustainable system must maintain a stable resource base, avoiding over-exploitation of renewable resource systems or environmental sink functions, and depleting non-renewable resources only to the extent that investment is made in adequate substitutes. This includes maintenance of biodiversity, atmospheric stability, and other ecosystem functions not ordinarily classed as economic resources.
- **Social:** A socially sustainable system must achieve distributional equity, adequate provision of social services

including health and education, gender equity, and political accountability and participation.[14]

Indicators

Traditional indicators such as unemployment rate or GDP growth, stockholder profits, asthma rates, and water quality measure changes in one part of a community as if they were entirely independent of the other parts. Its indicator on the other hand, reflect the reality that the three different segments are very tightly interconnected. The following are certain characteristics that all the SD indicators have in common: • Alert a problem before it gets too bad • Helps recognise what needs to be done to fix the problem • Build clarity and accountability • Reflect a sense of purpose • Illustrate relationships • Show trends.[15]

At the Sustainable Development Summit on 25 September, 2015, UN Member States will adopt the 2030 Agenda for Sustainable Development, which includes a set of 17 Sustainable Development Goals (SDGs) to end poverty, fight inequality and injustice, and tackle climate change by 2030. The SDGs, otherwise known as the Global Goals, build on the Millennium Development Goals (MDGs), eight anti-poverty targets that the world committed to achieving by 2015. The MDGs, adopted in 2000, aimed at an array of issues that included slashing poverty, hunger, disease, gender inequality, and access to water and sanitation.[16]

Criteria

Achieving a more sustainable lifestyle necessitates making the best use of scarce resources including land, while providing for a good quality of life. This may result in higher densities for new developments.[17] A sustainable development process must, at a minimum, • be founded on the principles of sustainable development • guarantee a process of continuous improvement • be capable of succeeding, on the basis of defined success factors.

The criteria have been classified into three groups: Respect for the fundamental principles of sustainable development is vital to any sustainable development process. These principles are what impart meaning; without them, the entire process could amount to nothing more than a quality management process that bears no relation to sustainable development. The criteria that contribute to the quality of the continuous improvement process allow a sustainable development process to be evolutionary. A sustainable development process needs not necessarily satisfy all of the criteria. Each process will take a different approach, depending on the context, and view such criteria above all as guiding lights in the quest for continuous improvement.[18]

Indian Perspectives

India is an entire world on its own. Its combination of spiritual depth, unparalleled physical beauty, and cultural diversity makes the country one of the most alluring destinations on the planet. India's development is another story. While the economy is growing rapidly, almost 800 million citizens (79.9 per cent) still live on less than US$2 each day. Grassroots and government efforts are making great strides to rectify poverty-related issues; however, the severity of the problem is astonishing. Water tables throughout the country have collapsed, public education is floundering, and HIV infects more people than any other nation in the world.[19]

Almost all ministries of the Government of India are involved in decision-making for sustainable development. However, major participation is by the Ministries of External Affairs, Environment and Forests, Agriculture, Water Resources, Finance, Industries, Rural Development, Commerce, Non Conventional Energy Sources, Finance and the Planning Commission. Government of India has have formulated legislation, regulations and policy instruments to address matters concerning cooperation for Sustainable Development at sub-regional, regional and International level. There are legislation regulations and policy instruments framed to fulfil obligation under the agreements signed under the International Conferences, MEAs, etc. India believes that environmentally harmful processes should be stopped and that over-exploitation of non-renewable resources should be controlled.[20]

Role of United Nations

In 1980, the International Union for the Conservation of Nature published a world conservation strategy that included one of the first references to sustainable development as a global priority. Two years later, the United Nations World Charter for

Nature raised five principles of conservation by which human conduct affecting nature is to be guided and judged. In 1987, the United Nations World Commission on Environment and Development released the report *Our Common Future*, commonly called the Brundtland Report. In 1992, the UN Conference on Environment and Development published in 1992 the Earth Charter, which outlines the building of a just, sustainable, and peaceful global society in the twenty-first century. Under the principles of the United Nations Charter the Millennium Declaration identified principles and treaties on sustainable development.[21]

Conclusion

At the United Nations Sustainable Development Summit on 25 September 2015, world leaders adopted the 2030 Agenda for Sustainable Development, which includes a set of 17 Sustainable Development Goals to end poverty, fight inequality and injustice, and tackle climate change by 2030. All 17 Sustainable Development Goals are connected to UNDP's Strategic Plan focus areas: development, democratic governance and peace building, and climate and disaster resilience. SDGs Number 1 on poverty, Number 10 on inequality and Number 16 on governance are particularly central to UNDP's current work and long-term plans.[22]

References

1. What is sustainable development, Available at http://www.hks.harvard.edu/sustsci/ists/docs/whatisSD_ env_kates_0504.pdf
2. Rachel Emas, The Concept of Sustainable Development: Definition and Defining Principles, https://sustainabledevelopment.un.org/content/documents/5839GSDR%202015_SD_concept_definiton_rev.pdf
3. Our Common Future, Chapter 2: Towards Sustainable Development, http://www.un-documents.net/ocf-02.htm
4. https://www.iisd.org/pdf/bellagio.pdf
5. https://www.iisd.org/sd/
6. http://www.energy.gov.za/files/esources/kyoto/Web%20info/Annex%203%20SA%20Sustainable %20Development%20Criteria.pdf
7. http://www.sustainabledevelopmentinfo.com/the-definition-of-sustainable-development/
8. Sustainable Development Goals (2015), Available at https://en.wikipedia.org/wiki/Sustainable_Development_Goals
9. http://www.worldbank.org/depweb/english/sd.html
10. http://ec.europa.eu/environment/eussd/
11. Sustainable Development in India: Perspectives, http://www.moef.nic.in/divisions/ic/wssd/doc4/consul_book_persp.pdf

12. Supriya Guru, Importance of Sustainable Development for the Economic Growth of a Country.
13. Sustainable Development: An Introduction, http://www.sayen.org/volume-i.pdf
14. Jonathan M. Harris (2000), Basic Principles of Sustainable Development, http://www.ase.tufts.edu/gdae/publications/working_papers/Sustainable %20Development.PDF
15. Sustainable Development: An Introduction, http://www.sayen.org/volume-i.pdf
16. http://www.undp.org/content/india/en/home/mdgoverview/post-2015-development-agenda.html
17. Guidelines for Sustainable Development, http://www.dlrcoco.ie/aboutus/councildepartments/planning/downloadit/guidelinesforsustainable development/criteriaforsustainabledevelopment/
18. Quality criteria for a sustainable development process, file:///C:/Users/sukanta/Downloads/quality_en.pdf
19. http://www.fsdinternational.org/country/india
20. Economic aspects of sustainable development of India, Available at http://www.un.org/esa/agenda21/natlinfo/countr/india/eco.htm
21. Sustainable development, Available at https://en.wikipedia.org/wiki/Sustainable_development
22. http://www.undp.org/content/undp/en/home/mdgoverview/post-2015-development-agenda.html

18

Renewable Energy

"Cities are the origins of global warming, impact on the environment, health, pollution, disease, finance, economies, energy are all problems that are confronted by having cities. That's where they - all these problems come from."

- Geoffrey West

Energy is the prime mover of economic growth, and is vital to sustaining a modern economy and society. Future economic growth significantly depends on the long-term availability of energy from sources that are affordable, accessible and secure. India's conventional energy reserves are limited and we must develop all available and economic alternatives. Simultaneously, a major stress must be laid on energy efficiency and conservation, with particular emphasis on efficiency of electricity generation, transmission, distribution and end-use. Energy efficiency is often viewed as a resource option like coal, oil or natural gas. It provides additional economic value by preserving the resource base and reducing pollution.

The proven global coal reserve was estimated to be 9,84,453 million tonnes by the end of 2003. The USA has the largest share of the global reserve (25.4 per cent) followed by Russia (15.9), China (11.6 per cent). India was fourth in the list with 8.6 per cent. The proven global oil reserve was estimated to be 1147 billion barrels by the end of 2003. Saudi Arabia had the largest share of the reserve with almost 23 per cent. India faces formidable challenges in meeting its energy needs and in providing adequate energy of desired quality in various forms in a sustainable manner and at competitive prices.[1]

Meaning

Renewable energy is generally defined as energy that comes from resources which are naturally replenished on a human timescale, such as sunlight, wind, rain, tides, waves, and geothermal heat. Renewable energy resources exist over wide geographical areas, in contrast to other energy sources, which are concentrated in a limited number of countries. Rapid deployment of renewable energy and energy efficiency is resulting in significant energy security, climate change mitigation, and economic benefits. Renewable energy resources and significant opportunities for energy efficiency exist over wide geographical areas, in contrast to other energy sources, which are concentrated in a limited number of countries.[2]

The key drivers for renewable energy are the following: (a) The demand-supply gap, especially as population increases; (b) A large untapped potential; (c) Concern for the environment; (d) The need to strengthen India's energy security; (e) Pressure on high-emission industry sectors from their shareholders; and (f) A viable solution for rural electrification.[3]

Indian Perspectives

India has a vast supply of renewable energy resources, and it has one of the largest programmes in the world for deploying renewable energy products and systems. Since the 1980's, and still currently, India has encountered a negative balance in overall energy consumption and production. India is a large consumer of coal, which makes up more than 57 per cent of its total consumption. Nearly 85 per cent of the villages have been electrified, and there is a nationwide grid for the transmission and distribution of power. In India, small hydro is the most utilised renewable energy source for energy production. Solar energy has several applications: photovoltaic cells are placed on the roof top of houses or commercial buildings, and collectors such as mirrors or parabolic dishes that can move and track the sun throughout the day are also used.

India is surpassed only by Germany as one of the world's fastest growing markets for wind energy. The ten machines near Okha in the province of Gujarat were some of the first wind turbines installed in India. India is very rich in biomass. It has a potential of 19,500 MW (3,500 MW from bagasse-based cogeneration and 16,000 MW from surplus biomass). Currently, India has 537 MW commissioned and 536 MW under construction. The most successful forms of biomass are sugar cane bagasse in agriculture, pulp and paper residues in forestry and manure in livestock residues.[4]

Renewable energy in India comes under the purview of the Ministry of New and Renewable Energy. India was the first country in the world to set up a ministry of non-conventional energy resources, in early 1980s. The development of wind power in India began in the 1990s, and has significantly increased in the last few years. Although a relative newcomer to the wind industry compared with Denmark or the US, domestic policy support for wind power has led India to become the country with the fifth largest installed wind power capacity in the world.

The Indian Solar Loan Programme, supported by the United Nations Environment Programme has won the prestigious Energy Globe World award for sustainability for helping to establish a consumer financing programme for solar home power systems. The Jawaharlal Nehru National Solar Mission is a major initiative of the Government of India and State Governments to promote ecologically sustainable growth while addressing India's energy security challenges. The objective of the National Solar Mission is to establish India as a global leader in solar energy, by creating the policy conditions for its diffusion across the country as quickly as possible. The programme was inaugurated by Former Prime Minister of India, Dr Manmohan Singh on 11th January, 2010.[5]

Government-funded solar electricity in India was approximately 6.4 MW per year as of 2005. India is ranked number one in terms of solar electricity production per watt installed, with an insolation of 1,700 to 1,900 kilowatt hours per kilowatt peak (kWh/KWp). Gujarat has been a leader in solar power generation and contributes two-third of the 900 MW of photovoltaics in the country. The State of Gujarat has commissioned Asia's largest solar park at Charanka village. The park is already generating 2 MW solar powers out of its total planned capacity of 500 MW. With regard to solar energy production, Rajasthan is one of India's most solar-developed states. There its total photovoltaic capacity has passed 500 MW, having reached 510.25 MW by the end of the 2012-13 fiscal year. The Welspun Solar MP project, the largest solar power plant in India set up at a cost of Rs 1,100 crore on 305 hectares of land, will supply power at Rs 8.05 a kWh. The project of a 130 MW solar power plant at Bhagwanpur in Neemuch was launched by the previous Gujarat Chief Minister, Narendra Modi.[6]

Currently, on an average, the country is adding 1,000 MW of solar power annually. At this rate, 100,000 MW in six years looks farfetched even if one was to assume that India can match China which has added solar capacity at an ever increasing rate. Solar power may have got greater policy impetus after the National Democratic Alliance came to power but ratcheting up capacity at rates no country has done before is a tough task when seen from where India sits at present.[7]

The development of wind power in India began in the 1990s, and has significantly increased in the last few years. Suzlon, an Indian-owned company, emerged on the global scene in the past decade, and by 2006 had captured almost 7.7 per cent of market share in global wind turbine sales. Wind power accounts nearly 8.5 per cent of India's total installed power generation capacity and generated 28,214 million kWh in the fiscal year 2014-15 which is nearly 2.6 per cent of total electricity generation. Tamil Nadu's wind power capacity is around 35 per cent of India's total. Gujarat government's focus on tapping renewable energy has led to sharp rise in the wind power capacity in the last few years. Maharashtra is one of the prominent states considering the installation of wind power projects second to Tamil Nadu in India. Odisha a coastal state has higher potential for wind energy. The Kargil, Ladakh, Pakisthan occupied Gilgit and China occupied Aksai Chin regions of Jammu and Kashmir state are having lucrative wind energy potential up to 80 meters height. India is planning to enter in to offshore wind power, with a 100 MW demonstration plant located off the Gujarat coast.[8]

The government plans to rapidly accelerate wind energy generation, adding an ambitious 10,000 MW every year, or five times the total new capacity that came up in the last fiscal, as the Modi government takes steps to reduce India's dependence on costly energy imports. Wind energy, which had been overshadowed by solar projects in recent years, got a big boost as the government has restored key tax incentives that had helped India emerge as one of the top countries in the world in gene. With installed capacity of over 21,000 MW, India is fifth-largest wind power producer in the world after China, US, Germany and Spain. According to Centre for Wind Energy Technology, India has potential to install over one lakh mw of wind turbines.[9]

Bioenergy

Bioenergy is a form of renewable energy derived from biomass to generate electricity and heat or to produce liquid fuels for transport. It is any organic matter of recently living plant or animal origin. It is available in many forms such as agricultural products, forestry products, and municipal and other waste.[10] Biomass means all materials which come from living organisms. For instance, waste material of plants and animals, wood, agricultural wastes, dead parts of plants and animals. Bioenergy is a carbon-neutral and renewable energy source that's attracting research and development worldwide.[11]

It is the energy which is contained inside plants and animals. This can include organic matter of all kinds: plants, animals, or waste products from organic sources. It is the material derived from recently living organisms, which includes plants, animals and their byproducts.[12] It is any organic material which has stored sunlight in the form of chemical energy. Biomass can be converted to other usable forms of energy like methane gas or transportation fuels like ethanol and biodiesel.[13] It is cheap and readily available source of energy. If the trees are replaced, biomass can be a long-term, sustainable energy source.[14]

Conventional biofuel technologies include well-established processes that are already producing biofuels on a commercial scale. These biofuels, commonly referred to as first-generation, include sugar- and starch-based ethanol, oil-crop-based biodiesel and straight vegetable oil, as well as biogas derived through anaerobic digestion. Advanced biofuel technologies are conversion technologies which are still in the research and development (R&D), pilot or demonstration phase, commonly referred to as second or third-generation.[15]

One of the advantages of biomass fuel is that it is often a by-product, residue or waste-product of other processes, such as farming, animal husbandry and forestry. Biomass energy creates no harmful carbon dioxide emissions. Biomass products are abundant and renewable. It has developed as an alternate source of fuel for many homeowners and has helped them to reduce their dependency on fossil fuels. Another benefit of this energy is that it can take waste that is harmful to the environment and turn it into something useful.[16]

Geothermal Energy

Geothermal energy is thermal energy generated and stored in the Earth. Thermal energy is the energy that determines the temperature of matter. Earth's internal heat is thermal energy generated from radioactive decay and continual heat loss from Earth's formation. From hot springs, geothermal energy has been used for bathing since Paleolithic times and for space heating since ancient Roman times, but it is now better known for electricity generation.[17] Resources of geothermal energy range from the shallow ground to hot water and hot rock found a few miles beneath the Earth's surface, and down even deeper to the extremely high temperatures of molten rock called magma.[18] To harness this geothermal energy, two holes are dug deep into the earth and cold water is pumped through the first one and steam comes out through the second long pipe which helps in generating electricity.[19]

Energy created from geothermal power is safe, clean, simple, reliable and environment friendly as it is extracted from deep within the earth's surface. To get geothermal energy, requires installation of power plants, to get steam from deep within the earth and this require huge one time investment and require hiring a certified installer and skilled staff needs to be recruited and relocated to plant location[20].

Geothermal energy generally involves low running costs since it saves 80 per cent costs over fossil fuels and no fuel is used to generate the power. Dependence on fossil fuels decreases with the increase in the use of geothermal energy. Since ancient times, people having been using this source of energy for taking bath, heating homes, preparing food and today this is also used for direct heating of homes and offices. Being the renewable source of energy, geothermal energy has helped in reducing global warming and pollution.[21]

Solar Energy

Solar energy is radiant light and heat from the Sun harnessed using a range of ever-evolving technologies. Solar power is the conversion of sunlight into electricity, either directly using photovoltaics or indirectly using concentrated solar power.[22] Solar energy is derived from the sun's radiation. The sun is a powerful energy source. Solar energy is a truly renewable energy source. It can be harnessed in all areas of the world and is available everyday.[23] Solar power is now very clearly one of the most important solutions to the global warming crisis.[24]

Solar energy is becoming increasingly popular as the world takes notice of the burgeoning carbon emission problems that come with burning fossil fuels. Another advantage of using solar energy is that beyond initial installation and maintenance, solar energy is free.[25] It can be harnessed as a renewable energy power source. Renewable energy resources are energy sources that regenerate in a short amount of time, allowing them to be used over and over again.[26] The possibility of much greater energy security is a major advantage of solar power that many people are not aware of.[27] Solar cells make absolutely no noise at all. They do not make a single peep while extracting useful energy from the sun.[28]

Wind Energy

Wind energy is extracted from air flow using wind turbines or sails to produce mechanical or electrical energy. Windmills are used for their mechanical power, wind pumps for water pumping, and sails to propel ships. Winds are caused by the uneven heating of the atmosphere by the sun, the irregularities of the earth's surface, and rotation of the earth. The earth's surface is made of different types of land and water. These surfaces absorb the sun's heat at different rates; giving rise to the differences in temperature and subsequently to winds.[29] Wind is a form of solar energy and is a result of the uneven heating of the atmosphere by the sun, the irregularities of the earth's surface, and the rotation of the earth.[30]

Hydroelectricity

Wind power is very consistent from year to year but has significant variation over shorter time scales. It is, therefore, used in conjunction with other electric power sources to give a reliable supply. The first windmill used for the production of electricity was built in Scotland in July 1887 by Professor James Blyth of Anderson's College, Glasgow. Offshore wind power refers to the construction of wind farms in large bodies of water to generate electricity. These installations can utilise the more frequent and powerful winds that are available in these locations and have less aesthetic impact on the landscape than land-based projects. The environmental impact of wind power when compared to the environmental impacts of fossil fuels is relatively minor.[31]

Ocean Energy

Ocean energy is a term used to describe all forms of renewable energy derived from the sea[32]. It refers to the energy carried by ocean waves, tides, salinity, and ocean temperature differences. The movement of water in the world's oceans creates a vast store of kinetic energy, or energy in motion. The term marine energy encompasses both wave power i.e. power from surface waves, and tidal power i.e. obtained from the kinetic energy of large bodies of moving water.[33]

Tidal energy is energy generated from tidal movements. Tides contain both potential energy, related to the vertical fluctuations in sea level, and kinetic energy, related to the horizontal motion of the water column. Wave energy is generated by converting the energy of ocean waves into other forms of energy. It can be harnessed using a variety of different technologies, several of which are currently being trialled to find the most efficient way to generate electricity from wave energy.[34]

Ministry of New and Renewable Energy

It is a ministry of Government of India. The Ministry is mainly responsible for research and development, intellectual property protection, and international cooperation, promotion, and coordination in renewable energy sources such as wind power, small hydro, biogas, and solar power. The broad aim of the Ministry is to develop and deploy new and renewable energy for supplementing the energy requirements of India. The ministry is headquartered in Lodhi Road, New Delhi.[35]

References

1. Renewable Energy and Energy Efficiency Status in India (2007), http://local-renewables.iclei.org/fileadmin/template/projects/localrenewables/files/Local_Renewables/Publications/RE_EE_report_India_final_sm.pdf
2. https://en.wikipedia.org/wiki/Renewable_energy
3. Peter Meisen (2006), Overview of Renewable Energy Potential of India, http://www.geni.org/globalenergy/library/energytrends /currentusage/renewable/Renewable-Energy-Potential-for-India.pdf
4. Peter Meisen (2006), Overview of Renewable Energy Potential of India, http://www.geni.org/globalenergy/library/energy trends/currentusage/renewable/Renewable-Energy-Potential-for-India.pdf
5. Jawaharlal Nehru National Solar Mission, Available at https://en.wikipedia.org/wiki/Jawaharlal_ Nehru_ National_ Solar_Mission
6. Solar power in India, Available at https://en.wikipedia.org/wiki/Solar_power_in_India
7. Business Standard (October 8, 2015), India's renewable energy targets may be overambitious, http://www.business-standard.com/article/

economy-policy/india-s-renewable-energy-targets-may-be-overambitious-115100801272_1.html

8. Wind power in India, Available at https://en.wikipedia.org/wiki/Wind_power_in_India
9. Government aims to add 10,000 MW per year to lift wind energy sector. Read more at:http://economictimes. indiatimes.com/articleshow/40079023.cms? utm_source=contentofinterest&utm_medium=text&utm_campaign=cppst
10. http://arena.gov.au/about-renewable-energy/bioenergy/
11. https://www.originenergy.com.au/blog/about-energy/advantages-and-disadvantages-of-bioenergy.html
12. http://www.conserve-energy-future.com/Advantages_ Disadvantages_BiomassEnergy.php
13. Bioenergy, https://en.wikipedia.org/wiki/Bioenergy
14. http://www.bioenergy.org/information/advantages-disadvantages-biomass/
15. https://www.iea.org/topics/renewables/subtopics/bioenergy/
16. http://www.conserve-energy-future.com/Advantages_ Disadvantages_BiomassEnergy.php
17. Geothermal energy, https://en.wikipedia.org/wiki/Geothermal_energy
18. http://www.renewableenergyworld.com/geothermal-energy/tech.html
19. http://www.ianswer4u.com/2012/02/geothermal-energy-advantages-and.html#axzz3stVfIDpe
20. http://www.conserve-energy-future.com/Disadvantages_GeothermalEnergy.php
21. http://www.conserve-energy-future.com/Advantages_ Geothermal Energy.php
22. https://en.wikipedia.org/wiki/Solar_energy
23. http://www.greenmatch.co.uk/blog/2014/08/5-advantages-and-5-disadvantages-of-solar-energy
24. http://cleantechnica.com/2013/10/08/advantages-disadvantages-solar-power/
25. http://exploringgreentechnology.com/solar-energy/advantages-and-disadvantages-of-solar-energy/
26. http://study.com/academy/lesson/what-is-solar-power-uses-advantages-disadvantages.html
27. http://cleantechnica.com/2014/09/22/solar-energy-advantages-vs-disadvantages/
28. http://www.alternate-power.org/solar-power-advantages-and-disadvantages/
29. http://www.eai.in/ref/ae/win/win.htm
30. http://energy.gov/eere/wind/how-do-wind-turbines-work
31. Wind power, Available at https://en.wikipedia.org/wiki/Wind_power
32. http://arena.gov.au/about-renewable-energy/ocean-energy/
33. Marine energy, Available at https://en.wikipedia.org/wiki/Marine_energy
34. http://www.ga.gov.au/scientific-topics/energy/resources/other-renewable-energy-resources/ocean-energy
35. Ministry of New and Renewable Energy, Available at https://en.wikipedia.org/wiki/Ministry_of_New_and_ Renewable_Energy

19

Non-Renewable Energy

"Have we failed to slow global warming pollution in part because climate and environmental activists have been too polite and well behaved?" - **Jeff Goodell**

Energy consumption is the consumption of energy or power. World energy consumption refers to the total energy used by all of human civilisation. Institutions such as the International Energy Agency, the US Energy Information Administration, and the European Environment Agency record and publish energy data periodically. Improved data and understanding of World Energy Consumption may reveal systemic trends and patterns. The twentieth century saw a rapid twenty-fold increase in the use of fossil fuels. Energy consumption is loosely correlated with gross national product and climate, but there is a large difference even between the most highly developed countries.[1]

Energy conservation refers to reducing energy consumption through using less of an energy service. Energy conservation differs from efficient energy use, which refers to using less energy for a constant service. Some countries that employ energy or carbon taxes are to motivate energy users to reduce their consumption. Carbon taxes can allow consumption to shift to nuclear power and other alternatives that carry a different set of environmental side effects and limitations.[2]

The Earth provides a vast range of resources that allow us to live healthily and to make things that we take for granted every day. Buildings, furniture, cars, plastics are all made from natural resources.[3] Energy is the ability to do work. There are many different sources of energy that we use everyday. Energy sources such as solar, wind, coal, and natural gas can be categorised either as being a renewable or a non-renewable energy source. Renewable energy does not have a limited supply, but can be used again and again without running out. Examples of renewable energy are: hydroelectric, solar, wind, and geothermal energy.[4] Today the greatest attention in the world is devoted to energy resources because their use is usually irreversible, but the supplies of traditional fossil fuels (oil, natural gas) are running out fast.[5]

Historically renewable energy was first energy humankind used. Going from use of fuel wood as a source of cooking and providing heat to using wind energy for transportation and later as a source of mechanical energy in first machinery renewable played absolutely essential role for development in pre-industrial time. Renewable sources of energy is a convenient label for the energy obtainable from biomass, solar radiation temperature differences that produce currents in deep oceans or that are found in rocks beneath the earth's surface, air pressure differences that produce winds, and natural or man-made differences in water levels.[6]

Meaning

Non-renewable resource is a resource that does not renew itself at a sufficient rate for sustainable economic extraction in meaningful human time-frames. It is energy from fossil fuels (coal, crude oil, natural gas) and uranium. Fossil fuels are mainly made up of carbon. Most non-renewable energy sources are fossil fuels: coal, petroleum, and natural gas. Carbon is the main element in fossil fuels. Fossil fuels are a valuable source of energy. They are relatively inexpensive to extract. Burning fossil fuels also upsets Earth's "carbon budget," which balances the carbon in the ocean, earth, and air.[7]

There are many countries, which have recorded significant reduction of these sources and are currently suffering from the side effects of drilling these energy reserves from deep underground. Examples of these countries include China and India.[8]

Indian Perspectives

India has a long history of commercial coal mining covering nearly 220 years starting from 1774 by M/s Sumner and Heatly of East India Company in the Raniganj Coalfield along the western bank of river Damodar. With the advent of Independence, the country embarked upon the five-year development plans. At the beginning of the 1st Plan, annual production went upto 33 mts. During the First Plan period itself, the need for increasing coal production efficiently by systematic and scientific development of the coal industry was being felt.[9] India is the third largest coal producing country in the world after China and USA. Domestic coal production is unlikely to meet expected demand growth over the next five years. PSU companies, who account for four-fifths of the country's coal production, are finding it difficult to accelerate production growth.[10]

The Ministry of Coal is an Indian government ministry headquartered in New Delhi. The portfolio is held by Minister of State with Independent Charge Piyush Goyal. The Ministry of Coal is charged with exploration of coal and lignite reserves in India, production, supply, distribution and price of coal through the government-owned corporations Coal India Limited and its subsidiaries, as well as Neyveli Lignite Corporation.[11] The Ministry of Coal has the overall responsibility of determining policies and strategies in respect of exploration and development of coal and lignite reserves, sanctioning of important projects of high value and for deciding all related issues.[12] It also fully owns a mining company in Mozambique christened as 'Coal India Africana Limitada'. It also manages 200 other establishments like workshops, hospitals etc. It having fulfilled the financial and other prerequisites was granted the Maharatna recognition in April 2011. It is a privileged status conferred by Government of India to select state owned enterprises in order to empower them to expand their operations and emerge as global giants.[13]

India had about 125 Million metric tonne of proven oil reserves as April 2010 or 5.62 billion barrels as per EIA estimate for 2009, which is the second-largest amount in the Asia-Pacific region behind China. Most of India's crude oil reserves are located in the western coast (Mumbai High) and in the northeastern parts of the country, although considerable undeveloped reserves are also located in the offshore Bay of Bengal and in the state of Rajasthan. India's oil sector is dominated by state-owned enterprises, although the government has taken steps in past recent years to deregulate the hydrocarbons industry and support greater foreign involvement. India's state-owned Oil and Natural Gas Corporation is the largest oil company.[14]

Digboi is known as the Oil City of Assam where the first oil well in Asia was drilled. The first refinery was started here as early as 1901. Digboi has the oldest oil well in operation. It is said that the town gets its name from the phrase "dig-boy-dig," which is what the English told the labourers as they dug for crude oil. Today, though the crude production is not high, Digboi has the distinction of being India's oldest continuously producing oilfield. The Digboi Refinery modernisation project was taken up in large scale in order to overcome the technological obsolescence of the old refinery.[15] The Digboi Refinery in North Eastern India is India's oldest refinery and was commissioned in 1901. Originally a part of Assam Oil Company, it became part of Indian Oil in 1981. Its original refining capacity had been 0.5 MMTPA since 1901. The Digboi Refinery processed 0.66 million tonnes of crude oil during the year 2013 as against 0.62 million tonnes of crude oil processed last year. Petroleum products are supplied mainly to north-eastern India primarily through road and by rail wagons.[16]

Bombay High is an offshore oilfield 162 kilometres (101 mi) off the coast of Mumbai, India, in about 75 m of water. As of 2004, it supplied 14 per cent of India's oil requirement and accounted for about 38 per cent of all domestic production. Crude oil produced from Bombay High is of very good quality as compared to crudes produced in Middle East. On 27 July 2005, a major fire destroyed the production platform, leaving at least 22 people dead despite rescue measures taken by the Indian Coast Guard.[17]

Seemandhra and Telangana regions are sitting on potential oil and natural gas reserve. The Pranahita-Godavari stretch in Adilabad district in the Telangana region and Krishna-Godavari stretch in Kadapa district in Rayalaseema region have been identified as potentially prospective categories. These regions can be lined up for bidding by New Exploration Licensing Policy. They are most likely to be focused in the coming day. As per a report by DGH, about 15,000 square kilometres area in Adilabad district is potential region for exploration of oil and natural gas. Over 39,000 sq. km. stretch in Kadapa district has been earmarked by Director General of Hydrocarbons as a potential exploration site for the rare natural resource.[18]

ONGC is a multinational oil and gas company headquartered in Dehradun, Uttarakhand. It is India's largest oil and gas exploration and production company. It produces around 69 per cent of India's crude oil and around 62 per cent of its natural gas. ONGC was founded on 14 August 1956 by Government of India, which currently holds a 68.94 per cent equity stake. It is involved in exploring for and exploiting hydrocarbons in 26 sedimentary basins of India, and owns and operates over 11,000 kilometers of pipelines in the country. Since its inception, ONGC has been instrumental in transforming the country's limited upstream sector into a large viable playing field, with its activities spread throughout India and significantly in overseas territories. Its operations include conventional exploration and production, refining and progressive development of alternate energy sources like coal-bed methane and shale gas. As on 31 March 2013, the company had 32,923 employees, out of which 2,091 were women (6.35 per cent) and 143 were employees with disabilities (0.43 per cent).[19]

Hindustan Petroleum Corporation Limited is an Indian state-owned oil and natural gas company with its headquarters at Mumbai, Maharashtra and with Navratna status. The Government of India owns 51.11 per cent shares in HPCL and others are distributed amongst financial institutes, public and other investors. HPCL operates two major refineries producing a wide variety of petroleum fuels and specialties, one in Mumbai (West Coast) of 6.5 Million Metric Tonnes Per Annum (MMTPA) capacity and the other in Visakhapatnam, (East Coast) with a capacity of 8.3 MMTPA. HPCL has a number of refineries in India: Mumbai Refinery, Visakhapatnam Refinery, Mangalore Refinery Pvt. Ltd, Guru Gobind Singh Refinery and Barmer Refinery.[20]

Indian Oil Corporation is India's largest commercial enterprise, with a sales turnover of Rs 4,50,756 crore and profits of Rs 5,273 crore for the year 2014-15. The main products of Indian Oil are petrol, diesel, LPG, aviation turbine fuel, lubricants and petrochemicals: naphtha, bitumen, kerosene etc. As of

31 March 2013, the company had 34,084 employees, out of which 2643 were women (7.8 per cent). Its workforce includes 14,981 officers. Indian Oil's equity shares are listed on the Bombay Stock Exchange and National Stock Exchange of India. Indian Oil Corporation has two major domestic competitors, Bharat Petroleum and Hindustan Petroleum. OCL has various refineries across India.[21]

The Digboi Refinery was set up at Digboi in 1901 by Assam Oil Company Ltd. The Indian Oil Corporation Ltd took over the refinery and marketing management of Assam Oil Company Ltd. with effect from 1981 and created a separate division. This division has both refinery and marketing operations.[22] Guwahati Refinery was set up at Noonmati in Guwahati on January 1, 1962. Guwahati Refinery is the first Public Sector refinery of India and belongs to Indian Oil Corporation Limited. The refinery was inaugurated by Late Pandit Jawahar Lal Nehru, the first Prime Minister of independent India.[23] Bongaigaon Refinery and Petrochemicals Limited were incorporated as Government of India Undertaking under the administrative control of the Ministry of Petroleum and Natural Gas on 20 February 1974. The company became a subsidiary of Indian Oil on 29 March 2001.[24]

Barauni Refinery in the Bihar state of India was built in collaboration with the Soviet Union at a cost of Rs 49.4 crores and went on stream in July, 1964. Barauni Refinery was built in collaboration with Russia and Romania. Situated 125 kilometres (78 mi) from Patna, it was built with an initial cost of Rs 49.40 crore. Barauni Refinery was initially designed to process low sulphur crude oil (sweet crude) of Assam.[25] The Gujarat Refinery is an oil refinery located at Koyali in Gujarat, Western India. It is the second largest refinery owned by Indian Oil Corporation after Panipat Refinery. The refinery's facilities include five atmospheric crude distillation units. The major secondary units include Catalytic Reforming Unit, Fluidised Catalytic Cracking Unit and the first hydrocracking unit of the country.[26]

The Haldia Refinery for processing was commissioned in January, 1975 with two sectors - one producing fuel products and the other Lube base stocks. The refinery is in Haldia near Kolkata. The fuel sector was built with French collaboration and the Lube sector with Romanian collaboration.[27] The Mathura Refinery, owned by Indian Oil Corporation, is located in Mathura,

Uttar Pradesh. The refinery, which cost Rs 253.92 crores to build, was commissioned in January, 1982. In 1998 the plant was awarded the "Best of all" Rajiv Gandhi National Quality Award.[28] Panipat Refinery is an oil refinery located in Baholi village, Panipat, Haryana. It was set up in 1998. Panipat Refinery is the seventh refinery belonging to Indian Oil Corporation Limited. The original cost of the refinery's construction was Rs 3868 crores. In order to produce low sulphur diesel, a Diesel Hydro Desulphurisation Unit was commissioned in 1999.[29]

Bharat Petroleum Corporation Limited is an Indian state-controlled oil and gas company headquartered in Mumbai, Maharashtra. The Corporation operates two large refineries of the country located at Mumbai and Kochi. Bharat Petroleum operates the following refineries:[30] Bharat Petroleum operates the following refineries: The Mumbai Refinery located Mumbai; Maharashtra came into stream in 1954 under the ownership of Esso.[31] The Kochi Refinery is a public crude oil refinery in the city of Kochi, in the state of Kerala. Kochi Refinery started on 15 August 1947 when Government of India, Phillips Petroleum Company of USA and Duncan Brothers of Calcutta signed an agreement for the construction of a petroleum refinery in south India, in Kochi, Kerala. In 2006, Kochi Refinery was acquired by the Bharat Petroleum Corporation Limited.[32] Bina Refinery is an oil refinery located at Bina in Sagar district of Madhya Pradesh state. The refinery is owned and operated by Bharat Oman Refineries Limited.[33]

The Numaligarh Refinery is located at Numaligarh, Golaghat district, Assam in India is a refinery owned by Numaligarh Refinery Limited, a joint venture between Bharat Petroleum, Oil India and Government of Assam.[34] Ministry of Petroleum and Natural Gas is a ministry of the Government of India. It is responsible for the exploration, production, refining, distribution, marketing, import, export, and conservation of petroleum, natural gas, petroleum products, and liquefied natural gas in India. The ministry has administrative control over various public-sector undertakings of the Government of India.[35]

India had 38 trillion cubic feet of proven natural gas reserves as of January 2007. The total gas production in India was about 31,400 mcm in 2002-03 compared with 2,358 mcm in 1980-81. At this production level, India's reserves are likely to last for around

29 years; that is significantly longer than the 19 years estimated for oil reserves.[36]

India's natural gas output will rise about 60 per cent in four years, sufficient for less than 30 per cent of the local gas demand then, according to a projection in the annual report of the oil ministry. The local gas production is expected to rise to 146.87 million metric standard cubic metres per day (mmscmd) in 2018-19, from 90.99 mmscmd in 2014-15. The projected output for 2014-15, however, was 98.15 mmscmd. The output is expected to touch 99.87 mmscmd in the current fiscal year. The demand for natural gas has been projected to increase to 523 mmscmd by 2018-19 from 405 mmscmd in 2014-15, mainly driven by the power, city gas and industrial customers. In the current fiscal year, the demand is expected to climb 10 per cent. The demand of gas is highly price sensitive, and the actual demand has varied widely from the projection in the past, the report warned.[37]

Coal

Coal is formed from the remains of ancient plants. Millions of years ago, much of the land on Earth was covered with warm, humid forests and swamps. When trees and plants died, they were buried by layers of other dead plants before they could rot.[38] Coal is traditionally looked upon as the most typical fossil fuel. Today coal is primarily used for energy and coke production for producing iron and steel. Coal of a lower quality is used in cement and food production as well as in several less important industries.[39]

There are several different types of coal that have different properties usually dependent on their age and the depth to which they have been buried under other rocks. Peat is the layer of vegetable material directly underlying the growing zone of a coal forming environment. Peat is widely used as a domestic fuel in rural parts. Lignite is geologically very young (upwards of around 40,000 years). It is brown and can be soft and fibrous, containing discernible plant material. Coals that get more deeply buried by other rocks lose more moisture and start to lose their oxygen and hydrogen. These coals are harder and shinier (bituminous coal). Anthracite is a hard, black, shiny form of coal that contains virtually no moisture and very low volatile content.

Because of this, it burns with little or no smoke and is sold as a "smokeless fuel".[40]

Although coal is considered a widely distributed deposit and found in all continents, extraction is economically grounded and concentrated only in four major countries: the USA (27 per cent), Russia (17 per cent), China (13 per cent) and India (10 per cent). These countries provide ~65 per cent of coal extraction in the world. There are a number of adverse health and environmental effects of coal burning especially in power stations, and of coal mining.[41]

Coal contains sulphur and nitrogen, and releases them to the atmosphere as sulphur and nitrous oxides during burning. These oxides react with water in the atmosphere to form sulphuric and nitric acids. These strong acids can decrease the pH of rainwater to values below four. Coal contains radioactive and toxic elements. It contains trace amounts of the naturally-occurring radioactive elements uranium and thorium. These elements get concentrated in the fly ash produced during burning. The toxic heavy metals mercury, arsenic, and lead also become concentrated in fly ash. The radioactive and toxic elements contained in coal are concentrated in the fly ash collected from coalfired power plants.[42]

Coal is the largest source of energy for the generation of electricity world wide, as well as one of the largest worldwide anthropogenic sources of carbon dioxide releases. In 1999, world gross carbon dioxide emissions from coal usage were 8,666 million tonnes of carbon dioxide. Coal is primarily used as a solid fuel to produce electricity and heat through combustion. Coal is an important feedstock in production of a wide range of chemical fertilisers and other chemical products.[43]

Oil

Oil and natural gas are believed to have formed from the remains of tiny sea animals and plants. These organisms were buried in sediments at the bottom of the oceans millions of years ago. As these plant and animal remains slowly decomposed, they were compressed by water and the layers of sediment that formed above them.[44] In nature oil is a liquid that fills in empty spaces, crevices and caverns, in rocks, forming deposits in anticlines, folds at plate boundaries and foothills. Oil can also be found in pores or on grains of rocks. Such oil can form oil-saturated sandstone and limestone rocks, or plastic and hard layers of crust, most often called natural asphalt or oil shale.[45]

Almost all of the world's cars run on petrol /gasoline which are derived from crude oil. Oil is not very difficult to produce though most of the low cost locations have already been depleted. Oil is widely distributed in almost all parts of the world. Oil has one of the highest energy densities which mean that a small amount of oil can produce a large amount of energy.[46] *Crude oil* is easy to handle, transport and store, but it emits high levels of carbon gas into the atmosphere that presents safety hazards.

Organisation of the Petroleum Exporting Countries is an international organisation headquartered in Vienna, Austria. OPEC was established in Baghdad, Iraq on 10–14 September 1960. OPEC's mandate is to "coordinate and unify the petroleum policies" of its members and to "ensure the stabilisation of oil markets in order to secure an efficient, economic and regular supply of petroleum to consumers, a steady income to producers, and a fair return on capital for those investing in the petroleum industry." OPEC has thirteen members: Algeria, Angola, Ecuador, Indonesia, Iran, Iraq, Kuwait, Libya, Nigeria, Qatar, Saudi Arabia, the United Arab Emirates, and Venezuela. According to the United States Energy Information Administration, OPEC crude oil production is an important factor affecting global oil prices.[47]

Peat

Peat is black, brown or yellowish-brown sedimentary rock which, when dry, consists of over 50 per cent organic substances. It is formed of plant material at different stages of decomposition, having accumulated in extremely wet conditions. According to historical data, peat extraction has fundamentally changed throughout the world in the last century. Since the mid-1990s, the world peat extraction has only slightly exceeded the amount extracted in the early years of the twentieth century. Today most peat goes to seed farms to propagate seedlings for forests, parks and gardens.[48]

Peat is now recognised worldwide for its exceptional restorative properties and potential healing benefits. The botanical peat bath is a soothing, exhilarating and rejuvenating full submersion bath at a therapeutic temperature range of 105 to 113 degrees Fahrenheit for a minimum of seven minutes and a maximum of 20 minutes.[49]

Natural Gas

Natural gas is a fossil fuel formed when layers of decomposing plant and animal matter are exposed to intense heat and pressure over thousands of years. Natural gas is found in deep underground rock formations or associated with other hydrocarbon reservoirs in coal beds and as methane clathrates. The World Bank estimates that over 150 billion cubic metres of natural gas are flared or vented annually. Natural gas flowing in the distribution lines and at the natural gas well head is often used to power natural gas powered engines. Natural gas is a major source of electricity generation through the use of cogeneration, gas turbines and steam turbines. Natural gas is also well suited for a combined use in association with renewable energy sources such as wind or solar.[50]

Natural gas is the cleanest burning fossil fuel. Because the combustion process for natural gas is almost perfect, very few byproducts are emitted into the atmosphere as pollutants.[51] Natural gas is cheaper compared to other fossil fuels and cheaper than electricity when used for supplying home appliances. It does not pollute the ground or the underground water because its byproducts are in gaseous form. Another important fact is that natural gas burns without releasing any soot or sulphur dioxide. Natural gas is a multi-use fuel. It is used inside the house for cooking, heating, drying, etc. It can be used for generating electric power, powering vehicles, producing plastics, paints, fertilisers, and many more uses.[52]

Nuclear Power

Nuclear power is the use of nuclear reactions that release nuclear energy to generate heat, which most frequently is then used in steam turbines to produce electricity in a nuclear power station. Along with other sustainable energy sources, nuclear fission power is a low carbon power generation method of producing electricity, meaning that it is in the renewable energy family of low associated greenhouse gas emissions per unit of energy generated.[53] The nuclear power generation is power station that applies fission fuel to generate electricity. About that system, it boils water by using the heat produced by fission reaction in a nuclear reactor in order to generate water vapour, and that water vapour rotates a steam turbine.[54]

Nuclear power is generated using Uranium, which is a metal mined in various parts of the world. The first large-scale nuclear power station opened at Calder Hall in Cumbria, England, in 1956. Nuclear power produces around 11 per cent of the world's energy needs, and produces huge amounts of energy from small amounts of fuel, without the pollution that you'd get from burning fossil fuels.[55] There are over 435 commercial nuclear power reactors operable in 31 countries, with over 375,000 MWe of total capacity. About 70 more reactors are under construction. Many countries have also built research reactors to provide a source of neutron beams for scientific research and the production of medical and industrial isotopes.[56]

Nuclear energy by far has the lowest impact on the environment since it does not release any gases like carbon dioxide, methane which are largely responsible for greenhouse effect. It can be produced from nuclear power plants even in the cases of rough weather conditions. The cost of uranium which is used as a fuel in generating electricity is quite low. The main reason behind the low fuel cost is that it requires little amount of uranium to produce energy. The best part is that this energy has a continuous supply.[57] Nuclear energy is by far the most concentrated form of energy - a lot of energy is produced from a small mass of fuel.[58] Nuclear energy is a clean, safe, reliable and competitive energy source. It is the only source of energy that can replace a significant part of the fossil fuels (coal, oil and gas) which massively pollute the atmosphere and contribute to the greenhouse effect. Tomorrow's nuclear electric power plants will also provide power for electric vehicles for cleaner transportation.[59]

The waste produced by nuclear reactors needs to be disposed off at a safe place since they are extremely hazardous and can leak radiations if not stored properly. Another practical disadvantage of using nuclear energy is that it needs a lot of investment to set up a nuclear power station. Nuclear energy uses uranium which is a scarce resource and is not found in many countries. Most of the countries rely on other countries for the constant supply of this fuel.[60]

References

1. World energy consumption, Available at https://en.wikipedia.org/wiki/World_energy_consumption
2. Energy conservation, Available at https://en.wikipedia.org/wiki/Energy_conservation

3. http://www.wiley.com/legacy/Australia/PageProofs/SQ7_AC_VIC/c07PreciousResources_WEB.pdf
4. Renewable and Non-Renewable Energy, http://www.nevadaoutdoorschool.org/Education/LessonPlans/grade6/6_RenewableAndNonRenewableEnergyFinal.pdf
5. http://www.geo.lu.lv/fileadmin/user_upload/lu_portal/projekti/gzzf/videunilgtspejigaattistiba/VidZ1000/7.LECTURE-Energy_resources.pdf
6. http://unstats.un.org/unsd/envaccounting/londongroup/meeting13/LG13_13a.pdf
7. http://education.nationalgeographic.org/encyclopedia/non-renewable-energy/
8. http://www.conserve-energy-future.com/NonRenewableEnergySources.php
9. http://coal.nic.in/content/coal-mining-india
10. http://www.ukessays.com/essays/economics/coal-and-lignite-sector-in-india-economics-essay.php
11. Ministry of Coal, https://en.wikipedia.org/wiki/Ministry_of_ Coal_(India)
12. http://coal.nic.in/content/about-ministry
13. https://www.coalindia.in/en-us/company/aboutus.aspx
14. Natural resources of India, Available at https://en.wikipedia.org/wiki/Natural_resources_of_India
15. Digboi, Available at https://en.wikipedia.org/wiki/Digboi
16. https://www.iocl.com/aboutus/DigboiRefinery.aspx
17. Bombay High, Available at https://en.wikipedia.org/wiki/Bombay_High
18. The Hindu (Feb 25, 2014), Rich oil, natural gas reserves in Seemandhra, Telangana, http://www.thehindu.com/todays-paper/tp-national/tp-andhrapradesh/rich-oil-natural-gas-reserves-in-seemandhra-telangana/article5724337.ece
19. Oil and Natural Gas Corporation Limited, Available at https://en.wikipedia.org/wiki/Oil_and_Natural_Gas_Corporation
20. Hindustan Petroleum, Available at https://en.wikipedia.org/wiki/Hindustan_Petroleum
21. Indian Oil Corporation, Available at https://en.wikipedia.org/wiki/Indian_Oil_Corporation
22. Digboi Refinery, Available at https://en.wikipedia.org/wiki/Digboi_Refinery
23. Guwahati Refinery, Available at https://en.wikipedia.org/wiki/Guwahati_Refinery
24. Bongaigaon Refinery, Available at https://en.wikipedia.org/wiki/Bongaigaon_Refinery
25. Barauni Refinery, Available athttps://en.wikipedia.org/wiki/Barauni_Refinery
26. Gujarat Refinery, Available at https://en.wikipedia.org/wiki/Gujarat_Refinery
27. Haldia Refinery, Available at https://en.wikipedia.org/wiki/Haldia_Refinery
28. Mathura Refinery, Available at https://en.wikipedia.org/wiki/Mathura_Refinery
29. Panipat Refinery, Available at https://en.wikipedia.org/wiki/Panipat_Refinery
30. Bharat Petroleum, Available at https://en.wikipedia.org/wiki/Bharat_Petroleum
31. Mumbai Refinery, Available at https://en.wikipedia.org/wiki/Mumbai_Refinery

32. https://en.wikipedia.org/wiki/Kochi_Refineries
33. Bina Refinery, https://en.wikipedia.org/wiki/Bina_Refinery
34. Numaligarh Refinery, Available at https://en.wikipedia.org/wiki/Numaligarh_Refinery
35. Ministry of Petroleum and Natural Gas, Available at https://en.wikipedia.org/wiki/Ministry_of_Petroleum_ and_ Natural_ Gas
36. http://www.eai.in/ref/fe/nag/nag.html
37. The Economic Times (June 2, 2015), India's natural gas output projected to rise 60 per cent in 4 years,Read more at:http://economictimes.indiatimes.com/articleshow/47513429.cms?utm_source =contentofinterest&utm_ medium= text&utm_ campaign=cppst
38. http://www.wiley.com/legacy/Australia/PageProofs/SQ7_AC_VIC/c07PreciousResources_WEB.pdf
39. http://www.geo.lu.lv/fileadmin/user_upload/lu_portal/projekti/gzzf/videunilgtspejigaattistiba/VidZ1000/7.LECTURE-Energy_resources.pdf
40. http://www.griffincoal.com.au/coal-education/coal-types/
41. http://www.geo.lu.lv/fileadmin/user_upload/lu_portal/projekti/gzzf/videunilgtspejigaattistiba/VidZ1000/7.LECTURE-Energy_resources.pdf
42. Chpt. 7: Non-renewable Energy Sources, http://www.vanderbilt.edu/Sustainability/book/S1C7.pdf
43. Coal, https://en.wikipedia.org/wiki/Coal
44. http://www.wiley.com/legacy/Australia/PageProofs/SQ7_AC_VIC/c07PreciousResources_WEB.pdf
45. http://www.geo.lu.lv/fileadmin/user_upload/lu_portal/projekti/gzzf/videunilgtspejigaattistiba/VidZ1000/7.LECTURE-Energy_resources.pdf
46. http://www.greenworldinvestor.com/2011/07/07/advantages-and-disadvantages-of-oil-cons-disregarded-by-powerful-lobbies/
47. Organisation of the Petroleum Exporting Countries, Available at https://en.wikipedia.org/wiki/OPEC
48. http://www.geo.lu.lv/fileadmin/user_upload/lu_portal/projekti/gzzf/videunilgtspejigaattistiba/VidZ1000/7.LECTURE-Energy_resources.pdf
49. http://billingsgazette.com/lifestyles/health-med-fit/naturopathic-medicine-peat-baths-offer-health-benefits/article_3848ae1e-ad57-11de-b82f-001cc4c03286.html
50. Natural Gas, Available at https://en.wikipedia.org/wiki/Natural_gas
51. https://www.pseg.com/business/small_large_business/convert/advantages.jsp
52. http://www.brighthubengineering.com/power-plants/114797-pros-and-cons-of-natural-gas-use/
53. Nuclear power, Available at https://en.wikipedia.org/wiki/Nuclear_power
54. https://storify.com/Ryotin_Tana/advantages-and-disadvantages-of-the-nuclear-power
55. http://www.darvill.clara.net/altenerg/nuclear.htm
56. http://www.world-nuclear.org/info/current-and-future-generation/nuclear-power-in-the-world-today/
57. http://www.conserve-energy-future.com/Advantages_ NuclearEnergy.php
58. http://nuclear-energy.net/advantages-and-disadvantages-of-nuclear-energy.html
59. Bruno Comby, The benefits of nuclear energy, http://ecolo.org/documents/documents_in_english/BENEFITS-of-NUCLEAR.pdf
60. http://www.conserve-energy-future.com/Disadvantages_NuclearEnergy.php

Part IV: Pollution

20

Water Pollution

"Cities all over the world are getting bigger as more and more people move from rural to urban sites, but that has created enormous problems with respect to environmental pollution and the general quality of life." **-Alan Dundes**

Clean and plentiful water provides the foundation for prosperous communities. Dirty water is the world's biggest health risk, and continues to threaten both quality of life and public health in the United States. From more severe and frequent droughts to unprecedented flooding, many of the most profound and immediate impacts of climate change will relate to water. Fish, birds and wildlife depend on clean water, just as people do.[1] Water they say is life, and indeed they were right. With about 70 per cent of the earth's cover being water, it undeniably becomes one of our greatest resources. Water is an important resource for the people and the environment. Water is the basis of life; it makes up to 60-95 per cent of the total weight of any functioning living cell.[2]

Since water plays such a vital role in life on the earth, good quality water is a precious resource. Often, water quality is more important than water quantity. Science provides many practical solutions to minimise the present levels at which pollutants are introduced into the environment and for remediating (cleaning up) past problems. All of these solutions come with some cost (both societal and monetary).[3] Pollution comes in many forms; air, water, soil, noise, radioactive, thermal, light and visual pollution. Those pollutants are very dangerous to the environment. There are many forms of water pollution; biological pollution, oxygen, nutrients and chemical.[4]

Meaning

Water pollution is the contamination of water bodies. It can be defined in many ways. Usually, it means one or more substances have built up in water to such an extent that they cause problems for animals or people. It is all about quantities: how much of a polluting substance is released and how big a volume of water it is released into.

A 1969 United Nations report defined ocean pollution as: "The introduction by man, directly or indirectly, of substances or energy into the marine environment (including estuaries) resulting in such deleterious effects as harm to living resources, hazards to human health, hindrance to marine activities, including fishing, impairment of quality for use of sea water and reduction of amenities."[5]

Causes of Pollution

Water pollutant sources can be grouped into two super categories: (a) point sources which can be attributed to discrete discharge from a factory or sewage outfall and (b) non-point sources that include agricultural runoff, urban storm water runoff and other area wide sources.[6] It occurs when a body of water is adversely affected due to the addition of large amounts of materials to the water. The sources of water pollution are categorised as being a point source or a non-source point of pollution.[7]

Point source water pollution comes from discrete conveyances and alters the chemical, biological, and physical characteristics of water. Non-point source pollution refers to diffuse contamination that does not originate from a single discrete source. NPS pollution is often the cumulative effect of small amounts of contaminants gathered from a large area. The specific contaminants leading to pollution in water include a wide spectrum of chemicals, pathogens, and physical changes such as elevated temperature and discolouration. Many of the chemical substances are toxic. Pathogens can produce waterborne diseases in either human or animal hosts. Thermal pollution is the rise or fall in the temperature of a natural body of water caused by human influence. Thermal pollution, unlike chemical pollution, results in a change in the physical properties of water.[8]

Oil spill pose a huge concern as large amount of oil enters into the sea and does not dissolve with water; there by opens problem for local marine wildlife such as fish, birds and sea otter. The garbage produce by each household in the form of paper, aluminum, rubber, glass, plastic, food if collected and deposited into the sea in some countries. Mining activities emit several metal waste and sulphides from the rocks and is harmful for the water. The sewage water carries harmful bacteria and chemicals that can cause serious health problems. Pathogens are known as a common water pollutant; the sewers of cities house several pathogens and thereby diseases. Many industries do not have proper waste management system and drain the waste in the fresh water which goes into rivers, canals and later in to sea. Nuclear energy is produced using nuclear fission or fusion. The element that is used in production of nuclear energy is Uranium which is highly toxic chemical.[9]

Religious faith and social practices also add to pollution of our river waters. Carcasses of cattle and other animals are disposed in the rivers. Dead bodies are cremated on the river banks. Partially burnt bodies are also flung into the river. Mass bathing in a river during religious festivals is another environmentally harmful practice.[10] Detergents; by-productions of disinfection, food processing waste, insecticides, petrochemicals, debris from logging operations, volatile organic compounds, personal hygiene and cosmetic products, drug pollution, chemical wastes, fertilisers, heavy metals, and sedimentation are other causes of water pollution.[11] The main sources of water pollution are the following:

(a) Discharge of untreated Raw Sewage from households and factories.

(b) Chemicals dumped from Factories.

(c) Agricultural run-offs that make their way into our rivers and streams and groundwater sources.

(d) Urbanisation.

(e) The rising use of synthetic organic substances.

(f) Oil Spills.

(g) Acid Rain caused by the burning of Fossil Fuels.

(h) Human littering in rivers, oceans, lakes and other bodies of water. Harmful litter includes plastics, aluminum, glass and Styrofoam.[12]

Effects of the Pollution

Adverse alteration of water quality presently produces large scale illness and deaths, accounting for approximately 50 million deaths per year worldwide, most of these deaths occurring in Africa and Asia. In China, for example, about 75 per cent of the population (or 1.1 billion people) are without access to unpolluted drinking water; according to China's own standards.[13] The rain washes away human excreta and animal dung into rivers, ponds and lakes. Drinking this polluted water may cause several water-borne diseases such as diarrhea, dysentery, jaundice, typhoid and cholera. Polluted river-water can cause diseases to the whole population.[14]

In developed countries, even where there are better purification methods, people still suffer from the health effects of water pollution. Animals, including water animals die when water is poisoned for various reasons. Other animals are stressed and their populations are endangered.[15] Water-borne diseases are infectious diseases spread primarily through contaminated water. Most intestinal (enteric) diseases are infectious and are transmitted through faecal waste. Pathogens that include virus, bacteria, protozoa, and parasitic worms are disease-producing agents found in the faeces of infected persons. Drinking water that gets contaminated with nitrates can prove fatal especially to infants that drink formula milk as it restricts the amount of oxygen that reaches the brain causing the 'blue baby' syndrome.[16]

Infectious diseases can be spread through contaminated water. Some of these water-borne diseases are *Typhoid, Cholera, Paratyphoid Fever, Dysentery, Jaundice, Amoebiasis and Malaria.*[17] One of the greatest dangers to human health is water pollution. After all, people can not survive without drinking water, and if their freshwater resources are polluted, they can become ill from drinking them. Organisms that cause disease are called pathogens. Pathogens include bacteria, viruses, and parasitic organisms that infect humans and cause illness. In some cases, organisms rather than the water itself carry pathogens. For example, insects whose eggs or larvae live in water carry malaria.[18]

Drinking, accidentally swallowing or swimming in water affected by a harmful algal bloom can cause serious health problems including: Rashes, stomach or liver illness, Respiratory problems, Neurological affects. Nitrate, a compound found in fertiliser, often contaminates drinking water in agricultural areas. Infants who drink water too high in nitrates can become seriously ill and even die. Storm water runoff carries nutrients directly into rivers, lakes and reservoirs which serve as sources of drinking water for many people.[19]

Global Perspectives

Water in adequate quantity and safe quality is essential for human survival. Rapid population growth and economic development puts tremendous pressure on limited freshwater resources. In addition, the availability and safety of water resources is threatened by climate change.[20] Although the global water crisis tends to be viewed as a water quantity problem, water quality is increasingly being acknowledged as a central factor in the water crisis. The fact that some five million persons, mainly children and infants, die annually from water-borne diseases was not enough to mobilise international action about water quality.[21]

Asia, as a whole region, faces severe stress on water availability, primarily due to high population density. Many regions of the continent face severe problems of water pollution on local as well as regional scale and these have to be tackled with a pan-Asian approach. Asia is a region with intense mining activities whereby serious environmental problems related to land/use, loss of top soil, water pollution and acid mine drainage are faced by various communities.[22] Improving the water quality throughout South Asia is difficult. Interventions to improve the water quality are generally implemented by water engineers. The health impact of these interventions is less-commonly assessed.[23]

Asia faces a serious and growing water quality challenge. Rapid population growth, urbanisation and industrialisation in the region threaten to limit the freshwater supply. Strong seasonal variations in precipitation due to monsoons and inadequate water and wastewater treatment facilities compound these issues even further.[24] Evidence of surface and groundwater pollution is growing. One-third of the agricultural areas in Association of Southeast Asian Nations countries lie in potential flood zones, and some are vulnerable to droughts. Urban areas are increasingly endangered by floods, partly caused by highland development.[25] China is facing a water crisis. Its per capita water supply is significantly lower than the global average, but its demand for water is astronomical. Both industry and agriculture use massive amounts of water and create massive water pollution.[26]

Rivers in Asia are highly polluted with domestic waste. Many of the region's rivers contain up to three times the world average of human waste derived bacteria. The traditional agriculture-based economies of Asia are giving way to industrial economies. This transformation is having serious environmental side-effects, particularly in the case of pollution. The Asian region continues to face serious water quality issues that contribute to freshwater scarcity, ill-health, and even deaths.[27] According to the survey done by Food and Water Watch cites that approximately 3.5 billion people in 2025 will face water shortage issues. This will be mainly due to water pollution. This is likely to happen because the world pollution is increasing tremendously with more water sources getting contaminated as a result of water pollution.[28]

Most people in Europe have access to drinking water of good quality. In some parts the quality still frequently does not meet basic biological and chemical standards. Clean unpolluted water is also essential for our ecosystems. Plants and animals in lakes, rivers and seas react to changes in their environment caused by changes in chemical water quality and physical disturbance of their habitat.[29] It's estimated there are about 100,000 organic chemicals in regular use in Europe, with 1,000 new ones entering the market each year.[30] Around half of Europe's rivers and lakes are still polluted, a major environmental review has found, despite a 15-year-old target to restore all the continent's waters to good ecological health by 2015.[31] Substantial improvements in freshwater quality by 2015 have been a declared objective of the EU member states, manifesting itself by the requirements of the Water Framework Directive.[32] The study reveals that chemical toxins threaten almost half of all

European bodies of water. And in approximately 15 per cent of cases, the biota in freshwater systems may even be subject to acute mortality.[33]

Africa faces huge challenges with multiple issues that adversely affect public health. One major challenge is the ability for both rural and urban Africans to access a clean water supply. The WHO (2006) stated that, in 2004, only 16 per cent of people in sub-Saharan Africa had access to drinking water through a household connection. Not only is there poor access to readily accessible drinking water, even when water is available in these small towns, there are risks of contamination due to several factors.[34] Africa suffers from a lack of environmental regulation as well as a lack of resources to enforce the few regulations that are in place. Mining is a booming industry throughout Africa. It produces everything from gold and diamonds to lithium used in electronic batteries. These mines often pump chemical waste into streams and rivers that work their way into the water supply.[35]

Water pollution in South Africa is caused by various industries, including the mining industries as well as the urbanisation of people moving to cities in search of jobs or a better life. Because South Africa is rich in natural resources, mining and ore-smelting industries do pose a threat to the pollution of underground water. Heavy metals such as zinc, lead and cadium, is spilled into rivers and, in the end, lands in the underground water system.[36]

In South Africa, Malaria is given very high priority. This disease, which also occurs as a cycle, is caused by a parasite that is transmitted by some species of female mosquitoes. The female mosquito requires a blood meal in order to obtain sufficient energy and nutrients to produce her eggs.[37] Many African children are not familiar with safe drinking water. Their only source of hydration is water from polluted rivers and other water reservoirs. When these children are weakened by lack of proper nutrition they are easily affected by various diseases caused by bacteria living in this unclean water.[38]

Indian Perspectives

Water pollution is a major environmental issue in India. The largest source of water pollution in India is untreated sewage. A 2007 study found that discharge of untreated sewage is the single most important source of pollution of surface and ground water in India. A 1992 World Health Organisation study reported that out of India's 3,119 towns and cities, just 209 have partial sewage treatment facilities, and only eight have full wastewater treatment facilities. Rivers Yamuna, Ganga, Gomti, Ghaghara, River, Chambal, Mahi, Vardha are amongst the other most coliform polluted water bodies in India.[39]

An alarming 80 per cent of India's surface water is polluted, a latest assessment by WaterAid, an international organisation working for water sanitation and hygiene, shows. The report, based on latest data from the ministry of urban development (2013), census 2011 and Central Pollution Control Board, estimates that 75-80 per cent of water pollution by volume is from domestic sewerage, while untreated sewerage flowing into water bodies including rivers have almost doubled in recent years. This in turn is leading to increasing burden of vector borne diseases, cholera, dysentery, jaundice and diarrhea etc. Water pollution is found to be a major cause for poor nutritional standards and development in children also. Between 1991 and 2008, the latest period for which data is available, flow of untreated sewerage has doubled from around 12,000 million litres per day to 24,000 million litres per day in Class I and II towns. The database defines Class I towns as those with a population of more than 1 lakh, whereas towns with population ranging between 50,000 to 1 lakh are classified as Class II.

According to the report, inadequate sanitation facilities, poor sepage management and a near absence of sanitation and waste water policy framework are primary reasons responsible for the groundwater and surface water pollution in the country. Findings of the report show nearly 17 million urban households, accounting for over 20 per cent of total 79 million urban households, lack adequate sanitation. "Among those with access to improved sanitation facilities, a vast majority relies on on-site sanitation systems, such as septic tanks and pit latrines. Today, these septic tanks and pit latrines have become a major contributor to groundwater and surface water pollution in many cities in the country. The report acknowledges that India has of late started focusing on the problem of sepage management, which is one of the most immediately implementable solutions to address urban waste water.[40]

More than two-thirds of the sewage generated in 118 towns, located along the Ganga river basin is discharged into the river untreated, says a report prepared by a team of experts. The towns collectively generate over 3,636 million litres per day (MLD) of sewage while the treatment capacity of the existing 55 sewage treatment plants is hardly 1,027 MLD.[41] Over the decades, numerous campaigns to clean the Ganges have come and gone. Billions of dollars have been thrown into the river. Good intentions have been felled by corruption and mismanagement. The Ganges flows for 2500 kilometres from the Himalayas through four states where 400 million Indians live through to the east coast where it empties into the Bay of Bengal. As it passes through 100 towns and cities, it absorbs all their human and industrial waste. Experts estimate that more than 3000 million litres of untreated sewage from these towns along the Ganges are pumped into the river every day.[42]

Preventive Measures

Water pollution may be analysed through several broad categories of methods: physical, chemical and biological. Most involve collection of samples, followed by specialised analytical tests. Water samples may be examined using the principles of analytical chemistry. Biological testing involves the use of plant, animal, and/or microbial indicators to monitor the health of an aquatic ecosystem. Sampling for biological testing involves collection of plants and/or animals from the surface water body.[43]

Non-point source control relates chiefly to land management practices in the fields of agriculture, silviculture, mining and urban design and sanitation. In the case of urban storm water control, the most important methods are achieved in urban planning by use of minimal net surface runoff of impermeable surfaces.[44] Mining is another of the major causes of water pollution. Mining activities consumes large amounts of water in processing the ores from the mines. In addition, mining also results in large amounts of chemicals, heavy metals soil and other waste rock materials contaminating and polluting the water bodies.

The key solutions to water pollution come down to individual responsibility because all people have a direct impact on the environment.[45] The best solution for water pollution is prevention. While pollution that has already occurred is a current threat to all life on Earth, attempts to clean it up may cause even more harm.[46]

Legal Mechanism

India's dependence on water is critical owing to its large agricultural base, the water needs of its billion-plus population, and the recent economic growth trends. Despite the plethora of material on environmental law, legal scholarship on water law in particular has been negligible.[47] Water law and policy framework in India has undergone significant changes in the last couple decades. Given the complex nature of the law and policy framework, the awareness among common people is minimal or nil. Gender and caste are two important factors to be given adequate attention in the law and policy framework related to water and sanitation. Women and lower caste people are quite often neglected sections.[48]

National water law is more developed than international water law. The early Northern India Canal and Drainage Act, 1873 sought, for instance, to regulate irrigation, navigation and drainage in Northern India. One of the long-term implications of this act was the introduction of the right of the government to use and control for public purposes the water of all rivers and streams flowing in natural channels, and of all lakes. The Madhya Pradesh Irrigation Act, 1931 went much further and asserted direct state control over water. While the Constitution does not specifically recognise a fundamental right to water, court decisions deem such a right to be implied in Article 21 (right to life). The right to water can be read as being implied in the recognition of the right to a clean environment. In Subhash Kumar v. State of Bihar, the Supreme Court recognised that the right to life 'includes the right of enjoyment of pollution free water and air for full enjoyment of life.'[49]

Water (Prevention and Control of Pollution) Act, 1974[50]

It applies in the first instance to the whole of the States of Assam, Bihar, Gujarat, Haryana, Himachal Pradesh, Jammu and Kashmir, Karnataka, Kerala, Madhya Pradesh, Rajasthan, Tripura and West Bengal and the Union Territories; and it shall apply to such other State which adopts this Act by resolution passed in that behalf under clause (1) of Article 252 of the Constitution. It shall come into force, at once in the States of Assam, Bihar,

Gujarat, Haryana, Himachal Pradesh, Jammu and Kashmir, Karnataka, Kerala, Madhya Pradesh, Rajasthan, Tripura and West Bengal and in the Union Territories, and in any other State which adopts this Act under clause (1) of Article 252 of the Constitution on the date of such adoption and any reference in this Act to the commencement of this Act shall, in relation to any State or Union territory, mean the date on which this Act comes into force in such State or Union territory.

The Central Government shall, with effect from such date (being a date not later than six months of the commencement of this Act in the States of Assam, Bihar, Gujarat, Haryana, Himachal Pradesh, Jammu and Kashmir, Karnataka, Kerala, Madhya Pradesh, Rajasthan, Tripura and West Bengal and in the Union Territories) as it may, by notification in the Official Gazette, appoint, constitute a Central Board to be called the 1[Central Pollution Control Board] to exercise the powers conferred on and perform the functions assigned to that Board under this Act. The Central Board shall be a body corporate with the name aforesaid having perpetual succession and a common seal with power, subject to the provisions of this Act, to acquire, hold and dispose of property and to contract, and may, by the aforesaid name, sue or be sued. The State Government shall, with effect from such date 1 as it may, by notification in the Official Gazette, appoint, constitute a 2[State Pollution Control Board], under such name as may be specified in the notification, to exercise the powers conferred on and perform the functions assigned to that Board under this Act.[51]

The government has power to restrict any unit, and to take samples of effluents and get them analysed in Central or State laboratories. Whoever fails to comply with any provision of this Act is punishable with imprisonment, fine or with both. The Central Board may perform all or any of the following functions, namely,

- Advise the Central Government on any matter concerning the prevention and control of water pollution;
- Co-ordinate the activities of the State Boards and resolve disputes among them;
- Provide technical assistance and guidance to the State Boards, carry out and sponsor investigations and research relating to problems of water pollution and prevention, control or abatement of water pollution;
- Plan and organise the training of persons engaged or to be engaged in programmes for the prevention, control or abatement of water pollution on such terms and conditions as the Central Board may specify;

- Organise through mass media a comprehensive programme regarding the prevention and control of water pollution;
- Collect, compile and publish technical and statistical data relating to water pollution and the measures devised for its effective prevention and control and prepare manuals, codes or guides relating to treatment and disposal of sewage and trade effluents and disseminate information connected therewith;
- Lay down, modify or annul, in consultation with the State Government concerned, the standards for a stream or well;
- Plan and execute a nation-wide programme for the prevention, control or abatement of water pollution;
- Perform such other functions as may be prescribed.

References

1. Water, Available at http://www.nrdc.org/water/
2. Water pollution, Available at http://biology.tutorvista.com/environmental-pollution/water-pollution.html
3. Puja Mondal, Essay on Controlling Water Pollution, Available at http://www.yourarticlelibrary.com/water-pollution/essay-on-controlling-water-pollution-689-words/4704/
4. http://www.exampleessays.com/viewpaper/210045.html
5. Chris Woodford, Water pollution: an introduction, Available at http://www.explainthatstuff.com/waterpollution.html
6. C Michael Hogan, Water pollution, Available at http://www.eoearth.org/view/article/156920/
7. Water pollution, Available at http://www.mbgnet.net/fresh/pollute.htm
8. Water pollution, Available at https://en.wikipedia.org/wiki/Water_pollution
9. What is water pollution? http://www.lenntech.com/water-pollution-faq.htm
10. Smriti Chand, 5 Major Causes of Water Pollution in India.
11. http://www.preservearticles.com/201012261673/what-are-the-major-causes-of-water-pollution.html
12. Is your water clean? Available at http://www. theworld counts.com/stories/how-does-water-pollution-affect-humans
13. C Michael Hogan, Water pollution, Available at http://www.eoearth.org/view/article/156920/
14. http://www.preservearticles.com/201012261673/what-are-the-major-causes-of-water-pollution.html
15. Effects of water pollution, Available at http://enviropol.com/index.php/effects-of-water-pollution
16. Health impacts of water pollution, Available at http://edugreen.teri.res.in/explore/water/health.htm
17. http://www.theworldcounts.com/stories/how-does-water-pollution-affect-humans
18. Alecia M. Spooner, How Does Water Pollution Endanger Human Health?, Available at http://www.dummies.com/how-to/content/how-does-water-pollution-endanger-human-health.html
19. The Effects: Human Health, Available at http://www2.epa.gov/nutrientpollution/effects-human-health

20. Drinking water quality in south-east Asia, See http://www.searo.who.int/entity/water_sanitation/documents/waterquality/en/
21. Somaya Abbaspour, Water Quality in Developing Countries, South Asia, South Africa, Water Quality Management and Activities that Cause Water Pollution, 2011 International Conference on Environmental and Agriculture Engineering IPCBEE Vol. 15 (2011), http://www.ipcbee.com/vol15/17-U10016.pdf
22. Asian Journal of Water, Environment and Pollution, See http://www.iospress.nl/journal/asian-journal-of-water-environment-and-pollution/
23. Water quality in South Asia, See http://www.ncbi.nlm.nih.gov/pmc/articles/PMC2740663/
24. http://www.envirotech-online.com/articles/water-wastewater/9/joep_van_den_broeke/water_pollution_in_asia_ a_brief_review_of_monitoring_technologies/1384/
25. http://www.gwp.org/gwp-in-action/Southeast-Asia/
26. Water pollution in China, See http://www.greenpeace.org/eastasia/campaigns/toxics/problems/water-pollution/
27. Water pollution in Asia: The urgent need for prevention and monitoring, Available at http://www.globalwaterforum.org/2012/06/09/water-pollution-in-asia-the-urgent-need-for-prevention-and-monitoring/
28. http://www.conserve-energy-future.com/various-water-pollution-facts.php
29. Water pollution: Overview, See http://www.eea.europa.eu/themes/water/water-pollution
30. Almost Half of Europe's Water is Threatened by Pollution, Retrieved from http://www.citylab.com/work/2014/06/almost-half-of-europes-water-is-threatened-by-pollution/372797/
31. Europe sounds alarm over freshwater pollution, See http://www.nature.com/news/europe-sounds-alarm-over-freshwater-pollution-1.17021
32. http://www.sciencedaily.com/releases/2014/06/140617093224.htm
33. Chemical Pollution of European Waters Worse than Previously Thought, Available at http://www.natureworldnews.com/articles/7645/20140618/chemical-pollution-of-european-waters-worse-than-previously-thought.htm
34. http://thewaterproject.org/water-in-crisis-rural-urban-africa
35. Water Pollution in Africa: Causes and Effects, Available at http://study.com/academy/lesson/water-pollution-in-africa-causes-and-effects.html
36. http://www.theinnovationdiaries.com/2668/water-pollution-in-south-africa/
37. http://www.randwater.co.za/corporateresponsibility/wwe/pages/waterpollution.aspx
38. https://www.aidorphansrelief.org/water-pollution-in-african-countries/
39. Water pollution in India, Available at https://en.wikipedia.org/wiki/Water_pollution_in_India
40. The Times of India (June 28, 2015), 80% of India's surface water may be polluted, report by international body says, Available at http://timesofindia.indiatimes.com/home/environment/pollution/80-of-Indias-surface-water-may-be-polluted-report-by-international-body-says/articleshow/47848532.cms

41. http://www.ibtimes.co.uk/india-million-litres-untreated-sewage-polluting-holy-river-ganga-says-report-1491715
42. http://www.smh.com.au/national/the-ganges-holy-river-from-hell-20140806-100xz9.html
43. Water pollution, Available at https://en.wikipedia.org/wiki/Water_pollution
44. C Michael Hogan, Water pollution, Available at http://www.eoearth.org/view/article/156920/
45. http://www.waterbenefitshealth.com/solutions-to-water-pollution.html
46. http://greenliving.lovetoknow.com/How_to_Stop_ Water_Pollution
47. Water Law in India: An Introduction to Legal Instruments, Available at http://www.oup.co.in/product/academic-general/law/law-society/217/water-law-india-introduction-legal-instruments/9780198070818
48. Water law and policy in India, Available at http://www.elrs.in/content/chitrakoot_up_report.pdf
49. Philippe Cullet, Water law in India, Available at http://www.ielrc.org/content/w0701.pdf
50. Water (prevention and control of pollution) Act, 1974, Available at http://www.indiawaterportal.org/articles/water-prevention-and-control-pollution-act-1974
51. http://indiankanoon.org/doc/867156/

21

Air Pollution

"Clean energy is about offering people the opportunity to do what's right for themselves and the people they love. It's about reducing the pollution that makes people sick. It's about helping the low-income families struggling to pay their gas and electricity bills."

- Gloria Reuben

Air is the Earth's atmosphere. Air around us is a mixture of many gases and dust particles. It is the clear gas in which living things live and breathe. It has an indefinite shape and volume. It has no colour or smell. It has mass and weight. It is a mixture of 78.09 per cent nitrogen, 20.95 per cent oxygen, 0.93 per cent argon, 0.039 per cent carbon dioxide, and small amounts of other gases. There is an average of about one per cent water vapour. Wind is moving air.[1]

Air is essential for organisms to live. Organisms do not produce energy in the absence of air. The smoke from vehicles and factories contain carbon-monoxide, carbondioxide and other gases which we cannot see. Coal mines, cement, granite factories, refrigerators and also sprayers produce dust and poisonous gases.[2] Across the globe, the issue of air pollution has become a hot topic, as scientists blame a large amount of deaths and respiratory disease on its widespread effects. Air pollution is a chemical, physical or biological agent that alters the natural characteristics regarding the atmosphere. An assortment of gases, such as carbon dioxide, which helps make the global warming problem worse, is also a newly recognised culprit for air pollution. The contributing factors of air pollution often come from two different sources: anthropogenic and natural.[3]

Meaning

Air pollution is the introduction of particulates, biological molecules, or other harmful materials into Earth's atmosphere, causing disease, death to humans, damage to other living organisms such as food crops, or the natural or built environment.[4] It is the introduction into the atmosphere of chemicals, particulates, and biological matter that cause harm to humans, other living organisms, or cause damage to the natural environment. Stratospheric ozone depletion (contributed to air pollution) has long been recognised as a threat to human health as well as to the Earth's ecosystems.[5]

H. Perkins (1974) has defined air pollution as, "the presence in the outdoor atmosphere of one or more contaminants such as dust, fumes, gases, mist, smoke or vapours in quantities of characteristics and of duration such as to be injurious to living organisms and to property which reasonably interferes with comfortable enjoyment of life and property. According to World Health Organisation, air pollution is defined as limited to situation in which the outdoor ambient atmosphere contains materials in concentration which are harmful to man and its environment. In general sense, air pollution may be defined as the imbalance or disequilibrium in the quality of air due to introduction of foreign materials from natural or anthropogenic sources to the air so as to cause adverse effect to biological communities in general and man in particular.[6]

Causes of Pollution

An air pollutant is a substance in the air that can have adverse effects on humans and the ecosystem. Pollutants are classified as primary or secondary. Primary pollutants are usually produced from a process, such as ash from a volcanic eruption. Other examples include carbon monoxide gas from motor vehicle exhaust, or the sulphur dioxide released from factories. Secondary pollutants are not emitted directly.[7] Air pollution is caused mainly by transportation, fuel combustion in stationary sources, burning of fossil fuels like coal, wood, dry grass, and construction activity. Motor vehicles produce high levels of Carbon monoxide (CO) and Hydrocarbons (HC) and Nitrogen Oxides (NO).[8]

Sulphur dioxide emitted from the combustion of fossil fuels like coal, petroleum and other factory combustibles is one of the major cause of air pollution. Pollution emitting from vehicles including trucks, jeeps, cars, trains, airplanes cause immense amount of pollution. Ammonia is a very common byproduct from agriculture related activities and is one of the most hazardous gases in the atmosphere. Manufacturing industries release large amount of carbon monoxide, hydrocarbons, organic compounds, and chemicals into the air thereby depleting the quality of air. Household cleaning products, painting supplies emit toxic chemicals in the air and cause air pollution.[9]

Traffic fumes from cars, buses, lorries and other vehicles are the main cause of air pollution.[10] Fires are another major source of air pollution and can lead to severe problems if the smoke is inhaled for a period of time. These fires can either be forest fires, oil well fires, burning of leaves in the backyard or as in the case of rural areas, large-scale burning of agricultural waste.[11]

Effects of the Pollution

The effects of air pollution are alarming. They are known to create several respiratory and heart conditions along with cancer, among other threats to the body. Another direct effect is the immediate alterations that the world is witnessing due to global warming.[12] The health effects caused by air pollutants may range from biochemical and physiological changes like difficulty in breathing, wheezing, coughing and aggravation of existing respiratory and cardiac conditions.[13] Air pollution causes damage to plants and animals, affecting biodiversity and crop yields.[14]

Air pollution often has long-term health impacts that build-up slowly over time. It has been linked to increased incidences of cancer, heart disease, stroke and respiratory illnesses. On a less severe level, it is associated with asthma in children, and thus impaired quality of life for many kids.[15] It may cause several health problems. Its impacts economic productivity reduces agricultural productivity, damages property and causes ecological changes that increase the risk of environmental disasters. Flight schedules are routinely disrupted in winter due to smog in

Delhi and other cities, when airports are shutdown for the lack of visibility. Exposure to indoor air pollutants also causes serious health problems like acute respiratory infections, chronic obstructive lung disease, lung cancer and possibly blindness and heart disease in women, children less than five years of age, and senior citizens who spend long periods indoors are particularly susceptible.[16]

Air pollution is a significant risk factor for a number of health conditions including respiratory infections, heart disease, COPD, stroke and lung cancer. Children aged less than five years that live in developing countries are the most vulnerable population in terms of total deaths attributable to indoor and outdoor air pollution. It is estimated that some seven million premature deaths may be attributed to air pollution. It is estimated to reduce life expectancy by almost nine months across the European Union.[17]

Carbon monoxide enters the bloodstream and reduces oxygen delivery to the body's organs and tissues. The health threat from CO is most serious for those who suffer from cardiovascular disease. Healthy individuals are also affected, but only at higher levels of exposure. Exposure to lead mainly occurs through inhalation of air and ingestion of lead in food, paint, water, soil, or dust. Lead accumulates in the body in blood, bone, and soft tissue. Excessive exposure to lead may cause anemia, kidney disease, reproductive disorders, and neurological impairments such as seizures, mental retardation, and/or behavioural disorders. The major health concerns associated with exposure to high concentrations of SO_2 include effects on breathing, respiratory illness, alterations in pulmonary defenses, and aggravation of existing cardiovascular disease. Particulate matter is the term for solid or liquid particles found in the air. Major concerns for human health from exposure to particulate matter are: effects on breathing and respiratory systems, damage to lung tissue, cancer, and premature death.[18]

The following table summarises some sources and effects of these air pollutants:[19]

Pollutant	*Anthropogenic Sources*	*Health Effects*	*Environmental Effects*
Ozone (O_3)	Secondary pollutant formed by chemical reaction of VOCs and NOx in the presence of sunlight.	Breathing problems, reduced lung function, asthma, irritates eyes, stuffy nose, reduces resistance to colds and infections, premature aging of lung tissue.	Damages crops, forests, and other vegetation; damages rubber, fabric, and other materials; smog reduces visibility
Volatile Organic Compounds (VOCs)	Fuel combustion, solvents, paint. (Cars are a major source of VOCs.)	Ozone (smog) effects, cancer, and other serious health problems.	Ozone (smog) effects, vegetation damage.
Carbon Monoxide (CO)	Burning of gasoline, natural gas, coal, oil.	Reduces ability of blood to bring oxygen to body cells and tissues.	-
Nitrogen Oxides (NOx)	Burning of gasoline, natural gas, coal, oil. (Cars are a major source of NOx.)	Lung damage, respiratory illnesses, ozone (smog) effects.	Ozone (smog) effects; precursor of acid rain which damages trees, lakes, and soil; aerosols can reduce visibility. Acid rain also causes buildings, statues, and monuments to deteriorate.
Particulate Matter	Emitted as particles or formed through chemical reactions; burning of wood, diesel, and other fuels; industrial processes; agriculture (plowing, field burning); unpaved roads.	Eye, nose, and throat irritation; lung damage; bronchitis; cancer; early death.	Source of haze which reduces visibility. Ashes, smoke, soot, and dust can dirty and discolour structures and property, including clothes and furniture.

Pollutant	*Anthropogenic Sources*	*Health Effects*	*Environmental Effects*
Mercury	Fossil fuel combustion, waste disposal, industrial processes (incineration, smelting, chlore-alkali plants), mining.	Liver, kidney, and brain damage; neurological and developmental damage.	Accumulates in food chain.
Sulphur Dioxide (SO_2)	Burning of coal and oil, especially high-sulphur coal; industrial processes (paper manufacturing, metal smelting).	Respiratory illness, breathing problems, may cause permanent damage to lungs.	Precursor of acid rain, which can damage trees, lakes, and soil; aerosols can reduce visibility. Acid rain also causes buildings, statues, and monuments to deteriorate.
Lead	Combustion of fossil fuels and leaded gasoline; paint; smelters (metal refineries); battery manufacturing.	Brain and nervous system damage (esp. children), digestive and other problems. Some lead-containing chemicals cause cancer in animals.	Harm to wildlife and livestock

Source: http://www.cleanerandgreener.org/resources/air-pollution.html

Global Perspectives

According to the World Health Organisation, it is estimated that about 4.6 million people die each year from complications received through various levels of air pollution. Often, it is indoor air pollution that threatens health and safety, but overall air pollution is also related to the number of asthma, emphysema, bronchitis, lung diseases, heart diseases, and respiratory allergies plaguing the United States.[20]

Air pollution is a major environmental issue affecting people across the world. According to the World Health Organisation, more than two million people worldwide die every year from air pollution. Of all the air pollutants, fine particulate matter (PM) is one of the most hazardous pollution for the human health. The particulate matter causes about nine per cent of lung cancer deaths worldwide, five per cent of cardiopulmonary deaths and about one per cent of respiratory infection deaths. According to the WHO, there is mounting evidence that concentration of particulate matter is increasing in Asia. According to the WHO, air pollution has worsened in Asian cities in recent years and presents a threat to human health. Over the last few years, China has been in the news for heavy pollution in its cities with the skies being completely blanketed by smog. India and Pakistan have the dubious distinction of having the most polluted cities in the region. The WHO global study ranks air pollution as one of the top 10 killers in the world, with 65 per cent of all air pollution deaths occurring in Asia. In 2010 alone, particulate matter pollution was the fourth-leading risk factor for deaths in China, behind high blood pressure and smoking.[21]

Asia is home to the world's 20 most polluted cities, but that dirty air does not stay put, as the above animation of aerosol emissions shows.[22]

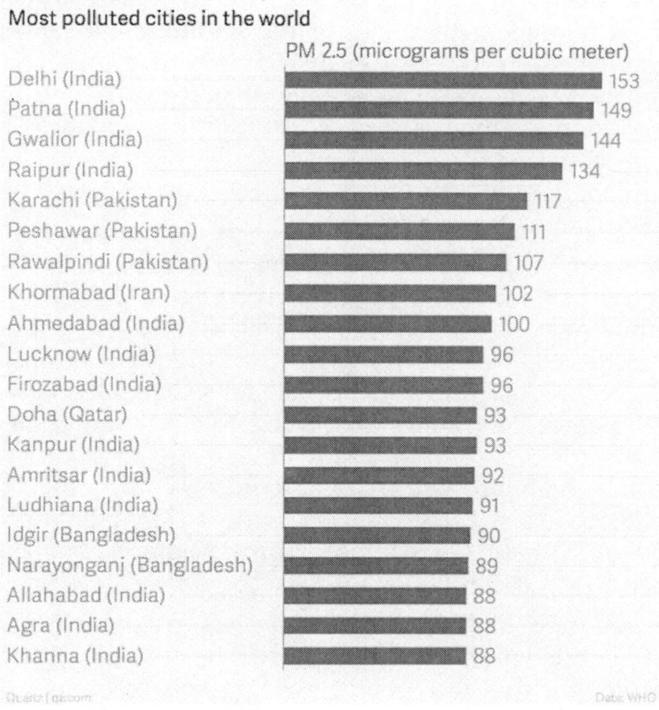

In Europe, emissions of many air pollutants have decreased substantially over the past decades, resulting in improved air quality across the region. However, air pollutant concentrations are still too high, and air quality problems persist.[23] Around 90 per cent of city dwellers in the European Union are exposed to one of the most damaging air pollutants at levels deemed harmful to health by the World Health Organisation. Vehicles, industry, agriculture and homes are contributing to air pollution in Europe. Alongside health concerns, the report also highlights environmental problems such as eutrophication, which is when excessive nutrient nitrogen damages ecosystems, threatening biodiversity. Eutrophication is still a widespread problem that affects most European ecosystems.[24]

Hundreds of thousands of Europeans will suffer a premature death in the next two decades as the result of governments' failure to act on air pollution, Europe's environmental watchdog has warned. Europe is also faring badly on other environmental indicators, including the loss of biodiversity to intensive farming and urbanisation, and the poor state of many inland freshwater systems, according to the State of the Environment report for 2015, published by the European Environment Agency. EU environment watchdog blames governments for failing to act on air pollution warnings saying it will lead to premature deaths across the countries.[25]

Campaigners have urged a crackdown on Europe's worst polluters after a report claimed dirty air is costing society up to 189 billion Euros a year. Half the damage is being done by just one per cent of industrial plants, according to data from the European Environment Agency (EEA). It said air pollution, chiefly from coal-fired power plants, cost Europe as much as 189 bn Euros in 2012, the same as Finland's GDP. Germany was Europe's biggest contributor, according to EEA figures. It was responsible for 38.2 billion Euros of damage to society as a result of air pollution, which was around one-fifth of Europe's total in 2012. Next was the United Kingdom (25.9 billion Euros), followed by Poland (24.8 billion Euros), France (14.3 billion Euros) and Italy (13.8 billion Euros).[26]

Air pollution in Asia and Europe has grabbed headlines. The problem is pervasive across Africa as well. Africa is urbanising quickly, and pollution from sources like vehicle exhaust, wood burning and dusty dirt roads has reached worrisome levels in many cities. Equally or more troubling is air pollution inside homes, caused by cooking with wood or other sooty fuels. Dirty air can cause lung damage as well as heart disease, strokes and cancer. The organisation found that air pollution in African homes contributed to nearly 600,000 deaths in 2012. Africa had the third highest level of deaths per capita from indoor air pollution of any region of the world, though it was still well behind areas of the western Pacific region and Southeast Asia.

The WHO figures for deaths per capita from outdoor air pollution in Africa are well below the world average, but the lack of data is a barrier. A survey several years ago by the WHO showed Gaborone, Botswana, as having the eighth-highest level of particulate pollution (particles of up to 10 micrometers in diameter) among a list of world cities. One recent study, published in the journal Environmental Research Letters, estimated that Africa could generate 20 per cent to 30 per cent of the world's combustion-driven sulphur dioxide and nitrogen oxides by 2030, up from about five per cent each in 2005.[27]

The two major types of pollution in South Africa are air and marine pollution. The industrial sector is the prime contributor to air pollution. More than 90 per cent of South Africa's electricity is generated from the combustion of coal that contains approximately 1.2 per cent sulphur and up to 45 per cent ash. Nitrogen dioxide levels in Cape Town, South Africa, for instance, were significantly higher than those measured in Calcutta, and surpassed the World Health Organisation's annual mean guideline for air quality standard of 50 micrograms per cubic meter.[28]

Air pollution in fast-growing West African cities is reaching dangerous levels. There's little monitoring of pollution, no emissions inventories, or statistical information on things like fuel consumption. Evans and the study's lead author, Peter Knippertz, from the Karlsruhe Institute of Technology in Germany, worry that these pollutants will change the West African monsoon, a sensitive atmospheric circulation system that controls everything from wind and temperature to rainfall across huge swathes of the region. The sources of pollution are many: car exhaust, wood burning, garbage burning, cooking indoors with fuel stoves, the use of millions of diesel electricity generators, petrochemical plants. As much as 94 per cent of

Nigeria's population is exposed to levels of air pollution that exceed what the World Health Organisation deems as safe. Gaborone in Botswana was the seventh-most polluted city in the world, according to WHO data in 2013.[29]

By world standards, Australia has very clean air. Strategies to manage air pollution in Australia have contributed to reducing the levels of pollutants in our air. However, levels of some pollutants, including ground-level ozone and particulate matter, can still exceed current air quality standards. The National Environment Protection (Ambient Air Quality) Measure (Ambient Air Quality NEPM) was established in 1998 to provide a common national goal to best protect human health and well being from the adverse impacts of air pollution. It provides a consistent framework to assess Australia's ambient (outdoor) air quality. In addition, population growth, urbanisation and increasing demands for transportation and energy consumption are ongoing challenges which impact air quality.[30]

Australia has set national standards for six criteria air pollutants in outdoor air: carbon monoxide, lead, nitrogen dioxide, ozone, particles and sulphur dioxide. Information about air quality in major urban air sheds in Australia is available in the State of the air: national ambient air quality status and trends report 1991-2001. The report presents an analysis of national air quality based on 2001 data for the criteria pollutants, and examines the trends over the past decade or so, with emphasis on the period from 1991 to 2001. This report indicates that particles and ozone are the air pollutants of concern in Australia, having peak concentrations at or above national air quality standards and showing no consistent downward trend in some major cities.[31]

A new report from the Organisation for Economic Co-operation and Development, called *The Cost of Air Pollution: Health Impacts of Road Transport,* shows Australia has failed to halt the dangerous rise in air pollution. It estimates the economic cost of that failure has run into the billions. The report shows that between 2005 and 2010, the number of deaths from air pollution in Australia jumped from 882 to 1483, representing a 68 per cent rise.[32] Auckland has New Zealand's worst air pollution which is at levels nearly double that of Sydney, World Health Organisation data out reveals. All Australia's major cities do better than New Zealand cities, including Melbourne which is currently the world's most liveable city. New Zealand air is much cleaner than that of Iran, India, Pakistan and Mongolia, but a lot worse than Canada.[33]

Air pollution in Canada is regulated by standards set by the Canadian Council of Ministers of the Environment (CCME), an inter-governmental body of federal, provincial and territorial Ministers responsible for the environment.[34] Canadians breathe easier than most people in the world, ranking third in an-air quality index released by the World Health Organisation. Estonia topped the list with the best air quality, Mauritius ranked second, and Canada tied with Australia for third. WHO spokesman Gregory Hartl said the air quality in all cities is affected by combination of four main factors: private transport, power generation, indoor combustion of fuels, and industry. Ahvaz, located in southwest Iran, earned the unfortunate distinction of worst air quality at the city level. Cities in Iran, India, Pakistan and Ulaanbaatar were among the worst on the planet for air pollution, whereas cities in Canada and the United States fared better.[35]

Air pollution in Mexico City is a continuing concern for citizens, health experts, and environmentalists. However, much improvement has been made in the city since 1992 when the United Nations named Mexico City "the most polluted city on the planet." In 1992, the United Nations described Mexico City's air as the most polluted on the planet.[37] Ever since the beginning of the Industrial Revolution in the United States, America has had much trouble with environmental issues, air pollution in particular. According to a 2009 report, around 60 per cent of Americans live in areas where air pollution has reached unhealthy levels that can make people sick. In the 1960s, 1970s, and 1990s, the United States Congress enacted a series of Clean Air Acts which significantly strengthened regulation of air pollution. Los Angeles has some of the most contaminated air in the country. With a population of over 18 million, the Los Angeles area is a large basin with the Pacific Ocean to the west, and several mountain ranges with 11,000-foot peaks to the east and south. Diesel engines, ports, motor vehicles, and industries are main sources of air pollution in Los Angeles.[38]

Almost half of the US population lives in areas where air pollution levels are often dangerously high for them to breathe, according to a report of American Lung Association. The group's annual "State of the Air" report finds 47 per cent of Americans live in counties with frequently unhealthy levels of either ozone or particulate pollution. That's up from 42 per cent in last year's report.[39]

Indian Perspectives

A sharp rise in cases of chest and throat disease in India is being blamed by doctors on worsening air pollution in the country, which is now home to 13 of the 20 most polluted cities in the world. According to India's National Health Profile 2015, there were almost 3.5 million reported cases of acute respiratory infection (ARI) last year, a 140,000 increase on the previous year and a 30 per cent increase since 2010.

The number of ARI cases has risen steadily in India over the last 15 years, even when population growth is taken into account. In 2001, less than 2,000 cases per 100,000 people had an ARI. In 2012, the number was 2,600 per 100,000, statistics show. The rise has occurred despite steady improvements in medical care and nutrition, as well as a shift away from using wood as fuel in rural areas. Together this has mitigated many factors long blamed for the high levels of respiratory diseases in India. Doctors are blaming the increasing severity of the problem on unprecedented decline in air quality across India.

Mumbai has pollution levels which, though lower than in Delhi, exceed safe limits set by the Indian government many times. Those limits are significantly higher than those set by international experts and western governments. The worst affected areas of Chennai, which has a population of around four million people, lie on its northern rim, where petrochemical works, car factories and coal-burning power stations exist close to residential areas. In other cities across the country the problem was even worse. In Ahmedabad, in the west, levels of PM_2.5s peaked at eight times the WHO limit for a 24-hour average. In Lucknow, in the north, levels reached seven times the limit. Levels of CO_2, nitrogen dioxide and ozone in less known cities have also regularly exceeded WHO guidelines by huge margins. India has the highest rate of death from respiratory disease in the world, according to the WHO. The rate was 159 per 100,000 in 2012, about 10 times that of Italy, five times that of the UK and twice that of China.[40]

Preventive Measures

There are various air pollution control technologies and land-use planning strategies available to reduce air pollution. Most effective is the switch to clean power sources such as wind power, solar power; hydro power which doesn't cause air pollution.[41] According to the US Environmental Protection Agency, saving energy can reduce carbon emissions. The process of manufacturing packaging are releases harmful emissions into the atmosphere, so patronise brands that use as little packaging as possible. Recycle everything you can: aluminum, paper, glass, plastic and cardboard are usually easy to recycle.[42]

Encourage people to use more and more public modes of transportation to reduce pollution. Switch off fans and lights when are going out. Large amount of fossil fuels are burnt to produce electricity. Do not throw away items that are of no use. Infact, reuses them for some other purpose. Clean energy technologies like solar, wind and geothermal are on high these days.[43] Some measures that can be adopted in this direction are:

1. Using unleaded petrol.
2. Using fuels with low sulphur and ash content.
3. Encouraging people to use public transport, walk or use a cycle as opposed to private vehicles.
4. Ensure that houses, schools, restaurants and playgrounds are not located on busy streets.
5. Plant trees along busy streets as they remove particulates, carbon dioxide and absorb noise.
6. Industries and waste disposal sites should be situated outside the city preferably on the downwind of the city.
7. Catalytic converters should be used to help control emissions of carbon monoxide and hydrocarbons.[44]

In the short-term, there are many intermediate solutions for air pollution. However, all of these solutions require governments to recognise the impact of air pollution on public health and the economy, and take action immediately.

- Make complete air quality information easily available to the public.
- Tighten the controls for power plant emissions to reduce emissions.
- Introducing cleaner fuel standards and switching to electric vehicles.

- Restrict the construction of power plants and other energy-intensive industries near residential areas.
- Improve urban planning to increase green spaces.
- Take air quality into consideration when conducting environmental assessments for major projects; for example, flyovers and highways should be far away from residential areas.[45]

London fog of 1952

Smoke is produced as a result of the incomplete combustion of fuels. The smoke contains various gases and suspended particulate matter. In addition, another substance responsible for smog formation is dust. Dust is nothing but small particle of solid matter that can be carried in suspension. Dusts are produced from forest fires, automobile exhaust, industrial combustion process, soil blowing by wind, ocean spray, mining areas, etc. The smog is caused either due to the presence of oxidising pollutants or due to reducing pollutants. If the smog is caused due to oxidising pollutants, it is known as oxidising smog and if it is caused due to reducing pollutants, it is known as reducing smog.[46]

The Great Smog of 1952 was a severe air-pollution event that affected London during December 1952. It lasted from Friday 5 December to Tuesday 9 December 1952, and then dispersed quickly after a change of weather. Government medical reports in the following weeks estimated that up until 8 December 4,000 people had died prematurely and 100,000 more were made ill because of the smog's effects on the human respiratory tract. In February 1953, Lieutenant-Colonel Lipton suggested in the House of Commons that the fog had caused 6,000 deaths and that 25,000 more people had claimed sickness benefits in London during that period. It led to several changes in practices and regulations, including the Clean Air Act 1956.[47]

Smog was nothing new in London, but this particular "pea souper" quickly thickened into a poisonous brew unlike anything the city had ever experienced. The 30-mile-wide noxious smog, teeming with acid sulphur particles, reeked like rotten eggs. It was so dense that residents in the Isle of Dogs section of the city reported they were unable to see their feet as they walked. For five days, the Great Smog paralysed London and crippled all transportation, except for its Underground. Boat traffic on the Thames came to a halt. Flights were grounded and trains cancelled. Authorities advised parents to keep their children home from school in fear they would get lost in the smog.[48]

Legal Mechanism

Environmental Management Bureau is committed to preventing air pollution due to the emissions of factories, cars, and the like, preventing pollution due to dioxins, and protecting the health of the Japanese people, as well as preserving our living environment by tacking such issues as noise, vibration, and offensive odours. Japan is pushing forward a comprehensive set of measures against environmental pollution from dioxins, including measures to reduce dioxin emissions based on the Law Concerning Special Measures against Dioxins. Environmental Management Bureau regulates dioxin emissions by factories and industrial facilities and regularly observes environmental conditions. In order to prevent air pollution due to nitrogen oxide, particulate matter, and other substances contained in automotive exhaust, and prevent noise pollution, the bureau regulates emissions of individual automobiles, as well as noise and fuel quality.[49]

The Air (Prevention and Control of Pollution) Act, 1981 is an Act of the Parliament to control and prevent air pollution. It was amended in 1987. The Act specifically empowers State Government to designate air pollution areas and to prescribe the type of fuel to be used in these designated areas. According to this Act, no person can operate certain types of industries including the asbestos, cement, fertiliser and petroleum industries without consent of the State Board. The government passed this Act in 1981 to clean up our air by controlling pollution. It states that sources of air pollution such as industry, vehicles, power plants, etc., are not permitted to release particulate matter, lead, carbon monoxide, sulphur dioxide, nitrogen oxide, volatile organic compounds or other toxic substances beyond a prescribed level. This Act is created to take appropriate steps for the preservation of the natural resources of the Earth which among other things includes the preservation of high quality air and ensures controlling the level of air pollution.

The main objectives of the Act are as follows: (a) To provide for the prevention, control and abatement of air pollution. (b) To provide for the establishment of Central and State Boards with a view to implement the Act. (c) To confer on the Boards the powers to implement the provisions of the Act and assign;

and to the Boards functions relating to pollution. The main function of the Central Board is to implement legislation created to improve the quality of air and to prevent and control air pollution in the country. The State Boards have the power to advise the State Government on any matter concerning the prevention and control of air pollution. A State Board may establish or recognise a laboratory to perform this function. The persons managing industry are to be penalised if they produce emissions of air pollutants in excess of the standards laid down by the State Board. The Board also makes applications to the court for restraining persons causing air pollution.[49]

References

1. Air, Available at https://simple.wikipedia.org/wiki/Air
2. Air its importance, Available at http://jsprasanna. hubpages.com/hub/Air-its-Importance
3. How to prevent air pollution, Available at http://www.howtoprevent.com/enviroment/how-to-prevent-air-pollution/
4. Air pollution, Available at https://en.wikipedia.org/wiki/Air_pollution
5. Causes of air pollution, Available at http://www.universetoday.com/81977/causes-of-air-pollution/
6. http://www.environmentalpollution.in/essay/air-pollution-essay-on-air-pollution-8634-words/336
7. Air pollution, Available at https://en.wikipedia.org/wiki/Air_pollution
8. http://mpcb.gov.in/envtdata/quicklinks.php
9. What is air pollution? Available at http://www.conserve-energy-future.com/causes-effects-solutions-of-air-pollution.php
10. http://www.southwark.gov.uk/info/200075/pollution/1360/air_pollution/5
11. Health impacts of air pollution, Available at http://edugreen.teri.res.in/explore/air/health.htm
12. What is air pollution? Available at http://www.conserve-energy-future.com/causes-effects-solutions-of-air-pollution.php
13. http://mpcb.gov.in/envtdata/quicklinks.php
14. http://uk-air.defra.gov.uk/air-pollution/effects
15. The problems of air pollution, Available at http://www.greenpeace.org/eastasia/campaigns/air-pollution/problems/
16. Dr V. Ramasammy, Studies on the effects of vehicular pollutants on road side plants of Puducherry, Available at http://dste.puducherry.gov.in/Dr.V.Ramasamy.pdf
17. Air pollution, Available at https://en.wikipedia.org/wiki/Air_pollution
18. Health effects of air pollution, Available at http://www.epa.gov/region07/air/quality/health.htm
19. Air pollution, Available at http://www.cleanerandgreener.org/resources/air-pollution.html
20. How to prevent air pollution, Available at http://www.howtoprevent.com/enviroment/how-to-prevent-air-pollution/
21. Air pollution in Asia, Available at http://ejap.org/environmental-issues-in-asia/AirPollution.html
22. http://www.onearth.org/earthwire/asia-pollution-us-weather
23. http://www.eea.europa.eu/themes/air

24. Air pollution still harming health across Europe, Available at http://www.eea.europa.eu/media/newsreleases/air-pollution-still-causing-harm
25. Air pollution will kill thousands in Europe, EEA warns, Available at http://www.theguardian.com/environment/2015/mar/03/air-pollution-will-kill-thousands-in-europe-eea-warns
26. http://www.euronews.com/2014/11/27/which-countries-in-europe-cause-the-most-air-pollution-damage/
27. Kate Galbraith, Measuring Africa's Air pollution, Available at http://www.nytimes.com/2014/04/17/business/energy-environment/measuring-africas-air-pollution.html?_r=0
28. Air pollution in South Africa, Available at http://corrosion-doctors.org/AtmCorros/mapSA.htm
29. http://qz.com/487128/west-africas-air-pollution-is-reaching-dangerously-high-levels-and-we-dont-know-the-worst-of-it/
30. https://www.environment.gov.au/protection/air-quality
31. http://www.environment.gov.au/protection/air-quality/air-pollutants
32. http://www.smh.com.au/federal-politics/political-news/air-pollution-takes-toll-on-australian-lives-economy-oecd-report-20140522-38rre.html
33. http://www.stuff.co.nz/auckland/local-news/5690153/Auckland-air-pollution-worst-in-NZ
34. https://en.wikipedia.org/wiki/Air_pollution_in_Canada
35. http://www.cbc.ca/news/health/canada-s-air-quality-3rd-best-in-world-1.980695
36. http://www.idrc.ca/EN/Resources/Publications/Pages/ArticleDetails.aspx?PublicationID=740
37. Air pollution in the United States, Available at https://en.wikipedia.org/wiki/Air_pollution_in_the_United_States
38. http://www.cbsnews.com/news/air-pollution-dangerously-high-for-almost-half-of-us/
39. The Guardian (23 Sep, 2015), India's doctors blame air pollution for sharp rise in respiratory diseases, Retrieved from http://www.theguardian.com/world/2015/sep/23/india-doctors-air-pollution-rise-respiratory-diseases-delhi
40. Air pollution, Available at https://en.wikipedia.org/wiki/Air_pollution
41. http://homeguides.sfgate.com/5-easy-steps-reduce-air-pollution-79154.html
42. What is air pollution? Available at http://www.conserve-energy-future.com/causes-effects-solutions-of-air-pollution.php
43. Air Pollution - causes, effects and control measures, Available at http://mjcetenvsci.blogspot.in/2013/11/air-pollution-causes-effects-and.html
44. The solution of air pollutions, Available at http://www.greenpeace.org/eastasia/campaigns/air-pollution/solutions/
45. http://www.environmentalpollution.in/essay/air-pollution-essay-on-air-pollution-8634-words/336
46. Great smog, Available at https://en.wikipedia.org/wiki/Great_Smog
47. http://www.history.com/news/the-killer-fog-that-blanketed-london-60-years-ago
48. For a Safe and Refreshing Environment, Available at https://www.env.go.jp/en/aboutus/pamph/html/00pan090.html
49. Puja Mondal, Summary on Air Prevention and Control of Pollution Act (1981) of India, See http://www.yourarticlelibrary.com/law/acts/summary-on-air-prevention-and-control-of-pollution-act-1981-of-india/30191/

22

Vehicular Pollution

"Greenhouse gas pollution, through its contribution to global climate change, presents a significant threat to Americans' health and to the environment upon which our economy and security depends."- **Gina McCarthy**

Air pollution has been aggravated by developments that typically occur as countries become industrialised. It is common in growing cities, increasing traffic, rapid economic development and industrialisation, and higher levels of energy consumption. Currently, in India, air pollution is widespread in urban areas where vehicles are the major contributors and in a few other areas with a high concentration of industries and thermal power plants.[1] Transport sector contributes around 14 per cent towards the global emissions of green house gases. Carbon dioxide represents the largest proportion of basket of greenhouse gas emissions. During, the past three decades, carbon dioxide emissions from transport have increased faster than those from all other sectors and are projected to increase more rapidly in future.[2]

The major sources of air pollution are the flue gases, emission from refineries and factories, etc., on one hand; and exhaust emissions from vehicles on the other hand. Control over urban air pollution turns out to be an enormous challenge due to not only the rising numbers of total vehicles but also the increased toxic risk of the growing numbers of diesel cars. Pollution from vehicles especially automobiles is responsible for about two-third of air pollution in the urban area.[3] Efforts to reduce black carbon emissions have become an increasingly important component of national and international efforts to fight global warming, particularly as recent studies have concluded that black carbon is the second most powerful climate warming pollutant after carbon dioxide.[4]

Air pollution is actually the addition of any harmful substances to the atmosphere, which causes the damaging of the environment, human health and the quality of life. With the development in industry, came along the increase in air pollution, which occurs inside homes, schools, offices even in the countryside. Consequently there has been an increase in the death rates resulting from various diseases caused by air pollution varying from breathing problem to lung cancer.[5] It comes from factories, businesses, consumer products, cars, trucks and buses. Pollution from vehicles causes two of our worst air pollution problems, smog, or low-level ozone, and carbon monoxide. Ozone is a colourless gas, which is composed of three oxygen atoms linked together. When found in the upper atmosphere, it is a natural barrier to the harmful rays of the sun. When found at ground level, it can be a hazard to the health of humans, animals and plants.[6]

Meaning

There are three broad sources of air pollution from human activities: stationary or point, mobile, and indoor. In urban areas both developing and developed countries, it is predominately mobile and vehicular pollution that contributes to air quality problem.[7] All motor vehicles release pollutants into the air, mostly through the exhaust fumes that come out of the tailpipe when the engine operates. Pollutants produced by vehicle exhausts include carbon monoxide, hydrocarbons, nitrogen oxides, particles, volatile organic compounds and sulphur dioxide. Hydrocarbons and nitrogen oxides react with sunlight and warm temperatures to form ground-level ozone.[8]

Motor vehicle emissions contribute to air pollution and are a major ingredient in the creation of smog in some large cities. In spark-ignition engines the gases resulting from combustion of the fuel and air mix are called exhaust gases. Exhaust gas from an internal combustion engine whose fuel includes nitro methane will contain nitric acid vapour, which is corrosive, and when inhaled causes a muscular reaction making it impossible to breathe.[9]

Causes of Pollution

The major pollutants emitted by motor vehicles including CO, NO_x, sulphur oxides, lead and suspended particulate matter, have damaging effects on both human health and ecology. The human health effects of air pollution vary in the degree of severity, covering a range of minor effects to serious illness, as well as premature death in certain cases.[10]

Cars release many different kinds of chemicals into the air such as and not limited too: Carbon Dioxide, Nitrogen Dioxide, Sulphur Dioxide, Benzene, Formaldehyde, and Polycyclic hydrocarbons. Hydrocarbon emissions result when fuel molecules in the engine do not burn or burn only partially. Hydrocarbons react in sunlight to form ground-level ozone. Carbon monoxide results from incomplete combustion of fuel and is released from cars tailpipes. Incomplete combustion is most likely to occur at low air-to-fuel ratio.[11] Some of the reasons of automobile pollution are summarised below:

1. Absence of effective mass rapid transport system and intra-city railway networks.
2. High population of humans and vehicles in the urban cities.
3. Improper traffic management systems and road conditions.
4. Inadequate inspection and maintenance facilities.
5. Adulteration of fuel and fuel products.
6. Older vehicles (with old inferior technology) still allowed operating on roads.
7. Faulty engine.[12]

Exponential growth in petrol and diesel fueled vehicles are responsible for deterioration of air quality in cities. Because of the increase in urbanisation, industrialisation and commercial activities in the urban areas, the demand for transport has also been increased. In addition to it the use of personal vehicles has also increase steadily. The various principle pollutants emit from vehicles are as follows:

1. Carbon monoxide (CO)
2. Suspended particulate matter (SPM)
3. Oxides of nitrogen (NOx)
4. Hydrocarbons (HC)
5. Polynuclear aromatic hydrocarbons (PAHs)[13]

Effects of the Pollution

The vehicular emissions have damaging effects on both human health and ecology. There is a wide range of adverse health/ environmental effects of the pollutants released from vehicles. In particular, high levels of sulphur dioxide and suspended particulate matter are associated with increased mortality, morbidity and impaired pulmonary function.[14] Scientific experts now believe the nation faces an epidemic of illnesses that are exacerbated by air pollution. These illnesses include cardiovascular disease, asthma, chronic obstructive pulmonary disease, lung cancer, and diabetes. Cardiovascular disease, hypertension, diabetes and cancer are all illnesses disproportionately borne by the elderly. Nearly one-half million Connecticut residents are over 65 years of age. Vehicle emissions are particularly harmful to people afflicted with chronic obstructive pulmonary disease, such as chronic bronchitis.[15]

Carbon monoxide is a colourless, odourless, poisonous gas emitted from the vehicle's exhaust as a result of incomplete combustion. Unborn or newborn children and people with heart disease are in greatest danger from this pollutant, but even healthy people can experience headaches, fatigue and reduced reflexes due to CO exposure. Ground-level ozone is the major component in what we know as smog. In the body, ozone reacts with lung tissue. It can inflame and cause harmful changes in breathing passages, decrease the lungs' working ability and cause coughing and chest pains. Even healthy people are found to be sensitive to ozone exposure.

Sulphur dioxide exposure constricts air passages, creating problems for people with asthma and for young children, whose small lungs need to work harder than adults' lungs. Nitrogen dioxide and related nitrogen oxides (NO_x) are produced when fuel is burned. The effect of NO_x exposure on the respiratory system is similar to that of ozone and sulphur dioxide. Lead poisoning can reduce mental ability, damage blood, nerves, and organs, and raise blood pressure. Even small ingestions or inhalations of lead can be harmful because lead accumulates in the body. Exposure to particulate matter can cause wheezing and similar symptoms in people with asthma or sensitive airways. Particulate matter can serve as a vector for toxic air pollutants.[16]

Vehicle emissions can affect the environment in several ways. Cars emit greenhouse gasses, such as carbon dioxide, which contribute to global warming. Some air pollutants and particulate matter from cars can be deposited on soil and surface waters where they enter the food chain; these substances can affect the reproductive, respiratory, immune and neurological systems of animals. Vehicles contain many different fluids, including motor oil, antifreeze, gasoline, air-conditioning refrigerants, and brake, transmission, hydraulic and windshield-wiper fluids. In most cases, these fluids are toxic to humans and animals, and can pollute waterways if they leak from a vehicle or are disposed of incorrectly.[17]

Global Perspectives

Vehicular pollution is a global problem. Emissions from motor vehicles are the single most significant source of air pollution in many Australian urban areas. Improved knowledge about the quantity of pollutants that the vehicle fleet is emitting into the air has become a high priority research question for authorities who are responsible for managing vehicle emission impacts on air quality - especially in urban areas.[18] In the past century, the automobile has come a far way from Henry Ford's Model T. In the United States there has always been a high demand for cars, and with that demand come the need for speed, and a need to have the best.[19]

The pollutant emissions from road vehicles are regulated separately for light-duty vehicles (cars and light vans) and for heavy-duty vehicles (trucks and buses).[20] Europe is to become the first place in the world to force 'real world' emissions tests on car makers, opening up a new front in the fight to tackle air pollution. Pollutants from diesel engines such as nitrogen oxide, carbon monoxide and particulates are thought to be responsible for at least one quarter of the 29,000 annual pollution-related deaths in the UK alone.[21] Road transport contributes about one-fifth of the EU's total emissions of carbon dioxide, the main greenhouse gas. While these emissions fell by 3.3 per cent in

2012, they are still 20.5 per cent higher than in 1990. Transport is the only major sector in the EU where greenhouse gas emissions are still rising.[22]

Air pollution levels in London are off the scale and more than 7,000 Britons die every year as a direct result of vehicle-derived air pollution. Americans, in contrast, stopped dying of smog a generation ago, when the smog laws swept the filthiest vehicles into the scrapyards.[23] Despite ongoing efforts to wean itself off the teat of foreign oil, the US car market is still almost twice as polluting as Europe and Japan.[24]

Indian Perspectives

The number of motor vehicles has increased from 0.3 million in 1951 to 37.2 million in 1997. Out of these, 32 per cent are concentrated in 23 metropolitan cities. Delhi itself accounts for about eight per cent of the total registered vehicles and has more registered vehicles than those in the other three metros (Mumbai, Calcutta, and Chennai) taken together. At the all-India level, the percentage of two-wheeled vehicles in the total number of motor vehicles increased from nine per cent in 1951 to 69 per cent in 1997, and the share of buses declined from 11 per cent to 1.3 per cent during the same period. Road-based passenger transport has recorded very high growth in recent years especially since 1980-81.[25]

The rapid urbanisation in India has also resulted in a tremendous increase the number of motor vehicles. The vehicle fleets have even doubled in some cities in the last one decade. This increased mobility, come with a high price. As the number of vehicles continues to grow and the consequent congestion increases, vehicles are now becoming the main source of air pollution in urban India.[26]

In major cities there exists a mandatory system for inspection and maintenance but it is now increasingly felt to upgrade the present system to a more effective one in the near future. The first initiative to regulate vehicle emissions in India started in the year 1989 when Ministry of Environment and Forests constituted an expert committee to notify the emission standards for both new and in-use vehicles under the Environment (Protection) Act. The in-use vehicle emission norms have been tightened with effect from 1st October 2004 and computerisation model for emission check has been developed by Society of

Indian Automobile Manufacturers, which is already in place in the major metro cities. Mass emission norms for vehicles for the first time at manufacturing stage as well as for in-use vehicles have been notified during 1990-91, the manufacturers did not require any major modification for meeting these norms.[27]

Delhi is a typical example of air pollution by vehicles. Delhi's vehicular population increased from an insignificant of 2.17 lakh in 1971 to 44 lakh in 2004. Over 2.5 lakh vehicles were registered in Delhi in 2004—more than twice the number registered in 2003. Of the total vehicular population in Delhi in 2004, 13.37 lakh were four wheelers, 27.8 lakh two wheelers, more than 80 thousand auto rickshaws, 18.4 thousand taxies, 26.9 thousand buses and 1.55 lakh goods vehicles. This figure is likely to rise to 60 lakh in 2011. A World Bank study in Delhi (1998) showed that diesel vehicles were responsible for as much as 62.5 per cent of the total particulate load coming from all vehicles. Even after the implementation of the CNG programme, a recent World Bank study of 2004 confirms, based on actual measurements and characterisation of PM 2.5 (a tiny fraction of the particulate), that diesel fuel's contribution could still rise as high as 23 per cent. According to a report of Centre for Science and Environment (CSE), air pollution claims one life in Delhi per hour. Another study from the Kolkata-based Chittaranjan National Cancer Institute stated that 64 per cent of Delhi's children suffer from lung function impairment and 71.4 per cent individuals display respiratory disorders.[28]

Preventive Measures

The main international systems of vehicle emission standards and test procedures are those of North America and Europe. North American emission standards and test procedures were originally adopted by the United States, which was the first country to set emission standards for vehicles. Under the North American Free Trade Agreement, these standards have also been adopted by Canada and Mexico. Other countries and jurisdictions that have adopted US standards, test procedures or both include Brazil, Chile, Hong Kong, Taiwan (China), several Western European countries, the Republic of Korea (South Korea), and Singapore (for motorcycles only).[29]

Motor vehicles are significant sources of pollution that can damage the environment and pose public health issues. Proper maintenance of car and truck emission control systems not only limits harmful emissions, but also can improve fuel efficiency and vehicle performance extending the life of the vehicle. Care in storing and handling gasoline and other solvents also reduces evapourative losses to the atmosphere. Zero-emission vehicles include battery-electric vehicles, plug-in hybrid-electric vehicles, and hydrogen fuel-cell-electric vehicles. These technologies can be used in passenger cars, trucks and transit buses.[30]

Vehicle emissions control is the study of reducing the motor vehicle emissions—emissions produced by motor vehicles, especially internal combustion engines. There are many ways to prevent vehicular pollution. By getting right to the sources and developing new transportation ideas, vehicular pollution can be greatly reduced. Currently there are trends towards encouraging less traffic through offering public transportation at reasonable costs. Hybrid vehicles are also popular with consumers because they save on fuel costs, but they also produce fewer emissions. To improve emissions from traffic we:

1. Hold open days where people can have their vehicle emissions checked and receive advice.
2. Check all council vehicles.
3. Use a diesel additive in council vehicles to reduce fuel consumption.
4. Use reduced-pollution emitting fuels such as biodiesel and ultra-low diesel in all council vehicles.[31]

Table 1: Prevention and Control of Vehicular Pollution[32]

Do's	*Don'ts*
Do you really need to drive a car everywhere? Walk to work, or ride a bicycle	Don't use extensively your private vehicles, try to use public transportation whenever possible
Carpool. Two - or four - can ride as cheaply as one	Avoid congested road and rush hours.
Clean the air filter and oil filter regularly.	Don't try to replicate mechanical works and experiment with your car.
Clean the carbon deposit from silencer.	Don't forget to replace your old battery with new battery when it required.
Maintain recommended tyre pressure.	Don't use clutch pedal as footrest.

Source: http://beed.nic.in/htmldocs/pdf/polution-do-dont.pdf

Legal Mechanism

The government has gotten involved, making the purchase of a hybrid vehicle a way to earn money and get tax cuts through special programmes. There has been more focus on traffic flow patterns and the creation of new roadways. This allows traffic to flow and cuts congestion which causes a great amount of pollution. Prevention of vehicular pollution is a great concern because it seems to just continue to be a problem that gets worse. As the population grows and more people take to the roadways the prevention of pollution is going to become even more important.[33]

Methods that helps in reducing automobile pollution:

1. Change oil at recommended time.
2. Use good quality lubricant.
3. Inspect spark-plug clearance and replace it, if necessary.
4. Maintain appropriate tyre pressure.
5. Tune and dirt free the carburetor.
6. Maintain and service the vehicle at regular intervals.
7. Drive at recommended speed.[34]

References

1. Air pollution with special reference to vehicular pollution in urban cities, Available at http://envfor.nic.in/soer/2001/ind_air.pdf
2. Status of the vehicular pollution control programme in India, Available at http://www.cpcb.nic.in/upload/NewItems/NewItem_157_VPC_REPORT.pdf
3. Shivaji Bhandarkar, Vehicular Pollution, Their Effect on Human Heatlh and Mitigation Measures, Vehicle Engineering (VE) Volume 1 Issue 2, June 2013, see file:///C:/Documents%20 and%20Settings/Administrator/My%20Documents/Downloads/VE004.pdf
4. http://www.nrdc.org/international/latin-america-diesel-pollution.asp
5. http://www.megaessays.com/viewpaper/101598.html
6. http://www.deq.louisiana.gov/portal/DIVISIONS/Assessment/MotorVehicleInspectionProgram/MotorVehicleEmissionsAirPollution.aspx
7. http://www.studymode.com/essays/Vehicular-Pollution-129265.html
8. http://www.tmr.qld.gov.au/Community-and-environment/Environmental-management/How-you-can-make-a-difference/Motor-vehicle-pollution.aspx
9. Exhaust gas, Available at https://en.wikipedia.org/wiki/Exhaust_gas
10. Shivaji Bhandarkar, Vehicular Pollution, Their Effect on Human Heatlh and Mitigation Measures, Vehicle Engineering (VE) Volume 1 Issue 2, June 2013, see file:///C:/Documents %20and%20Settings/Administrator/My%20Documents/Downloads/VE004.pdf
11. Pollution caused by vehicle, Available at http://www.directessays.com/viewpaper/30288.html
12. Raghav Agarwal, Short Essay on the Automobile Pollution in India, See http://www.shareyouressays.com/93486/short-essay-on-the-automobile-pollution-in-india

13. http://www.shareyouressays.com/89127/412-words-essay-on-automobile-pollution
14. Status of the vehicular pollution control programme in India, Available at http://www.cpcb.nic.in/upload/NewItems/NewItem_157_VPC_REPORT.pdf
15. http://www.ehhi.org/reports/exhaust/summary.shtml
16. Health Effects from Automobile Emissions, Available at https://fortress.wa.gov/ecy/publications/documents/0002008.pdf
17. Jennifer King, How Does Car Pollution Affect the Environment and Ozone Layer?, Available at http://homeguides.sfgate.com/car-pollution-affect-environment-ozone-layer-79358.html
18. Assessing Vehicle Air Pollution Emissions, Available at https://www.environment.gov.au/system/files/resources/73c55f4c-9b4f-4ae8-a09e-d089a703d29a/files/vehicle-pollution.pdf
19. http://www.exampleessays.com/viewpaper/83691.html
20. http://ec.europa.eu/environment/air/transport/road.htm
21. The Guardian (Feb 3, 2015), Car makers face 'real world' emissions tests in EU pollution clampdown, Available at http://www.theguardian.com/environment/2015/feb/03/car-makers-face-real-world-emissions-tests-in-eu-pollution-clampdown
22. Road transport: Reducing CO_2 emissions from vehicles, Available at http://ec.europa.eu/clima/policies/transport/vehicles/index_en.htm
23. The Telegraph (Sep 20, 2015), Europe must now come clean on diesel, Available at http://www.telegraph.co.uk/news/earth/environment/11878435/Europe-must-now-come-clean-on-diesel.html
24. http://www.gizmag.com/us-european-japanese-car-market-co2-pollution/15485/
25. Air pollution with special reference to vehicular pollution in urban cities, Available at http://envfor.nic.in/soer/2001/ind_air.pdf
26. Status of the vehicular pollution control programme in India, Available at http://www.cpcb.nic.in/upload/NewItems/NewItem_157_VPC_REPORT.pdf
27. Status of the vehicular pollution control programme in India, Available at http://www.cpcb.nic.in/upload/NewItems/NewItem_157_VPC_REPORT.pdf
28. Smriti Chand, Vehicular pollution in India, Available at http://www.yourarticlelibrary.com/pollution/vehicular-pollution-in-india-2118-words/19796/
29. Air Pollution from Motor Vehicles Standards and Technologies for Controlling Emissions, Available at http://www.un.org/esa/gite/iandm/faizpaper.pdf
30. Controlling Air Pollution from Motor Vehicles, Available at http://www.dec.ny.gov/chemical/8394.html
31. http://www.royalgreenwich.gov.uk/info/413/pollution_ control_-_air_quality/586/major_causes_of_ air_pollution
32. http://beed.nic.in/htmldocs/pdf/polution-do-dont.pdf
33. https://in.answers.yahoo.com/question/index?qid=20101207040205AAqPaiO
34. http://www.shareyouressays.com/93486/short-essay-on-the-automobile-pollution-in-india

23

Soil Pollution

"The prevailing ideology of the modern west - which is political economy - is in the doghouse. Having failed to notice atmospheric pollution, the economists then frightened themselves with the sort of financial crisis they said they had abolished."
-James Buchan

Soil is the mixture of minerals, organic matter, gases, liquids, and the countless organisms that together support life on earth. It is considered to be the "skin of the earth" and interfaces with its lithosphere, hydrosphere, atmosphere, and biosphere. Most soils have a density between 1 and 2 g/cm^3. Soil science has two basic branches of study: edaphology and pedology. Soil acts as an engineering medium, a habitat for soil organisms, a recycling system for nutrients and organic wastes, a regulator of water quality, a modifier of atmospheric composition, and a medium for plant growth.[1]

Soil is the material found on the surface of the earth that is composed of organic and inorganic material. It varies due to its structure and composition. There are three basic types of soil: sand, silt and clay. But most soils are composed of a combination of the different types. One type of soil is sand. Sand within soil is actually small particles of weathered rock. Sand is fairly coarse and loose so water is able to drain through it easily. Silt is another type of soil. Silt can be thought of as fine sand, and it will hold water better than sand. Clay is very fine-grained soil. Its particles are even smaller than silt, so there is very little space between the fine grains for air or water to circulate.[2]

In terms of soil texture, soil type usually refers to the different sizes of mineral particles in a particular sample. Each component, and their size, plays an important role. In addition to the mineral composition of soil, humus also plays an important role in soil characteristics and fertility for plant life.[3] In modern economies, various types of activity, including agriculture, industry and transportation, produce a large amount of wastes and new types of pollutants. Soil, air and water have traditionally been used as sites for the disposal of all these wastes.[4] The widespread industrialisation and increasing consumption have changed the composition and complexion of earth strata. It can be said that soil is being heavily polluted day by day by the toxic materials coming out of industries and domestic circles.[5]

Meaning

Soil pollution is defined as the build-up in soils of persistent toxic compounds, chemicals, salts, radioactive materials, or disease causing agents, which have adverse effects on plant growth and animal health. **Soil pollutants** include a large variety of contaminants or chemicals (organic and inorganic), which could be both naturally-occurring in soil and man-made. In both cases, the main **soil pollution causes** are the human activities.[6] It is the contamination of soil with harmful substances that can adversely affect the quality of the soil and the health of those living on it. Pollution can be the result of an accident or carelessness, or done on purpose through illegal dumping. It is a by-product of activities as normal as driving or maintaining a farm.[7]

The soil pollution is defined as the presence of materials in the soil which are harmful to the living beings when they cross their threshold concentration levels.[8] It comprises the pollution of soils with materials, mostly chemicals that are out of place or are present at concentrations higher than normal which may have adverse effects on humans or other organisms.[9] *It* is when humans introduce harmful objects, chemicals or substances, directly or indirectly into the *soil* in a way that causes harm to other living things or destroys *soil* or water ecosystems.[10]

It is the occurrence of pollutants in soil above a certain level causing a deterioration or loss of one or more soil functions. Soil contamination can be considered as the presence of man-made chemicals or other alteration in the natural soil environment. This type of contamination typically arises from the rupture of underground storage tanks, application of pesticides, percolation of contaminated surface water to subsurface strata, leaching of wastes from landfills or direct discharge of industrial wastes to the soil.[11]

Causes of Pollution

Industrial activity has been the biggest contributor to the problem in the last century, especially since the amount of mining and manufacturing has increased. As a result, the industrial waste lingers in the soil surface for a long time and makes it unsuitable for use. Chemical utilisation has gone up tremendously since technology provided with modern pesticides and fertilisers. They are full of chemicals that are not produced in nature and cannot be broken down by it. Oil leaks can happen during storage and transport of chemicals. This can be seen at most of the fuel stations. Acid rain is caused when pollutants present in the air mixes up with the rain and fall back on the ground.[12]

Hazardous waste means a waste or combination of wastes, which because of quantity or concentration can cause serious illness and irreversible hazards to the humans. These mainly include radioactive wastes, biomedical wastes and non-radioactive industrial wastes.[13] Thermal power plants generate a large quantity of 'Fly ash'. Huge quantities of these wastes are dumped on land which cause land pollution. Mining also affects ground and surface waters, the aquatic life, vegetation, soils, animals, and the human health.[14]

Mining waste is generally left on site in the form of spoil heaps. These spoil heaps may contain a wide variety of toxic or poisonous substances which then leach into the soil due to rainfall, or are blown around by wind. Heavy industry often produces quantities of unwanted chemicals, which, if allowed to come in contact with the soil, can cause extensive pollution. Vehicles are a major cause of pollution to the soil close to roads, especially where vehicles are running on the old leaded petrol.[15] Soil pollution occurs when the presence of toxic chemicals, pollutants or contaminants in the soil is in high enough concentrations to be of risk to plants, wildlife, humans and of course, the soil itself. The redundant, ever-increasing use of chemicals such as pesticides, herbicides, insecticides and fertilisers is one of the main factors causing soil pollution by increasing its salinity making it imperfect for crop bearing and adversely affecting the microorganisms present in the soil.[16]

Soil is getting polluted through the toxic substances released by the use of chemical fertilisers, pesticides, insecticides, industrial wastes, etc which are badly affecting the fertility of land. Main cause of the soil pollution are excessive soil erosion, forest fires, use of chemical fertilisers to improve crop production, pesticides, biocides to get control over insects, urban and industrial wastes, leaching, drought, untreated industrial water irrigation, water logging, over irrigation, deforestation, etc. Soil pollution is the polluted soil because of the presence of toxic chemicals in very high concentration to the soil of fertile land. Soil pollution is the contamination of the soil of fertile land which is gradually increasing day by day mainly because of the use of fertilisers and industrialisation. Soil pollution is the contamination of the fertile soil which reduces the productivity of soil because of various toxic pollutants. Toxic pollutants are very dangerous and adversely affect the physical, chemical and biological properties of the soil.[17]

In shortly, various causes of soil pollution are: Increasing urbanisation; disposal of untreated wastes; indiscriminate use of Agrochemicals and Agricultural; Unscientific mining; Dumping Industrial Wastes; Accidental Pollution/Leakages; Outdated technology; inadequate treatment and safety management of chemicals and waste, and Lack of Designed Engineered Landfills.[18]

Effects of the Pollution

Health consequences from exposure to soil contamination vary greatly depending on pollutant type, pathway of attack and vulnerability of the exposed population. Chronic exposure to chromium, lead and other metals, petroleum, solvents, and many pesticide and herbicide formulations can be carcinogenic, can cause congenital disorders. Chronic exposure to benzene at sufficient concentrations is known to be associated with higher incidence of leukemia. Mercury and cyclodienes are known to induce higher incidences of kidney damage, some irreversible.

Many chlorinated solvents induce liver changes, kidney changes and depression of the central nervous system. There is an entire spectrum of further health effects such as headache, nausea, fatigue, eye irritation and skin rash for the above cited and other chemicals.[19]

The ecological balance of any system gets affected due to the widespread contamination of the soil. The fertility slowly diminishes, making land unsuitable for agriculture and any local vegetation to survive. The toxic chemicals present in the soil can decrease soil fertility and therefore decrease in the soil yield. The emission of toxic and foul gases from landfills pollutes the environment and causes serious effects on health of some people.[20] The harmful effects of soil pollution may come from direct contact with polluted soil or from contact with other resources, such as water, that have come in direct contact with the polluted soil.[21] Soil pollution is considered as a major challenge for healthy environment. The weathering of earth's crust forms, soil over the centuries that supports the variety of microscopic and macroscopic life-forms. The top most layer of soil is composed of minerals of various sizes and organic matters along with pores filled with air and water.[22]

Industrial wastes containing toxic metals kill bacteria and beneficial micro-organisms in the soil. Industrial effluents causing high acidity or high basicity of the soil cause severe agricultural crop damage. Direct discharge of industrial effluents through sewage system is causes poisoning of biological purification mechanism of sewage treatment inducing several soil-borne and water- borne diseases. The dumped urban wastes along highways and other places in cities spread several chronic diseases posing a serious threat to human health. Solid wastes result in offensive odour and cause clogging of ground water filters. The excessive use of nitrogenous fertilisers in land leads to accumulation of nitrate in the soil which subsequently enters into human body through food chain. The pesticides present in the soil sometimes appear in fruits and vegetable and make them unusable. Herbicides and chlorinated pesticides affect soil texture and function thereby disturbing the natural eco-system. Since radioactive wastes are produced in huge quantities and these have high activation energies, these cause a number of hazards to public health system.[23]

Global Perspectives

Along with industrial expansion, arable lands have been gradually degraded or contaminated with heavy metals and organic pollutants in most Asian countries. During the past two decades, this trend led to significant deterioration of the quality of soils and crops as the concentration of pollutants continues to increase. Approximately 25 per cent of the world's crop yield is estimated to be directly attributed to the use of chemical fertilisers. The use of chemical fertilisers has increased significantly over the last few decades and is expected to raise even more.[24] Millions of tonnes of urban waste are produced every year from polluted cities. The inadequately treated or untreated sewage sludge not only poses serious health hazards but also pollutes soil and decreases its fertility and productivity. Other waste materials such as rubbish, used plastic bag, garbage sludge, dead animals, hospital wastes, skins, tyres shoes etc. cause land and soil pollution. Suspended matter present in sewage can act as a blanket on the soil and interfere with its productivity.[25]

Soil pollution is a serious concern in China, particularly with respect to the human health implications resulting from contaminated water and food.[26] Soil contamination is the presence of man-made chemicals or other alteration to the natural soil environment.[27] Conducted between 2005 to 2013, it found that 16.1 per cent of China's soil and 19.4 per cent of its arable land showed contamination. The report, by the Environmental Protection Ministry, named cadmium, nickel and arsenic as top pollutants. There is growing concern, both from the government and the public, that China's rapid industrialisation is causing irreparable damage to its environment.[28]

China's troubles with air and water pollution are widely known with its smog-clouded cities and chemical-filled rivers drawing international attention. Soil pollution is not only affecting the health and well-being of Chinese citizens, it is also putting the nation's food security at risk. A Chinese government report released in April this year said that 16.1 per cent of the country's soil was polluted. Soil pollution in China has attracted little public attention, in spite of the health threats. Until recently, the government also resisted media attempts to spotlight local cancer epidemics in the country's newly industrial areas, the report claims. Indeed, the Chinese government previously refused to divulge information on soil pollution terming it a state secret.[29]

There may be as many as 2.5 million potentially contaminated sites across Europe, which need to be investigated. Of these, approximately 14 per cent are expected to be contaminated and likely to require remediation. Approximately one-third of these contaminated sites have already been identified and around 15 per cent have been remediated. Municipal and industrial waste disposal and treatment causes around a third of Europe's soil contamination problem. Metal industries and petrol stations are also common sources of soil contamination.[30] Eight major aspects of soil degradation in Europe have been identified: *biodiversity decline, compaction, contamination, erosion, landslides, organic matter decline, salinisation and sealing.* Further, *acidification, desertification* or *biofuels production* are other potential threats to soil integrity considered in this report. All these problems have considerable economic and environmental consequences and could eventually compromise food production.[31]

United Nation's carbon offset mechanism is rewarding pollution and could cause unsustainable land grabs in Africa, according to an international charity. The Gaia Foundation says the current market is pushing industrial biofuels, genetically modified crops and biochar regardless of the problems caused to land in the long term.[32] The fact that Antarctica is one of the cleanest places on earth makes it an ideal location for measuring the spread of global pollutants. It is one of the first places on earth where the effects of increased atmospheric carbon dioxide are being seen, and hence has a central role in research into global climate change. Like many countries operating in Antarctica, Australia has inherited problems resulting from the way we used to build and operate our stations in the past.[33]

Indian Perspectives

The committee appointed by the Indian Council of Agricultural Research, classified the Indian soil in the following main groups: Alluvial Soils, Black Soils, Red Soils, Laterite Soils, Mountain Soils, and Desert Soils. The alluvial soil is found mostly in the Northern Plains, starting from Punjab in the west to West Bengal and Assam in the east. It is found in the deltas of the Mahanadi, Godavari, Krishna and Kaveri rivers in the Peninsular

India. The black soil is mostly found in the Deccan Trap, covering large areas of Maharashtra, Gujarat and western Madhya Pradesh. It is also found in some parts of Godavari and Krishna river valleys, covering parts of Karnataka, Andhra Pradesh and Tamil Nadu.

The red soil occupies about 10 per cent area of India, mostly in the south-eastern part of the Peninsular India. The red soil is found in Tamil Nadu, parts of Karnataka, southeast Maharashtra, eastern parts of Andhra Pradesh, Madhya Pradesh, Odisha and Jharkhand. Laterite soil is well- developed in southern Maharashtra, and parts of Odisha, West Bengal, Karnataka, Andhra Pradesh, Kerala, Bihar, Assam and Meghalaya. The mountain soil is generally found on the hill slopes covered with forests. Apart from the Himalayan region, this soil is also found in the Western and Eastern Ghats and in some parts of the Peninsular India. The desert soil is found mostly in the arid and semi-arid regions, receiving less than 50 cm of annual rainfall. Such regions are mostly found in Rajasthan and the adjoining areas of Haryana and Punjab.[34]

There are many environmental issues in India. Air pollution, water pollution, garbage, and pollution of the natural environment are all challenges for India. Environmental issues are one of the primary causes of disease, health issues and long-term livelihood impact for India. There is a long history of study and debate about the interactions between population growth and the environment. Trash and garbage is a common sight in urban and rural areas of India. It is a major source of pollution. Indian cities alone generate more than 100 million tonnes of solid waste a year. Street corners are piled with trash. In 2000, India's Supreme Court directed all Indian cities to implement a comprehensive waste-management programme that would include household collection of segregated waste, recycling and composting.[35]

The increasing use of chemical fertilisers and biocides particularly after Green Revolution, the use of untreated industrial water in irrigation, over irrigation, deforestation, defective land use practices etc. have led to the degradation of soils in many parts of the country. The increasing use of chemical fertilisers and biocides particularly after Green Revolution, the use of untreated industrial water in irrigation, over irrigation, deforestation, defective land use practices etc. have led to the degradation of soils in many parts of the country. Coal dust spreads over the agricultural fields of the mining areas. Numerous mica chips are seen scattered over the agricultural fields in Kodarma mica belt of Jharkhand. Magnesite dusts mixed with soils increases pH value of the soils. Soils near copper mining and smelting near Khetri, Dariba, Ghatsila, Rakha etc. are so polluted that no plant growth becomes possible.[36]

Preventive Measures

Soil may be polluted and converted into acidic soil or alkaline soil. It should be corrected by suitable technology, before cultivation. Air sparging is an in situ remedial technology that reduces concentrations of volatile constituents in petroleum products that are adsorbed to soils and dissolved in groundwater. Soil washing is a water-based process for scrubbing soils *ex-situ* to remove contaminants. The process removes contaminants from soils in one of the following two ways: (a) By dissolving or suspending them in the wash solution (which can be sustained by chemical manipulation of pH for a period of time); or (b) By concentrating them into a smaller volume of soil through particle size separation, gravity 6 separation, and attrition scrubbing (similar to those techniques used in sand and gravel operations). Biopile treatment is a technology in which excavated soils are mixed with soil amendments and placed on a treatment area that includes leachate collection systems and some form of aeration.

Land farming is a bioremediation treatment process that is performed in the upper soil zone or in biotreatment cells. Contaminated soils, sediments, or sludges are incorporated into the soil surface and periodically turned over to aerate the mixture. Soil conservation is the protection of soil against excessive loss of fertility by natural, chemical, or artificial means. Organic farming is a holistic approach which aims for the production of quality and safe agriculture products for consumption. Organic farming is a production method which does not pollute the soil and ground water with chemical residues and provides safe and quality food for consumption. Organic farming aspires to a complex mix of agronomic, environmental, agricultural and processing and is based on a number of principles.[37] Land pollution can be controlled by adopting as follows:

1. Soil erosion should be checked.
2. Controlled and judicious use of chemical fertilisers and pesticides, insecticides and herbicides.

3. Proper disposal of industrial and urban wastes.
4. After proper treatment the urban and industrial effluents should be used for irrigation purposes.
5. Proper land use and management.
6. Proper use of fertilisers and biocides.[38]

Legal Mechanism

The Indian Association of Preventive and Social Medicine and The Indian Public Health Association had urged the Indian government and the civil society to take prompt action to prevent the effects of global warming on health. According to the fourth assessment report of UN Intergovernmental Panel on Climate Change, it is important to study the impact of global warming at the grass root level and chalk out ways to tackle it. The Anti-pollution law should be strictly practiced. In order to check water pollution, the sewage and the factory waste should be properly treated and cleaned before being discharged. Trees should be planted everywhere and vehicles should be made eco-friendly. Public education and awareness of the relationship between climate change and human health is key to deal with problems more effectively.[39]

References

1. Soil, Available at https://en.wikipedia.org/wiki/Soil
2. What is Soil? - Definition, Structure and Types, Available at http://study.com/academy/lesson/what-is-soil-definition-structure-types.html
3. Soil type, Available at https://en.wikipedia.org/wiki/Soil_type
4. Diah Setyorini, Tini Prihatini and Undang Kurnia, Pollution of soil by agricultural and agricultural assets, Available at http://www.fao.org/prods/gap/database/gap/files/1284_SOIL_POLLUTION_INDONESIA.PDF
5. http://www.shareyouressays.com/89133/516-words-essay-on-soil-pollution
6. http://www.environmentalpollutioncenters.org/soil/
7. Suzanne S. Wiley (2015), Definition of soil pollution, Available at http://www.livestrong.com/article/192150-definition-of-soil-pollution/
8. What is soil pollution? Available at http://www.thebigger.com/biology/pollution/what-is-soil-pollution/
9. Soil pollution, Available at http://www.pollutionissues.com/Re-Sy/Soil-Pollution.html
10. http://eschooltoday.com/pollution/land-pollution/what-is-soil-contamination.html
11. Soil contamination, Available at http://esdac.jrc.ec.europa.eu/themes/soil-contamination
12. What is soil pollution?, Available at http://www.conserve-energy-future.com/causes-and-effects-of-soil-pollution.php
13. http://www.preservearticles.com/2012011320632/short-essay-on-the-sources-and-effects-of-soil-pollution.html

14. http://www.yourarticlelibrary.com/land-pollution/land-pollution-sources-effects-and-control-of-land-pollution-783-words/9951/
15. Soil pollution, Available at http://www.soil-net.com/dev/page.cfm?pageid=casestudies_soilpollution&loginas=anon_casestudies
16. http://www.everythingconnects.org/soil-pollution.html
17. http://www.indiacelebrating.com/essay/environmental-issues/pollution/soil-pollution/
18. http://sgw.epa.gov.tw/resag/Update_Data/Information 883128Nov30_08INDIA-Taipei%20Presentation.pdf
19. Soil contamination, Available at https://en.wikipedia.org/wiki/Soil_contamination
20. What is soil pollution?, Available at http://www.conserve-energy-future.com/causes-and-effects-of-soil-pollution.php
21. A.L. Kennedy (2014), The effects of soil pollution on humans, Available at http://www.livestrong.com/article/176005-the-effects-of-soil-pollution-on-humans/
22. http://www.importantindia.com/11080/essay-on-soil-pollution/
23. http://www.environmentalpollution.in/essay/land-pollution-essay-on-land-pollution-4204-words/353
24. Emerging Soil Pollution Problems in Rice and their Amelioration, Available at http://www.rkmp.co.in/sites/default/files/ris/research-themes/Emerging%20Soil%20Pollution% 20Problems% 20in%20Rice%20and% 20their% 20Amelioration. pdf
25. Lecture 10 Causes, effects and control of soil pollution, Available at http://agridr.in/tnauEAgri/eagri50/ENVS302/pdf/lec10.pdf
26. Angel Hsu and William Miao (2014), Soil Pollution in China Still a State Secret Despite Recent Survey, Available at http://blogs.scientificamerican.com/guest-blog/soil-pollution-in-china-still-a-state-secret-infographic/
27. http://www.sciencedaily.com/terms/soil_contamination.htm
28. http://www.bbc.com/news/world-asia-china-27076645
29. http://www.dw.com/en/soil-pollution-is-a-severe-problem-in-china/a-17807733
30. Soil contamination widespread in Europe, Available at http://www.eea.europa.eu/highlights/soil-contamination-widespread-in-europe
31. http://www.greenfacts.org/highlights/2012/02/farming-erosion-biodiversity-or- contamination-the-declining-state-of-soil-in-europe/
32. http://www.edie.net/news/3/Africas-land-pollution-threat-from-carbon-market/19516/
33. http://www.antarctica.gov.au/environment/pollution-and-waste
34. R Jain, 6 major types of soil found in India, Available at http://www.shareyouressays.com/110930/6-major-types-of-soil-found-in-india
35. Environmental issues in India, Available at https://en.wikipedia.org/wiki/Environmental_issues_in_India
36. http://www.preservearticles.com/2012013022186/short-essay-on-soil-pollution.html
37. Lecture 10 Causes, effects and control of soil pollution, Available at http://agridr.in/tnauEAgri/eagri50/ENVS302/pdf/lec10.pdfhttp://www.importantindia.com/11719/what-are-the-causes-and-effects-of-land-pollution/
38. http://www.publishyourarticles.net/knowledge-hub/essay/an-essay-on-the-pollution/1221/
39. http://www.publishyourarticles.net/knowledge-hub/essay/an-essay-on-the-pollution/1221/

24
Plastic Pollution

> *"Must we wait for selection to solve the problems of overpopulation, exhaustion of resources, pollution of the environment and a nuclear holocaust, or can we take explicit steps to make our future more secure? In the latter case, must we not transcend selection?"* **-B.F. Skinner**

Plastic is a material consisting of any of a wide range of synthetic or semi-synthetic organics that are malleable and can be molded into solid objects of diverse shapes. In the 1800s, as industrial chemistry developed during the Industrial Revolution, many materials were reported. The development of plastics also accelerated with Charles Goodyear's discovery of vulcanisations to thermo set materials derived from natural rubber. Parkesine is considered the first man-made plastic. After World War I, improvements in chemical technology led to an explosion in new forms of plastics, with mass production beginning in the 1940s and 1950s.

Most plastics contain organic polymers. The vast majority of these polymers are based on chains of carbon atoms alone or with oxygen, sulfur, or nitrogen as well. Plastics are usually classified by their chemical structure of the polymer's backbone and side chains. There are two types of plastics: thermoplastics and thermosetting polymers. Thermoplastics are the plastics that do not undergo chemical change in their composition when heated and can be molded again and again. The properties of plastics are defined chiefly by the organic chemistry of the polymer such as hardness, density, and resistance to heat, organic solvents, oxidation, and ionising radiation.

Pure plastics have low toxicity due to their insolubility in water and because they are biochemically inert, due to a large molecular weight. Most plastics are durable and degrade very slowly; the very chemical bonds that make them so durable tend to make them resistant to most natural processes of degradation. Plastics can be pyrolysed into hydrocarbon fuels, since plastics have hydrogen and carbon.[1] The plastics industry manufactures polymer materials and offers services in plastics important to a range of industries, including aerospace, building and construction, electronics, packaging, and transportation.[2]

Plastic is very popular material that is today part of all transport vehicles on the world. Because of its toughness, durability, lightness, and ease of colouring, plastic can be found in fenders, trunk lids, bumpers, housing for headlights and mirrors, hoods, doors, wheel covers, and many more other places.[3] The key problem with plastic however is that a major portion of plastic produced each year is used to make disposable packaging items or other short-lived products that are permanently discarded within a year of manufacture. Plastics have an array of unique properties: they are inexpensive, lightweight, strong, durable, corrosion resistant, and with high thermal and electrical insulation properties.[4]

Meaning

Plastic pollution involves the accumulation of plastic products in the environment that adversely affects wildlife, wildlife habitat, or humans. The prominence of plastic pollution is correlated with plastics being inexpensive and durable, which lends to high levels of plastics used by humans.[5] It is cheap and easy to buy. Hard plastics can be used in making chairs, toys etc. Can be putted in other materials and strengthens them. It takes a hundred of years to decompose. Plastic recycling is a process in which old plastics is turned into another more useful products.[6]

There are three major forms of plastic that contribute to plastic pollution: micro-plastics as well as mega- and macro-plastics. Micro debris is plastic pieces between 2 μm and 5 mm in size. Plastic debris is categorised as macro debris when it is larger than 20 mm. These include items such as plastic grocery bags.[7]

Causes of Pollution

Plastic is the general common term for a wide range of synthetic or semi-synthetic organic solid materials suitable for the manufacture of industrial products. The major chemicals that go into the making of plastic are highly toxic and pose serious threat to living beings of all species on earth. There are many aspects that affect the plastic: the environmental and include human, plants and animals and in economic terms.[8] Plastic can be a very useful material, but by design it is durable, lightweight, convenient and now everywhere.[9]

Plastic bags are one of the most dangerous substances to the environment. For one, plastic bags litter the environment. Forests, rivers, lakes, and oceans are littered all over the world. Wind carries these bags everywhere. We are destroying our own planet and most people don't even realise the harmful effects of these bags. Plastic bags have been one of the most lethal inventions of mankind. They have a major negative impact on humanity, animals, and our environment.[10] Most marine debris comes from trash and debris in urban runoff, i.e. land-based sources. Key components of land-based sources include litter, trash and debris from construction, ports and marinas, commercial and industrial facilities, and trash blown out of garbage containers, trucks, and landfills.[11]

As plastic is less expensive, it is overused. When it is disposed of in landfill sites, it does not decompose at a fast rate, and pollutes the land or soil in that area. Most people tend to throw plastic bottles and polythene bags away, even after a single use. This drastically increases its pollution rate on land as well as in the oceans, mainly in the developing and underdeveloped countries. Every year, about 100 million tonnes of plastic are produced all over the world. Out of this, 25 million tonnes of no degradable plastic gets accumulated in the environment. Approximately 70000 tonnes of plastic are dumped in the oceans and seas globally.[12]

Effects of the Pollution

Plastic pollution has the potential to poison animals, which can then adversely affect human food supplies. Some marine species, such as sea turtles, have been found to contain large proportions of plastics in their stomach. Entanglement in plastic debris has been responsible for the deaths of many marine organisms, such as fish, seals, turtles, and birds. It has been estimated that over 400,000 marine mammals perish annually due to plastic pollution in oceans. Sea turtles are affected by plastic pollution. This plastic debris can kill the sea turtle by obstructing the esophagus.

Plastic pollution does not only affect animals that live solely in oceans. Seabirds are greatly affected. Similar to humans, animals exposed to plasticisers can experience developmental defects. Due to the use of chemical additives during plastic production, plastics have potentially harmful effects that could prove to be carcinogenic or promote endocrine disruption. Due to the pervasiveness of plastic products, most of the human population is constantly exposed to the chemical components of plastics.[13] Animals and sea creatures are hurt and killed every day by discarded plastic bags. Plastic clogs their intestines and leads to slow starvation. Others become entangled in plastic bags and drown. Because plastic bags take hundreds of years to break down, every year our seas become 'home' to more and more bags that find their way there through our sewers and waterways.[14]

A large number of marine creatures become trapped and killed in ghost nets. These are pieces of gill nets which have been lost by fishing vessels. Other pieces of fishing equipment such as lobster pots may also keep trapping creatures. There is great concern about the effect of plastic rubbish on marine mammals in particular, because many of these creatures are already under threat for a variety of other reasons e.g. whale populations have been decimated by uncontrolled hunting. Turtles get entangled in fishing nets, and many sea turtles have been found dead with plastic bags in their stomachs. It is believed they mistake these floating semi-transparent bags for jellyfish and eat them.[15]

Global Perspectives

Plastic pollution in the world's oceans is ubiquitous. The EU estimates that there are 100,000 tonnes of plastic in the world oceans; a recent study on plastic accumulation in the North Atlantic and Caribbean found the highest concentration of plastic debris to exceed 200,000 pieces per square kilometre. The watery realm, upon which so much life depends, has quite simply become a plastic soup.[16] Seventy-five per cent of ocean pollution is due to onshore activities and plastic trash accounts for 90 per cent of all trash floating on the ocean's surface.[17]

Dozens of millions of tonnes of plastic debris end up floating in world oceans broken into micro plastic, the so-called plastic soup. Micro plastics are found in the most remote parts of our oceans. Entanglement of turtles by floating plastic bags, sea mammals and birds that die from eating plastic debris and ghost fishing through derelict fishing gear produce shocking pictures. The massive pollution of world oceans with plastic debris is therefore emerging as a global challenge that requires a global response. The European Union should be a showcase for how to build a coherent strategy to optimise plastic waste policy.[18]

Eight Asia-Pacific nations were among the top ten contributors to a staggering eight million tonnes of plastic trash in global oceans in 2010, which is predicted to increase ten-fold by 2025 unless waste management practices are improved. According to a study published in the journal Science (13 February), China was the world's worst offender along with five countries in South-East Asia — Indonesia, which ranked second; Philippines, third; Vietnam, fourth; Thailand, sixth; and Malaysia, eighth. The other top ten countries are Sri Lanka in fifth spot; Egypt, seventh; Nigeria, ninth; and Bangladesh, tenth.[19]

Plastic pollution is found in all of the world's oceans. Ocean currents throughout the globe converge in five large gyres, one of which is located in the Pacific Ocean. Plastic pollution gets concentrated in all of these gyres, but these are not the only places in the ocean that plastic is found.[20] Land-based sources account for approximately 80 per cent of marine pollution, globally. Seven of the EU Member States plus Norway and Switzerland recover more than 80 per cent of their used plastics. These countries adopt an integrated waste and resource management strategy to address each waste stream with the best options. Waste and disposal remain an issue in most of the world. The United Nations Environment Programme estimated in 2006 that every square mile of ocean contains 46,000 pieces of floating plastic.[21]

Each square kilometre of Australian sea surface water is contaminated by around 4,000 pieces of tiny plastics, according to study published in journal PLOS ONE and data repository Figshare. These small plastic fragments, mostly less than 5 mm across, are loaded with pollutants that can negatively affect several marine species, from tiny fish and zooplankton to large turtles and whales. Marine plastic pollution is a global issue caused by massive production of plastic waste. In Australia, 1,476,690 tonnes of plastics were used in 2011-2012, of which just 20.5 per cent was recycled. Most of these plastics (around 37 per cent) were used for manufacturing single-use disposable packaging, including plastic bottles, cups, and bags.[22]

The Great Pacific garbage patch was predicted in a 1988 paper published by the National Oceanic and Atmospheric Administration of the United States. Estimates of size range from 700,000 square kilometres to more than 15,000,000 square kilometers. The Great Pacific garbage patch has one of the highest levels known of plastic particulate suspended in the upper water column.[23]

Indian Perspectives

The measure was proposed after local municipalities had complained of blocked sewer lines, drainage systems and water distribution pipelines due to plastics buried in the soil, providing breeding grounds for malaria and dengue fever. In Mumbai, in 2005, India experienced massive monsoon flooding partially as a result of drains blocked by plastic bags, resulting in over 1,000 deaths. Only a few per cent of all plastic bags are recycled and the rest of the bags can theoretically persist for centuries in landfills, floating in the breeze or, as in India plugging water lines and creating disease sources.[24]

Deployment of proper plastic waste management techniques is vital. Increase in population, urbanisation and life-style changes were leading to increase in plastic waste. As per industry estimates, the per capita consumption of plastic in India was at about eight kg during 2011-12 and is expected to increase to around 12 kg by 2017. According to the Central Pollution Control Board of India, around 15,342 tonnes of plastic waste is generated in the country every day. Proper waste management techniques and recycling of plastics has many advantages such as conservation of non-renewable fossil fuels and reduced consumption of energy among others. Government of Andhra Pradesh said 175 municipalities in the State apart from those in Hyderabad had achieved 99 per cent collection and segregation of waste on a regular basis. There should be renewed efforts in reduction, recycling and reuse of plastic.[25]

The Supreme Court of India has reprimanded big cities for their poor waste management. The Supreme Court said: "We are sitting on a plastic time bomb," responding to information given by the Central Pollution Control Board that India generates 56 lakh tonnes of plastic waste annually, with Delhi accounting for a staggering 689.50 tonnes a day. The metro cities are major culprits with Delhi producing 690 tonnes a day, Chennai 429 tonnes, Kolkata 426 tonnes and Mumbai producing 408 tonnes. The CPCB told the court that the "total plastic waste which is collected and recycled in the country is estimated to be 9,205 tonnes per day (approximately 60 per cent of total plastic waste) and 6,137 tonnes remain uncollected and littered." After reviewing the situation, the Bench directed the commissioners of civic bodies in the cities of Delhi, Bangalore, Agra, Faridabad and Jaipur to file affidavits within four weeks detailing steps taken under the Municipal Solid Waste (Management and Handling) Rules, 2000 and the Plastic Waste (Management and Handling) Rules, 2011 to dispose of the waste responsibly.[26]

"Total plastic waste which is collected and recycled in the country is estimated to be 9,205 tonnes per day (approximately 60 per cent of total plastic waste) and 6,137 tonnes remain uncollected and littered," the CPCB said. The four metros are major culprits in generating such waste, with Delhi producing 689.5 tonnes a day, followed by Chennai (429.4 tonnes), Kolkata (425.7 tonnes) and Mumbai (408.3 tonnes). The figures only serve to confirm the common sight of mounds of plastic in industrial, residential and slum areas of Indian cities and towns. A shocked court asked civic authorities of five cities — Delhi, Agra, Jaipur, Faridabad and Bangalore — to submit reports on the steps taken to contain dumping of plastic waste and implementing the ban on gutka.

As 40 per cent of plastic waste is not recycled, the daily addition to untreated plastic in Delhi is estimated at 275.6 tonnes, followed by Chennai (171.6 tonnes), Kolkata (170 tonnes) and Mumbai (163.2 tonnes). This waste is a source of continuing pollution as plastic is not bio-degradable and poisons the environment for decades. The CPCB said a survey conducted in 60 major cities found that 15,342.46 tonnes of plastic waste was generated every day, amounting to 56 lakh tonnes a year.[27]

Preventive Measures

Efforts to reduce the use of plastics and to promote plastic recycling have occurred. Some communities and businesses have put a ban on some commonly used plastic items, such as bottled water and plastic bags. Protecting large areas of ocean is necessary to give marine life time to recover, from overfishing and other destructive practise, as well as protecting vital habitats.[28] In order to legitimately tackle the problem, strategies must work to stem the tide of plastic pollution in both developed and developing countries. The developed world has the resources to tackle this problem, while the developing world does not. Efforts must be made to design and export the appropriate low-cost and workable strategies from the developed world to developing countries.[29]

Some countries have introduced so-called "environmentally friendly plastic bags" that are biodegradable. These bags take about three years to break down into practically nothing and while that sounds like an attractive solution, the truth is that the process of breaking down these petrol-based bags causes carbon to become methane which is a greenhouse gas. Until a real alternative is freely available, the only solution is a re-think of attitude: (a) Re-use bags when shopping; (b) Choose biodegradable bags to use for litter; (c) Re-use large plastic sacks whenever possible; and (d) Refrigerate food in containers rather than plastic bags.[30]

Recycling is a making new product out of the waste materials. All types of plastics cannot be recycled. Plastic recycling involves the process of recovering scrap plastic and this waste plastic is then reprocessed to form new materials that may be different from their original state. Compared to other materials like glass and metal, recycling of plastic is expensive and complex. Recycling plastic has many advantages: (a) Use of non-renewable fossil fuels is reduced by recycling as manufacturing new plastic materials require more of these fuels; (b) Consumption of energy is also reduced as already prepared plastic is recycled for new use; (c) Amount of plastic that reach the landfill sites are greatly reduced. This will eliminate land pollution to some extent; and (d) Carbon emissions are reduced as manufacturing units emit more carbon.[31]

The problem of plastic pollution is serious and requires further urgent study. Immediate action is also required such as: (a) Reduction of the amount of plastic used in packaging which is usually immediately thrown away. Re-use of plastics should be encouraged; and (b) Plastic wrapping and bags should carry a warning label stating the dangers of plastic pollution, and shoppers should be encouraged to use their own bags, or recycled paper bags.[32]

Legal Mechanism

Plastic bags have been in the spotlight a lot this year. From bans in Los Angeles and Manila to tax levies in Scotland, it seems that the tide is turning on disposable, single-use plastic bags.[33] The European Parliament has voted to limit the use of plastic bags in Europe, in a drive to curb pollution. The vote has been hailed as an important environmental step. But critics say the targets should not be mandatory and countries should be allowed to take their own measures. The law applies to lightweight plastic bags thinner than 0.05 mm - the most commonly used in the EU. Such bags are less reusable and often pollute seas and rivers. In the future, EU countries will have two ways to implement the agreement: (a) Either to reduce annual average consumption to 90 lightweight bags per citizen by the end of 2019, and 40 by the end of 2025; (b) to ensure that no more light plastic bags are handed out free of charge to shoppers by 2018.[34]

Governments all over the world have taken action to either ban the sale of lightweight bags, charge customers for lightweight bags or generate taxes from the stores who sell them. Countries such as Rwanda, China, Taiwan and Macedonia have a total ban on the bag. In the United States only cities and counties have outlawed their use; however in September 2014, California became the first state to pass a law imposing a ban. Botswana introduced a levy on plastic bags that became effective in 2007. Eritrea banned plastic bags in 2005. Kenya banned the manufacture and import of plastic bags from January 2011 as a way to protect the environment. Mauritania banned the use, manufacture and import of plastic bags from January 2013 as a way to protect the environment, livestock, and marine species.

Rwanda prohibited shops from giving away plastic bags to their customers in 2004. Plastic bags were a major issue in South Africa before the bag levy was introduced in 2004. The Revolutionary Government of Zanzibar banned plastic bags in 2005. Uganda introduced legislation in 2007 to ban the sale of lightweight plastic bags under 30 μm thick and tax thicker bags. A strict ban was introduced in Bangladesh in 2002 after the occurrence of floods from 1988 to 1998 that submerged two-thirds of the country in water. A total plastic bag ban on ultra thin plastic bags and a fee on plastic bags was introduced in China on June 1, 2008.

Hong Kong forbids retailers from giving plastic bags under a certain thickness and for free. In 2002, India banned the production of plastic bags below 20 μm in thickness to prevent plastic bags from clogging of the municipal drainage systems and to prevent the cows of India ingesting plastic bags as they confuse it for food. Malaysia enforces taxes on plastic bags on every Saturday since 2011 in state of Selangor. All stores in Germany that provide plastic bags must pay a recycling tax. In 2003, Denmark introduced a tax to retails for giving out plastic bags. In January 2011, Italy banned the distribution of plastic bags that are not from biodegradable sources.[35]

References

1. Plastic, Available at https://en.wikipedia.org/wiki/Plastic
2. Plastic industry, Available at https://en.wikipedia.org/wiki/Plastics_industry
3. http://www.historyofplastic.com/plastic-facts/benefits-of-plastic/
4. Colette Wabnitz and Wallace J. Nichols, Editorial: Plastic Pollution: An Ocean Emergency, Available at http://www.seaturtle.org/plasticpollution/MTN129p1-4.pdf
5. Plastic pollution, Available at https://en.wikipedia.org/wiki/Plastic_pollution
6. http://www.bubblews.com/posts/advantages-and-disadvantages-of-using-plastics
7. Plastic pollution, Available at https://en.wikipedia.org/wiki/Plastic_pollution
8. The Effects of Plastic Waste Environmental Sciences Essay, Read more: http://www.ukessays.com/essays/environmental-sciences/the-effects-of-plastic-waste-environmental-sciences-essay.php#ixzz3mo72JPZ8
9. http://sailorsforthesea.org/resources/ocean-watch/plastic-pollution-and-its-solution
10. Plastic Bags Will Be the Death of Us, Available at http://www.teenink.com/hot_topics/environment/article/242153/Plastic-Bags-Will-Be-the-Death-of-Us/
11. The Problem of Marine Plastic Pollution, Available at http://www.cleanwater.org/feature/problem-of-marine-plastic-pollution
12. N. M. Dana Gopal, P. Phebe, E.V. Suresh Kumar, and B.K.K. Vani, Impact of plastic leading environmental pollution, National Seminar on Impact of Toxic Metals, Minerals and Solvents leading to Environmental Pollution-2014 Journal of Chemical and Pharmaceutical Sciences, http://www.jchps.com/pdf/si3/20%20jchps%20si3%20N.%20M.%20dana%20Gopal%2096-99.pdf
13. Plastic pollution, Available at https://en.wikipedia.org/wiki/Plastic_pollution
14. Sharon Jacobsen, Plastic Bag Pollution, Available at http://dpw.lacounty.gov/epd/PlasticBags/Articles/Googobits_07-21-05.pdf

15. Prevent plastic pollution, Available at http://www.botany.uwc.ac.za/envFacts/plastic/index.htm
16. file:///C:/Documents%20and%20Settings/Administrator/My%20Documents/Downloads/Fact-sheet-why-is-it-a-problem%20(1).pdf
17. http://ec.europa.eu/maritimeaffairs/maritimeday/en/events-europe/fighting-ocean-plastic-pollution
18. Plastic waste, Available at http://ec.europa.eu/environment/waste/plastic_waste.htm
19. http://www.scidev.net/asia-pacific/environment/news/asian-states-top-global-list-of-ocean-plastic-polluters.html
20. http://www.nrdc.org/oceans/plastic-ocean/faq.asp
21. http://www.unesco.org/new/en/natural-sciences/ioc-oceans/priority-areas/rio-20-ocean/blueprint-for-the-future-we-want/marine-pollution/facts-and-figures-on-marine-pollution/
22. http://theconversation.com/australian-waters-polluted-by-harmful-tiny-plastics-20790
23. Great Pacific garbage patch, Available at https://en.wikipedia.org/wiki/Great_Pacific_garbage_patch
24. Plastic Bag Problems in India, Available at http://www.enn.com/top_stories/article/41640
25. Business Line (March 15, 2013), Plastic waste disposal turning a serious problem, Available at http://www.thehindub usinessline.com/news/national/plastic-waste-disposal-turning-a-serious-problem/article4547522.ece
26. Plastic waste a ticking time bomb in India: Supreme Court, Available at http://southasia.oneworld.net/news/plastic-waste-a-ticking-time-bomb-in-india-supreme-court#. VgbNKNJViko
27. The Times of India (April 4, 2013), Plastic waste time bomb ticking for India, SC says, Available at http://times ofindia.india times.com/home/environment/pollution/Plastic-waste-time-bomb-ticking-for-India-SC-says/articleshow/19370833.cms
28. Plastic pollution a growing threat to the health of our oceans, Available at http://www.greenpeace.org/international/Global/international/planet-2/report/2007/8/plastic-pollution.pdf
29. Matt Prindiville (2015), The solution to plastic pollution, Available at http://upstreampolicy.org/the-solution-to-plastic-pollution/
30. Sharon Jacobsen, Plastic Bag Pollution, Available at http://dpw.lacounty.gov/epd/PlasticBags/Articles/Googobits_07-21-05.pdf
31. N. M. Dana Gopal, P. Phebe, E.V. Suresh Kumar, and B.K.K. Vani, Impact of plastic leading environmental pollution, National Seminar on Impact of Toxic Metals, Minerals and Solvents leading to Environmental Pollution-2014 Journal of Chemical and Pharmaceutical Sciences, http://www.jchps.com/pdf/si3/20%20jchps%20si3%20N.%20M.% 20dana %20Gopal% 2096-99.pdf
32. http://www.botany.uwc.ac.za/envFacts/plastic/index.htm
33. Closing the Loop of Materials, Phasing out Toxics and Emissions, Available at http://www.zerowasteeurope.eu/tag/plastic-pollution/
34. Bethany Bell (2015), EU to curb thinnest plastic bags in anti-pollution push, Available at http://www.bbc.com/news/world-europe-32495059

25

Electronic Waste

"It isn't pollution that's harming the environment. It's the impurities in our air and water that are doing it."

-Dan Quayle

Industrial revolution followed by the advances in information technology during the last century has radically changed people's lifestyle. Although this development has helped the human race, mismanagement has led to new problems of contamination and pollution. Disposal of e-wastes is a particular problem faced in many regions across the globe. Computer wastes that are land filled produces contaminated leachates.[1]

The Indian electronic goods industry forms a small part of the global electronics industry. In the recent years, the domestic market has witnessed a robust growth driven by several factors such as manufacturing growth, ICT penetration, rising disposable income, retail boom and attractive finance schemes. The Indian electronics industry is broadly divided into consumer electronics, industrial electronics, computer hardware, strategic electronics, communication and broadcasting equipment and electronic components. Industrial electronics comprises of critical hardware technologies and systems with built-in software. The important devices used in this segment relate to power electronics, medical electronics and other intermediates like semiconductor.[2]

Meaning

The term "e-waste" is an abbreviation of "electronic waste". A key part of the definition is the word "waste" and what it logically implies that the item has no further use and is rejected as useless or excess to the owner in its current condition. It includes almost any household or business item containing circuitry or electrical components with either power or battery supply.

E-waste are items such as TV appliances, computers, laptops, tablets, mobile phones, white goods - for example, *fridges, washing machines, dryers* - home entertainment and stereo systems, toys, toasters and kettles.[3] It is the term used to describe old, end-of-life or discarded appliances using electricity. It includes computers, consumer electronics, fridges etc which have been disposed of by their original users.[4] Rapid growth of technology, upgradation of technical innovations, and a high rate of obsolescence in the electronics industry have led to one of the fastest growing waste streams in the world which consist of end of life electrical and electronic equipment product.[5]

The waste generated due to the discarded, obsolete, end of life electrical and electronics equipments is known as E-waste world over. It is well known by acronym WEEE (Waste from Electrical and Electronics Equipments). E-waste is generated by both indigenous and outsourced electrical and electronics equipments besides Basel Convention. The knowhow and compatible infrastructure for e-waste treatment is limited in India and informal recycling survived under the ambit of flexible legislative framework.[6]

Causes of Pollution

Disposing of e-waste is a global concern. While the developed world has consumed the largest share of the more than one billion personal computers sold, the less-developed countries have tended to pay the environmental price. Cheap labour and lax environmental laws have created an e-waste trail from the developed world to Asia and Africa, where many of the digital discards are sent for reprocessing. Workers often take the computers and their toxic monitors apart with no protection from such hazardous substances as lead, cadmium, or beryllium and that can easily compromise their health and pollute their land and water.[7]

One reason e-waste is occurring is because the growth of technological devices. In the modern era, technology is growing at a lightning fast speed which may result in new products coming out more frequently. This causes people to discard their old computers more frequently and let that waste build up. Another reason e-waste is occurring is because of the growth of population. E-waste is occurring is because of human mentality.[8]

E-waste is both valuable as source for secondary raw material, and toxic if handled and discarded improperly. Rapid technology change, low initial cost and even planned obsolescence have resulted in a fast growing problem of stock-piled and mismanaged around the globe. Due to lower environmental standards and working conditions in China and India, e-waste is being sent to these countries for processing– in most cases illegally.[9]

Effects of the Pollution

E-waste is a serious environmental problem, from toxic chemicals and heavy metals leaching into soils in landfills, to the pollution to air and water supplies caused through improper recycling techniques in developing countries. The researchers found that e-waste pollution in the air, that workers in this e-waste dumps breath in constantly, cause inflammation and stress that lead to heart disease, DNA damage and possibly even cancer.[10]

Electronic waste is not just waste, it contains some very toxic substances, such as mercury, lead, cadmium, arsenic, beryllium and brominated flame retardants. When the latter are burned at low temperatures they create additional toxins, such as halogenated dioxins and furans – some of the most toxic substances known to humankind. Lead is toxic to the kidneys, accumulating in the body and eventually affecting the nervous and reproductive systems. Children's mental development can be impaired by low-level exposure to lead. Cadmium is a carcinogen and long-term exposure leads to kidney and bone damage. Beryllium causes acute or chronic beryllium disease, a deadly ailment affecting the lungs. Hexavalent chromium damages kidneys, the liver, and DNA. Asthmatic bronchitis has been linked to this substance.[11]

Exposure to high concentrations of selenium compounds cause selenosis. The major signs of selenosis are hair loss,

Table 1: Effects of E-Waste Constituent on Health

Source of e-wastes	*Constituent*	*Health e*
Solder in printed circuit boards, glass panels and gaskets in computer monitors	Lead (PB)	• Damage to central and pe systems and kidney dama • Affects brain development
Chip resistors and semiconductor	Cadmium (CD)	• Toxic irreversible effects o • Accumulates in kidney anc • Causes neural damage. • Teratoenic.
Relays and switches, printed circuit boards	Mercury (Hg)	• Chronic damage to the bra • Respiratory and skin diso fishes.
Corrosion protection of untreated and galvanised steel plates, decorator for steel housings	Hexavalent-chromium (Cr)	• Asthmatic bronchitis. • DNA damage.
Plastic housing of electronic equipments and circuit board	Brominated flame retardants	• Disrupts endocrine systen
Front panel of CRTs	Barium (Ba)	• Short term exposure caus to heart, liver and spleen.
Motherboard	Beryllium (Be)	• Carcinogenic (lung cancer • Inhalation of fumes and disease or beryllicosi. • Skin diseases such as wa

Source: http://wgbis.ces.iisc.ernet.in/energy/paper/ewaste/ewaste%20management.pdf

nail brittleness, and neurological abnormalities. Dioxins and furans are a family of chemicals comprising 75 different types of dioxin compounds and 135 related compounds known as furans. Dioxins are taken to mean the family of compounds comprising polychlorinated dibenzo-p-dioxins and polychlorinated dibenzofurans. Dioxins are known to be highly toxic to animals and humans because they bio-accumulate in the body and can lead to malformations of the foetus, decreased reproduction and growth rates and cause impairment of the immune system among other things. Arsenic is a poisonous metallic element which is present in dust and soluble substances. Chronic exposure to arsenic can lead to various diseases of the skin and decrease nerve conduction velocity.[12]

Many thousands of tonnes of old electronics, games, stereos, computers, and cell phones are sitting at home in garages, closets, and drawers. Many informed consumers know not to throw e-waste in the trash, and refuse to take it to a recycler for fear it'll be exported, or their data read.[13] Due to the crude recycling process, many pollutants, such as persistent organic pollutants and heavy metals, are released from e-waste, which can easily accumulate in the human body through the inhalation of contaminated air.[14]

Global Perspectives

Much of the 40 million tonnes of electronic waste produced around the world (example: old smartphones, TVs, laptops and obsolete kitchen appliances) finds its way illegally to Asia and Africa every year, says a report by the United Nations Environment Programme (UNEP). Close to 90 per cent of the world's electronic waste is illegally traded or dumped each year, to destinations half way across the world. While the European Union, the US and Japan are the primary origins of e-waste shipments, China, India, Malaysia and Pakistan are the main destinations, says the report. In Africa, Ghana and Nigeria are the biggest recipients of e-waste.

Illegal trade is driven by the relatively low costs of shipment and the high costs of treatment in the developed countries. Quoting an US Environmental Protection Agency study, the UNEP report says that exporting e-waste to Asia worked out 10 times cheaper than processing it in within these countries. The Indian subcontinent has turned into an important destination for European waste. This goes beyond e-waste to include household waste, metals, textiles and tires which are exported to India and Pakistan, says the report "Waste Crimes, Waste Risks: Gaps and Challenges in the Waste Sector."[15]

E-waste accounts for two to five per cent of the US municipal solid waste stream and continue to rise by three to five per cent each year, increasing the amount of harmful toxins leaked into our ecosystem. To stop this deadly trend, businesses and individuals need to recycle used cell phones and other electronics only with e-Stewards certified recyclers to ensure their toxic e-waste does not end up in a landfill.[16]

China and the United States were the worst offenders when it came to dumping electronics in 2014. In Europe, Scandinavia has the most effective e-waste collection programme. European countries have been hesitant to penalise wrongful e-waste dumpers, the CWIT study says. In a typical year, only 2,000 tonnes of wrongfully exported e-waste leads to penalties. There are costs associated with sorting, testing and packaging items for proper disposal, and illegal re-sale values can be profitable.[17] Every year 40 million tonnes of electronic waste produced in the world, and 28 million tonnes of this is disposed in China. Although the illegal disposal of electronic waste is prohibited by local governments, many people still do the job to make a living, polluting the air, soil and water.[18]

According to Frost and Sullivan, the European e-waste recycling market earned revenues of US$1.30 billion in 2012 and estimates this to reach US$1.79 billion in 2020. In addition to the momentum being generated by current market forces, the authors noted that European legislation is also increasingly driving the sector. Strict European Union legislations, escalating landfill prices, and awareness on the environmental impact of WEEE have heightened demand for recycling of waste electrical and electronic equipment in Europe.[19]

The EPA estimates that in 2011, the US generated nearly 3.4 million tonnes of e-waste. But only about 25 per cent of that was collected for recycling. The other 75 per cent went to landfills and incinerators, despite the fact that hazardous chemicals in them can leach out of landfills into groundwater and streams, or that burning the plastics in electronics can emit dioxin. Electronic recycling operations are increasingly active within

America's prison systems. Inmate labourers are not automatically afforded the same degree of worker health and safety protections as are people employed on the outside, nor are they paid comparable wages. Reliance on high tech chain gangs may frustrate development of the free market infrastructure necessary to safely manage our mountains of e-waste.[20]

Globally, 100 million tonnes of plastic are generated each year and at least 10 per cent of that is finding its way into the sea. The United Nations Environmental Programme now estimates that there are 46,000 floating pieces of plastic for every square mile of ocean. Some of that trash circulating the globe is 30 metres deep. Worldwide, each year 113 billion kilograms of small plastic pellets called nurdles–the feedstock for all disposable plastics–is shipped and billions are spilled during transfer in and out of railroad cars. Those spilled nurdles are ending up in gutters and drains and eventually carried into the ocean. The US produces about 6.8 billion kilograms of plastic each year and only one per cent of it is recycled. As a matter of fact, the average American uses 101 kilograms of plastic each year and by 2011 it's projected to be as high as 148 kilograms per annum.[21]

Indian Perspectives

All over the world, the quantity of electrical and electronic waste generated each year, especially computers and televisions, has assumed alarming proportions. According to the Comptroller and Auditor-General's (CAG) report, over 7.2 MT of industrial hazardous waste, 4 lakh tonnes of electronic waste, 1.5 MT of plastic waste, 1.7 MT of medical waste, 48 MT of municipal waste are generated in the country annually. There are 10 States that contribute to 70 per cent of the total e-waste generated in the country, while 65 cities generate more than 60 per cent of the total e-waste in India. The main sources of electronic waste in India are the government, public and private (industrial) sectors, which account for almost 70 per cent of total waste generation. A report of the United Nations predicted that by 2020, e-waste from old computers would jump by 400 per cent on 2007 levels in China and by 500 per cent in India.[22]

Over 95 per cent of the e-waste in India is handled by the informal sector. The issue with informal e-waste recycling is the usage of inefficient and polluting techniques for processing e-waste and poor environmental safety measures. These crude techniques not only release hazardous toxins into the eco-system causing pollution, but also cause serious health hazards among workers.[23]

India is emerging as a significant generator of E-waste in its own right. In India, the current estimate projects 2.7 million tonnes of E-waste generation annually. The ICT sector accounts for 34 per cent of this. The Rajya Sabha (2011) observed that there are 10 States that contribute to 70 per cent of the total E-waste generated in the country, while 65 cities generate more than 60 per cent of the total E-waste. Among the 10 largest e-waste generating States, Maharashtra ranks first followed by Tamil Nadu, Andhra Pradesh, Uttar Pradesh, West Bengal, Delhi, Karnataka, Gujarat, Madhya Pradesh and Punjab. Among the top ten cities generating E-waste, Mumbai ranks first followed by Delhi, Bangalore, Chennai, Kolkata, Ahmedabad, Hyderabad, Pune, Surat and Nagpur. The main sources of E-waste in India are the government, public and private (industrial) sectors, which account for almost 70 per cent of total generation.[24]

The E-waste (Management and Handling) Rules 2011 are based on EPR (Extended Producer Responsibility) concept. Since the Rules came into force from May 2012, E-waste management infrastructure has slowly been on the rise in India. As of February 2014 there were a total of 98 number of registered recyclers and dismantlers having recycling/ dismantling capacity of 2,93,572 MTA for environmentally sound management of E-waste.[25]

Preventive Measures

E-Waste Africa is the first proudly South African company to have officially commissioned the award winning Balcan MP8000 bulb recycling plant in 2014, thus making us a certified market leader in our industry. E-Waste Africa also officially received its HH Waste Management license from the Department of Environment making it the first legally compliant and operational recycling facility in South Africa.[26] The e-waste Association of South Africa was established in 2008 to manage the establishment of a sustainable environmentally sound e-waste management system for the country.[27]

The two methods found for proper treatment of e-waste are recycling and refurbishing. For recycling, there may be products that cannot be recycled completely. PVC layers, for example, stay as such for ages and cannot be recycled. If electronics are refurbished, they can be sold again at a lower price. Thus, both the society and environment will benefit.[28] E-waste avoidance and minimisation can play a significant role in GHG-emission reduction. Reduction of waste is achieved through reuse and recycling. From a climate perspective, the benefits of both reuse and recycling are realised in avoided GHG emissions from waste treatment and disposal. Moreover, GHG benefit is achieved through avoiding resource extraction and reducing manufacture of new products.

E-waste processing can be three major steps; collection, sorting/dismantling/mechanical processing, and end-processing. Collection generally takes place at a regional or national level and is achieved through take-back programmes sponsored by retails and manufacturers of electronics, municipal drop-off collection centres, and non-profit and for-profit collection programmes. Sorting, dismantling and pre-processing generally takes place at a regional level or national level, and has the end goal of separating device streams into material streams, primarily metals, glass and plastics, for end-processing. End-processing takes place at a global level and is dictated by the material stream. The goal of this step is to recover valuable components and remove impurities. Pyrometallurgical is the primary method used to recover precious metals, however hydrometallurgical and biometallurgical methods have been gaining in popularity over the last two decades. Approaches to financing e-waste recycling depend on many factors including state legislation and policies, social preferences, commodity prices, and available recycling facilities. Extended Producer Responsibility assigns collection and recycling responsibility to the manufacturer.[29]

The need for e-waste recycling and processing capacity is widely recognised by the global leaders in smelting. Hazardous components, such as batteries, cathode ray tubes and mercury bulbs, are removed at designated sorting stations. Once the electronics have been removed of their hazardous components, they are shredded into scrap metals and fines. Plastic components of e-waste cannot easily be recycled due to the mix of flame retardants, pigments and mixed types of plastics. However, smelting processes are able to use the energy content of the plastics.

Hydrometallurgy processing of e-waste has become more popular in the last two decades, due to the fact that hydrometallurgical methods are more exact, predictable and more easily controlled than pyrometallurgical methods. Currently the smelting and refining industry dominates e-waste recycling and hydrometallurgical processing of e-waste is just emerging as a potential domestic solution for treating e-waste. Biometallurgy for the recovery of valuable components from e-waste has been gaining popularity over the years. Biometallurgy is built on the concept that microbes interact and depend on metals to carry out their cellular functions.[30]

Legal Mechanism

In the European Union, the recycling of Electrical and Electronic Equipment is regulated through the WEEE Directive and its national transpositions in the different Member States.[30] The Basel Convention on the Control of Transboundary Movements of Hazardous Wastes and their Disposal, usually known as the Basel Convention, is an international treaty that was designed to reduce the movements of hazardous between nations and specifically to prevent transfer of hazardous waste from developed to less developed countries. The Convention was opened for signature on 22 March 1989, and entered into force on 5 May 1992. As of January 2015, 182 states and the European Union are parties to the Convention. Haiti and the United States have signed the Convention but not ratified it. After the initial adoption of the Convention, some least developed countries and environmental organisations argued that it did not go far enough. Many nations and NGOs argued for a total ban on shipment of all hazardous waste to LDCs.[31]

In 1995, the Amendment to the Basel Convention was adopted by decision III/1 of the third meeting of the Conference of the Parties. The Ban Amendment provides for the prohibition by each Party included in the proposed new Annex VII to the Convention (Parties and other States which are members of the OECD, EC, Liechtenstein) of: (a) all transboundary movements to States not included in Annex VII of hazardous wastes covered by the Convention that are intended for final disposal, and (b) all transboundary movements to States not included in Annex VII tof hazardous wastes covered by paragraph 1 (a) of Article 1 of the Convention that are destined for reuse, recycling or recovery operations. This decision III/1 added a paragraph in the preamble; inserted an Article 4A; and added the Annex VII. In 1998, Annexes VIII and IX were added to the Convention by the fourth meeting of the Conference of the Parties, to provide further elaboration as to the wastes regulated by the Convention as listed in Annexes I and III. Since then, the Conference of the Parties has adopted various changes to these Annexes VIII and IX.[32] The Basel Protocol on Liability and Compensation for Damage resulting from Transboundary Movements of Hazardous Wastes and their Disposal was adopted by COP 5 in 1999. The Basel Protocol regulates civil liability for damage resulting from the transboundary movement of hazardous wastes and other wastes, including incidents occurring as a result of illegal traffic.[33]

The Bamako Convention is a treaty of African nations prohibiting the import of any hazardous (including radioactive) waste. The Convention was negotiated by twelve nations of the Organisation of African Unity at Bamako, Mali in January, 1991, and came into force in 1998. The Bamako Convention uses a format and language similar to that of the Basel Convention, but is much stronger in prohibiting all imports of hazardous waste.[34]

The Bamako convention is a response to Article 11 of the Basel convention which encourages parties to enter into bilateral, multilateral and regional agreements on Hazardous Waste to help achieve the objectives of the convention. The impetus for the Bamako convention arose also from: (a) The failure of the Basel Convention to prohibit trade of hazardous waste to less developed countries; and (b) The realisation that many developed nations were exporting toxic wastes to Africa.

The Convention covers more wastes than covered by the Basel Convention as it not only includes radioactive wastes but also considers any waste with a listed hazardous characteristic or a listed constituent as a hazardous waste. The Convention also covers national definitions of hazardous waste. Finally, products that are banned severely restricted or have been the subject of prohibitions are also covered under the Convention as wastes. Countries should ban the import of hazardous and radioactive wastes as well as all forms of ocean disposal. For intra-African waste trade, parties must minimise the transboundary movement of wastes and only conduct it with consent of the importing and transit states among other controls. They should minimise the production of hazardous wastes and cooperate to ensure that wastes are treated and disposed of in an environmentally sound manner.[35]

E-Waste (Management and Handling) Rules, 2011[36]

The E-waste (Management and Handling) Rules, 2011 have been notified with primary objective to channelise the E-waste generated in the country for environmentally sound recycling which is largely controlled by the unorganised sector who are adopting crude practices that results into higher pollution and less recovery, thereby causing wastages of precious resources and damage to environment. As the E-waste Rules place main responsibility of e-waste management on the producers of the electrical and electronic equipment by introducing the concept of "extended producer responsibility".

The rules were notified in May 2011 and aim at reduction in the use of hazardous substances in electrical and electronic equipment by specifying threshold for use of hazardous material including lead, mercury and cadmium. These rules were notified in advance to give the various stakeholders adequate time to prepare themselves and also to put in place the required infrastructure. They will apply to every producer, consumer or bulk consumer, collection centre, dismantler and recycler of e-waste involved in the manufacture, sale, purchase and processing of electrical and electronic equipment or components. The rules place the main responsibility of e-waste management on the producers of the electrical and electronic equipment by introducing the concept of "extended producer responsibility". They will not apply to lead acid batteries as covered under the batteries (Management and Handling) Rules, 2001, micro and small enterprises as defined in the Micro, Small and Medium Enterprises Development Act, 2006 (27 of 2006) and radio-active wastes as covered under the provisions of the Atomic Energy Act, 1962 (33 of 1962).[37]

The e-waste (Management and Handling) Rules, 2011 have been notified in May 2011 and are effective from 01-05-2012. These rules were notified in advance to give the various stakeholders adequate time to prepare themselves and also to place the required infrastructure for the effective implementation of these rules. As per Rule 4(3), the producer is responsible for 'setting up collection centres or take-back systems either individually or collectively'. The decision about the mechanism for collection can be decided by the individual producer in accordance with their company policy. However, such details shall be specified while obtaining authorisation from SPCBs/PCCs. These guidelines suggest the following options and requirements for setting up Collection Centres.

1. Collection centres can be established by various ways. If a collection centre is set up for a particular producer, it may be called individual collection centre. If a collection centre caters the EPR requirements of multiple producers it may be called common collection centre. All collection centres require authorisation from SPCBs/PCCs of respective States.
2. In case a producer himself sets up a collection centre, he shall take separate authorisation from SPCBs/PCCs for setting up such individual collection centre.
3. Producer may organise take-back system through their retailers or through service centres and set up collection points or bins or drop-off points and link them to their authorised individual collection centres. Such collection points can also be set-up by authorised common collection centres.
4. Producer may organise take-back system through their retailers or service centres and set up collection points or bins and channelise the E-waste directly to registered dismantlers or recyclers.
5. The collection points can be designated places where e-waste can be collected through residential areas, office complexes, commercial complexes, retail outlets, customer care stores, educational and research institutions, resident welfare associations (RWAs), NGOs working with rag pickers, etc.
6. Collection bins could be installed in public places such as kerbsides, restaurants, malls, offices etc. which can be owned by the authorised collection centres or the producer.
7. Mobile collection vans can also act as collection systems for door to door collection of ewaste or from institutions/

individuals/small enterprises and such vans shall be linked to collection centre or provided by producer to channelise the e-waste to collection centres or registered dismantler or recyclers.

8. SPCBs shall ensure that authorised collection centres comply with the provisions of the Rules and ensure that the e-waste collected by them is stored in a secured manner and no damage is caused to the environment during storage and transportation till the e-waste reaches registered dismantler (s) or recycler (s) by undertaking periodic inspections and verifications.
9. The Rules specify that Collection Centres are allowed to store e-waste for a maximum period of 180 days.

References

1. http://wgbis.ces.iisc.ernet.in/energy/paper/ewaste/ewaste.html
2. Electronic goods, https://www.dnb.co.in/Axis_bank_SME_ awards/PDF/INdustry_Overview/Electronic%20Goods.pdf
3. http://www.step-initiative.org/what-is-ewaste.html
4. http://ewasteguide.info/introduction/e-waste
5. http://www2.epa.gov/sites/production/files/2014-05/documents/india.pdf
6. Mahesh C. Vats and Santosh K. Singh, Status of E-Waste in India - A Review, International Journal of Innovative Research in Science, Engineering and Technology, Volume 3, Issue 10, October 2014, http://www.ijirset.com/upload/2014/october/71_Status.pdf
7. http://ngm.nationalgeographic.com/geopedia/E-Waste
8. http://www3.jjc.edu/ftp/wdc12/rlebeck/The%20Cause.html
9. http://www.ewasa.org/
10. Jaymi Heimbuch (2011), E-Waste Harms Human Health; New Research Details How, http://www.treehugger.com/clean-technology/e-waste-harms-human-health-new-research-details-how.html
11. https://www.causesinternational.com/ewaste/e-waste-facts
12. http://ewasteguide.info/hazardous-substances
13. http://e-stewards.org/learn-more/for-consumers/overview/where-does-your-e-waste-go/
14. http://www.iop.org/news/11/may/page_51103.html
15. The Hindu (May 15, 2015), India, a victim of e-waste crime, http://www.thehindu.com/sci-tech/energy-and-environment/india-a-victim-of-ewaste-crime/article7202265.ece
16. http://www.e-cycle.com/tag/e-waste-effects-to-the-human-body/
17. http://www.newsweek.com/only-third-europes-e-waste-goes-where-it-should-366884
18. http://english.caixin.com/2012-10-17/100448595.html
19. http://waste-management-world.com/a/huge-potential-for-e-waste-recycling-growth-in-europe
20. http://www.electronicstakeback.com/resources/problem-overview/

21. More plastic than plankton in Pacific Ocean, http://ewasteguide.info/more-plastic-plankto
22. E-Waste in India, http://rajyasabha.nic.in/rsnew/publication_electronic/E-Waste_in_india.pdf
23. http://www.cleaneindia.org/
24. http://cbs.teriin.org/pdf/researchreports/EWasteManagementReport.pdf
25. E-Waste Management in India - The Corporate Imperative, http://cbs.teriin.org/pdf/researchreports/EWasteManagementReport.pdf
26. http://www.ewasteafrica.net/47-2/
27. http://www.ewasa.org/
28. http://www.thewindowsclub.com/e-waste-management
29. Jennifer Namias (2013), The future of electronic waste recycling in the United States: Obstacles and Domestic Solutions, http://www.seas.columbia.edu/earth/wtert/sofos/Namias_Thesis_07-08-13.pdf
30. http://www.seas.columbia.edu/earth/wtert/sofos/Namias_Thesis_07-08-13.pdf
31. http://www.te.com/usa-en/utilities/product-compliance/e-waste-in-europe.html
32. Basel Convention, Available at https://en.wikipedia.org/wiki/Basel_Convention
33. http://www.basel.int/TheConvention/Overview/TextoftheConvention/tabid/1275/Default.aspx
34. http://www.basel.int/TheConvention/Overview/Milestones/tabid/2270/Default.aspx
35. Bamako Convention, https://en.wikipedia.org/wiki/Bamako_Convention
36. http://www.unep.org/delc/BamakoConvention
37. E-Waste (Management and Handling) Rules, 2011, http://www.cpcb.nic.in/ImplimentationE-Waste.pdf
38. The Hindu (April 30, 2012), E-waste management rules kick in today, http://www.thehindu.com/news/national/ewaste-management-rules-kick-in-today/article3371455.ece

26

Nuclear Waste

"Sooner or later, we will have to recognise that the Earth has rights, too, to live without pollution. What mankind must know is that human beings cannot live without Mother Earth, but the planet can live without humans."- **Evo Morales**

Nuclear has long been considered a great way to generate the power that lights and heats our homes. It can generate electricity without greenhouse gas emissions. After a few terrible disasters in Nuclear power plants around the world, people have become more and more aware that, when not treated carefully, nuclear power poses rather a significant threat to our way of life.[1] Nuclear Waste is generally a variety of solids, liquids and gases which are produced during the generation of nuclear energy during fission, mining of uranium, nuclear research and weapons production.[2]

Radioactivity was discovered about a hundred years ago. Following the Second World War and discovery of the fission process, human activity added radioactivity artificially to the natural one. Two main sources have been: (a) the civilian nuclear programmes, including nuclear power production, medical and industrial applications of radioactive nuclides for peaceful purposes, and (b) the military nuclear programme, including atmospheric and underground nuclear-weapon testing and weapon production.[3]

Nuclear waste is not limited to the plutonium and uranium left over from unused nuclear weapons. Nuclear waste is generated at several steps of the nuclear weapon production process. High-level waste is waste generated during the reprocessing of spent fuel rods. Spent fuel consists of the highly radioactive material found in the core of a nuclear reactor following irradiation but before constituent elements are separated by reprocessing. Transuranic waste, made up of the transuranic elements, is generated during the production of nuclear weapons. Low-level waste is any radioactive waste that does not fall into one of the above categories. Waste which contains both chemical and radioactive waste is classified as mixed waste.[4]

Radiation is the transport of energy through space. The energy can be in the form of particles or electromagnetic waves. Radioactivity is the property of certain unstable atoms to disintegrate spontaneously, releasing radiation and forming a different "daughter" nuclide. The release of radioactive contamination into the environment is of concern because of the potential harm to people and ecosystems from radionuclides. Several means are used to measure or estimate human exposure to hazardous agents. Biological markers can be used in some instances to measure agents in the biological fluids or tissues of exposed individuals.[5]

Meaning[6]

Radioactive waste is waste that contains radioactive material. Radioactive waste is usually a by-product of nuclear power generation and other applications of nuclear fission or nuclear technology, such as research and medicine. Radioactive waste typically comprises a number of radionuclides: unstable configurations of elements that decay, emitting ionizing radiation which can be harmful to humans and the environment. Radioactive waste comes from a number of sources. The majority of waste originates from the nuclear fuel cycle and nuclear weapons reprocessing.[7]

Nuclear power plants produce two kinds of radioactive wastes, low-level and high-level. Low-level radioactive wastes are produced by nuclear power plants, hospitals, medical and educational research institutions, biomedical companies, and other commercial activities that use radioactive materials. There are three existing low-level waste disposal facilities in the United States that accept various classes of low-level waste. Fuel used in nuclear power plants is routinely used for three cycles of reactor operation, until it can no longer produce enough heat to generate electricity. When fuel is removed from the reactor for the last time, it is stored in a "spent fuel" pool at the power plant for a minimum of five to seven years.[8]

Classifications of nuclear waste vary by country. The IAEA, which publishes the Radioactive Waste Safety Standards, also plays a significant role.

1. Uranium tailings are waste by-product materials left over from the rough processing of uranium-bearing ore. They are not significantly radioactive.
2. Low-level waste is generated from hospitals and industry, as well as the nuclear fuel cycle. Low-level wastes include paper, rags, tools, clothing, filters, and other materials which contain small amounts of mostly short-lived radioactivity.
3. Intermediate-level waste contains higher amounts of radioactivity and in general requires shielding, but not cooling. Intermediate-level wastes include resins, chemical sludge and metal nuclear fuel cladding, as well as contaminated materials from reactor decommissioning.
4. High-level waste is produced by nuclear reactors. After a nuclear fuel rod serves one fuel cycle and is removed from the core, it is considered HLW. HLW accounts for over 95 per cent of the total radioactivity produced in the process of nuclear electricity generation.

Causes of Pollution

Nuclear waste is the material that nuclear fuel becomes after it is used in a reactor. It looks exactly like the fuel that was loaded into the reactor — assemblies of metal rods enclosing stacked-up ceramic pellets. In practice, the spent fuel is never unshielded. It is kept underwater for a few years until the radiation decays to levels that can be shielded by concrete in large storage casks.[9]

Radioactive wastes are the leftovers from the use of nuclear materials for the production of electricity, diagnosis and treatment of disease, and other purposes. The materials are either naturally occurring or man-made. Certain kinds of radioactive materials, and the wastes produced from using these materials, are subject to regulatory control by the federal government or the states. The Department of Energy is responsible for radioactive waste related to nuclear weapons production and certain research activities. The Nuclear Regulatory Commission and some states regulate commercial radioactive waste that results from the production of electricity and other non-military uses of nuclear material.[10]

Radioactive waste has been created by humans as a by-product of various endeavours since the discovery of radioactivity in 1896 by Antoine Henri Becquerel. There are approximately five thousand natural and artificial radionuclides that have been identified, each with a different half-life. A half-life is a measure of time required for an amount of radioactive material to decrease by one-half of its initial amount. Radioactive waste can vary greatly in its physical and chemical form. It can be a solid, liquid, gas, or even something in between, such as sludge. Radioactive waste management includes the possession, transportation, handling, storage, and ultimate disposal of waste. The safe management of radioactive waste is necessary to protect public health.[11]

The sources of radioactive wastes are" (1) Natural sources: Solar radiation, Radionuclides in the earth Crust, Human Internal radiation, environmental Radiations; and (2) Anthropogenic Sources. The sources of such waste include: (a) nuclear weapon testing or detonation; (b) the nuclear fuel cycle, including the mining, separation, and production of nuclear materials for use in nuclear power plants or nuclear bombs; and (c) accidental release of radioactive material from nuclear power plants.[12] It comes from:

1. military weapons production
2. testing
3. mining
4. electrical power generation
5. medical diagnosis and treatment
6. consumer product development, manufacturing, and treatment

7. biological and chemical research
8. other industrial uses
9. during fission
10. mining of uranium
11. nuclear research[13]

Effects of the Pollution

The products of nuclear fission have long half lives, which mean that they will continue to be radioactive and therefore hazardous- for many thousands of years. Another problem with nuclear waste disposal is the storage. Many different storage methods have been discussed throughout history, with very few being implemented because of the problematic nature of storing such hazardous material that will remain radioactive for thousands of years. Nuclear waste can have drastically bad effects on life, causing cancerous growths, for instance, or causing genetic problems for many generations of animal and plants.[14]

Nuclear wastes are normally classified as low, medium or high-level, according to the amount and types of radioactivity they contain. The high-level waste produced by nuclear reactors is the longest lasting contamination risk of a nuclear power plant.[15] E-waste has become both an immediate and long-term problem. The rapid growth of technology usage, up-gradation of technical innovations and a high rate of obsolescence in the electronics industry have led to one of the fastest growing waste streams in the world - end-of-life electrical and electronic equipment products.[16]

Numerous studies have been done on possible effect of nuclear power in causing cancer. Such studies have looked for excess cancers in both plant workers and surrounding populations due to releases during normal operations of nuclear plants and other parts of the nuclear power industry, as well as excess cancers in workers and the public due to accidental releases. Nuclear power plants, uranium enrichment plants, fuel fabrication plants, and even potentially uranium mines are vulnerable to attacks which could lead to widespread radioactive contamination. Terrorists could target nuclear power plants in an attempt to release radioactive contamination into the environment and community.[17]

Adverse health effects are to be expected as soon as radioactive substances are released into the environment. To assess nuclear health risks knowledge is needed on the frequency and extent of possible discharges, on the amounts of radioactivity involved and on the biomedical characteristics of the released radionuclides.[18] Some important cost considerations treated elsewhere are the measurement of potential health impacts and the cost of emergency preparation strategies in the presence of radioactive materials. However, these direct financial costs often do not include the social cost of "esthetic damages," such as fear and distress caused by the presence of potentially hazardous nuclear substances. As with many environmental quality goods, measurement of these costs which are chacterised by "publicness" is problematical due to the lack of complete price information in private markets.[19]

Global Perspectives

For hundreds of years, the seas have been used as a place to dispose of wastes resulting from human activities. Although no high-level radioactive waste (HLW) has been disposed of into the sea, variable amounts of packaged low-level radioactive waste (LLW) have been dumped at more than 50 sites in the northern part of the Atlantic and Pacific Oceans. In 1946, the first sea dumping operation took place at a site in the North East Pacific Ocean, about 80 kilometres off the coast of California.[20]

The 1986 Chernobyl disaster in Ukraine remains one of the worst nuclear incidents in history and highlighted the risks of generating power by splitting atoms. Scattered across the ocean floor in the cold waters of the Arctic are nuclear submarines and reactors dumped by the Soviets up until the early 1990s. Before the London Convention of 1972, an international agreement that prohibited marine dumping, countries were free to use the oceans as a trash heep for nuclear waste.[21]

Enormous quantities of decommissioned Russian nuclear reactors and radioactive waste were dumped into the Kara Sea in the Arctic Ocean north of Siberia over a course of decades, according to documents given to Norwegian officials by Russian authorities and published in Norwegian media.[22] According to a joint Russian-Norwegian report issued in 2012, there are 17,000 containers of nuclear waste, 19 rusting Soviet nuclear ships and

14 nuclear reactors cut out of atomic vessels at the bottom of the Kara Sea. When the Soviets first began dumping the spent nuclear fuel, the disposal method was standard practice across the globe. Some of the thousands of containers have already shown signs of leakage. The experts polled by The Moscow Times agreed the greatest and most immediate environmental threat posed by Soviet nuclear dumping comes from the carcass of the K-27 Soviet nuclear submarine. The K-27 was sunk in the early 1980s after the Soviets tried to tame its dangerous reactors for a decade before sinking it in the Kara Sea.[23]

According to the United Nations, some companies have been dumping radioactive waste and other hazardous materials into the coastal waters of Somalia, taking advantage of the fact that the country had no functioning government from the early 1990s onwards. Disposal projects attempted to locate ideal dumping sites based on depth, stability and currents, and to treat, solidify and contain the waste. Dumping occurred from 1948 to 1982. 78 per cent of dumping in the Atlantic was done by UK (35,088TBq), followed by Switzerland (4,419TBq), USA (2,924TBq) and Belgium (2,120TBq). USSR dumped 749TBq in the Sea of Japan, Japan dumped 15.1TBq south of Main Island. South Korea dumped 45 tonnes (unknown radioactivity value) in the Sea of Japan. Dumping was undertaken by UK, Switzerland, Belgium, France, the Netherlands, Sweden, German and Italy.[24]

Ocean floor disposal is a method of sequestering radioactive waste in ocean floor sediment where it is unlikely to be disturbed either geologically or by human activity. Large regions of the ocean floor are thought to be completely geologically inactive and it is not expected that there will be extensive human activity there in the future. Water absorbs essentially all radiation within a few metres provided the waste remains contained. One of the problems associated with this option includes the difficulty of recovering the waste.[25]

Indian Perspectives

Disposal as a final step in the management of radioactive waste involves confinement or isolation of these wastes from biosphere in the repositories. India has extensive and varied experience in the operation of near surface disposal facilities in widely different geohydrological and climatological conditions. Disposal of long-lived and high level waste in deep underground geological formation is one option which has received worldwide attention. In India, the most promising formation is granitic rocks.[26]

Over the next five years, scientists are going to study a set of physical and geological parameters required for setting up the nuclear waste storage facility before zeroing in on its location. The options vary from underground storage in rocky central India to plains where the storage may be housed inside layers of clay. Nuclear waste generated in India so far is too small to deserve a separate repository. India's existing nuclear waste site is located at Tarapur where high-level radioactive waste is first converted into inert and stable materials which are kept inside stainless steel canisters sealed with lead covers. A second waste disposal unit will come up in Kalpakkam during the 13th plan period. The two sites could take care of the nuclear waste in the next two decades as India's nuclear generation is rather small.[27]

The recycling of E-waste is a major concern in India. The workers in the recycling sector are dominated by the urban poor with very low literacy levels and hence they have very little awareness regarding the potential hazards of E-waste. According to a Delhi-based non-governmental organisation Toxics Link, India annually generates US$1.5 billion worth of e-waste domestically, with the booming IT sector being the largest contributor, as 30 per cent of its machines reach obsolescence annually. Bangalore, the IT hub of India, alone generates 8,000 tonnes a year. In India, primarily two types of disposal options based on the composition are in practice. These are Land filling and Incineration. The assessment of e-waste recycling sector in India indicates that E-waste trade starts from formal dismantling sector and moves to informal recycling sector.[28]

Preventive Measures

One of the difficulties in comparing hazardous chemical and nuclear wastes knows what they are. Section 3001, Subtitle C, of the Resource Conservation and Recovery Act of 1976 (RCHA), directs appropriate federal and state agencies to "develop and promulgate criteria for identifying the characteristics of hazardous [chemical] wastes, which should be subject to the provisions of this subtitle, taking into account toxicity [including carcinogenicity], persistence, and degradability in nature, potential for accumulation in tissue and other related factors such as flammability, corrosiveness and other hazardous characteristics."[29]

Pretreatment is the initial step that occurs just after waste generation. It may involve collection, segregation, chemical adjustment and decontamination and may also include a period of interim storage. The aim of this step is to segregate waste into streams that will be managed in similar ways, and to isolate non-radioactive wastes or those materials that can be recycled. Treatment involves changing the characteristics of the waste by volume reduction, radionuclide removal or change of composition. Conditioning involves transforming radioactive waste into a form that is suitable for handling, transportation, storage and disposal. Storage of radioactive waste may take place at any stage in the radioactive waste management process and aims to isolate the radioactive waste help protect the environment and make it easier to control its disposal.[30]

The international community has voiced concern about Russia's practice of dumping low-level radioactive waste into the seas's. Russia confirmed on October 18, 1993, that "one of its tankers dumped 900 tonnes of liquid nuclear waste in the Sea of Japan." It also confirmed plans to dump another 800 tonnes by November 15. The Russian Federation is a signatory to the London Convention-formally the Convention on the Prevention of Marine Pollution by Dumping of Wastes and Other Matter, 1972-which is a treaty under the International Maritime Organisation. Since 1993, the Office of Naval Research has been managing a programme of research that is assessing the fate of radioactive waste material deposited in the Arctic by the former Soviet Union. This Arctic Nuclear Waste Assessment Programme includes basic and applied research in both the terrestrial and oceanic portions of the Arctic, in adjoining regions in the North Pacific and in Russia.[31]

Legal Mechanism

In 1982, the US Congress enacted the Nuclear Waste Policy Act (Public Law 97-425). The NWPA created the Office of Civilian Radioactive Waste Management, within the Department of Energy. The OCRWM is responsible for developing a system to manage the disposal of commercial spent nuclear fuel. In 1987, Congress amended the Nuclear Waste Policy Act and designated Yucca Mountain, Nevada, as the sole site to be characterised for the possible development of the first high-level radioactive waste repository. The Nuclear Regulatory Commission is an independent federal agency responsible for regulating and licensing civilian (not defense-related) nuclear facilities. The US programme is funded by ratepayer fees collected by nuclear utilities and deposited into a special Nuclear Waste Fund. In 1998, the DOE intends to prepare a viability assessment of the Yucca Mountain site's potential to host an engineered repository.[32]

Greenpeace's campaign against ocean dumping has been successful in changing the mind-sets of most governments and industries. The ocean is no longer considered as the ultimate dustbin for wastes, and those still carrying out the limited ocean dumping practices that are still allowed are on the defensive and often carry them out with shame. The year 1998 marked the twentieth anniversary of Greenpeace's campaign against ocean dumping. It was July 1978 when Greenpeace first encountered a vessel routinely and deliberately dumping wastes at sea, approximately 400 miles South West of Cornwall in an area that had been specified by the Nuclear Energy Agency of the Organisation for Economic Co-operation and Development as the designated dumpsite of the Western European nuclear industry.[33]

The London Convention was originally signed in 1972 by the world's major maritime and industrial states. The Convention outlined certain rules as to what could be dumped in the sea. A ban on dumping heavily radioactive waste was instituted at once, followed by a ten-year moratorium in 1983 on depositing slightly or moderately radioactive substances in the sea. A motion proposed by Denmark and adopted in November, 1993, calls for an absolute and unconditional ban on dumping any nuclear waste in the seas. This agreement follows the Ocean Dumping Ban Act of 1988, enacted by the United States, which is an attempt to end dumping of industrial waste and sewage sludge at sea.[34]

In 1975, the Convention on the Prevention of Marine Pollution by Dumping of Wastes and Other Matter was ratified and entered into force. The Annexes to the Convention [2] called upon the IAEA to develop a definition of high level radioactive waste unsuitable for disposal at sea and Recommendations governing the disposal at sea of all other radioactive wastes. In 1977, the Council of the OECD/NEA established a Multilateral Consultation and Surveillance Mechanism to co-ordinate the sea disposal of its Member States. In 1980, the Council established a Coordinated Research and Environmental Surveillance Programme to keep the suitability of the disposal site under review.[35]

Under the auspices of the United Nations Environment Programme, on March 22, 1989, over 116 nations endorsed the Basel Convention on the Control of Transboundary Movements of Hazardous Wastes and Their Disposal (Basel Convention or Convention). The Convention is designed to provide a global framework for regulating the movement of hazardous waste across international borders. Although final implementation awaits ratification by twenty signatories, there is no mistaking the dimension of UNEP's achievement.[36]

References

1. Nuclear waste disposal, Available at http://www.conserve-energy-future.com/dangers-and-effects-of-nuclear-waste-disposal.php
2. Abhishek Shah (2011), Effects of Nuclear Waste: Mostly Negative for Life, Available at http://www.greenworldinvestor.com/2011/04/13/effects-of-nuclear-waste-mostly-negative-for-life/
3. K. R. Rao, Radioactive waste: The problem and its management, Available at http://tejas.serc.iisc.ernet.in/currsci/dec252001/1534.pdf
4. Patsy T. Mink, Nuclear Waste: The Most Compelling Environmental Issue Facing the World Today, Fordham Environmental Law Review, 1 (1), 2011, pp. 165-180.
5. Environmental and Health Effects of Nuclear Waste Dumping in the Arctic, Available at https://www.princeton.edu/~ota/disk1/1995/9504/950405.PDF
6. Radioactive waste (2015), Available at https://en.wikipedia.org/wiki/Radioactive_waste
7. *Ibid.*
8. https://psc.wi.gov/thelibrary/publications/electric/electric06.pdf
9. What is Nuclear waste?, Available at http://www.whatisnuclear.com/articles/waste.html
10. http://www.nrc.gov/reading-rm/doc-collections/nuregs/brochures/br0216/
11. Radioactive waste, Available at http://www.pollutionissues.com/Pl-Re/Radioactive-Waste.html
12. Lecture 12 Causes, effects and management of nuclear hazards and industrial wastes, p. 1, Available at http://agridr.in/tnauEAgri/eagri50/ENVS302/pdf/lec12.pdf
13. Kasey, Nuclear waste and its effects, Available at https://honchemistry.wikispaces.com/Nuclear+Waste+and+its+Effects
14. Nuclear waste disposal, Available at http://www.conserve-energy-future.com/dangers-and-effects-of-nuclear-waste-disposal.php
15. Impact of nuclear waste, Available at http://www.greenpeace.org/india/en/What-We-Do/Nuclear-Unsafe/Nuclear-Power-in-India/Jaitapur-nuclear-power-plant/Environmental-Impacts/Whats-wrong-with-the-Jaitapur-EIA/Impacts-of-nuclear-waste/
16. E-Waste Management in India - The Corporate Imperative, http://cbs.teriin.org/pdf/researchreports/EWaste ManagementReport.pdf

17. Environmental impact of nuclear power, Available at https://en.wikipedia.org/wiki/Environmental_ impact_ of_ nuclear_ power
18. Jan Willem Storm van Leeuwen (2010), Health risks of nuclear power, Available at http://static1.1.sqspcdn.com/static/f/356082/11430430/1301260306473/nuclearhealthrisks-final.pdf?token=K6gPDBvsuQr%2BDHJZFjgyP83JvtM%3D
19. Ronda K.Hagman, Nuclear waste proposal: Potential property value impacts,http://lawschool.unm.edu/nrj/volumes/21/4/08_hageman_nuclear.pdf
20. Dominique P. Calmet, Ocean disposal of radioactive waste: Status report, Available at https://www.iaea.org/sites/default/files/31404684750.pdf
21. Laura Dattaro (2015), The Soviet Union Dumped a Bunch of Nuclear Submarines, Reactors, and Containers into the Ocean, Available at https://news.vice.com/article/the-soviet-union-dumped-a-bunch-of-nuclear-submarines-reactors-and-containers-into-the-ocean
22. http://bellona.org/news/nuclear-issues/radioactive-waste-and-spent-nuclear-fuel/2012-08-russia-announces-enormous-finds-of-radioactive-waste-and-nuclear-reactors-in-arctic-seas
23. Matthew Bodner (2014), Sunken Soviet Submarines Threaten Nuclear Catastrophe in Russia's Arctic, http://www.themoscowtimes.com/business/article/nuclear-catastrophe-looms-in-arctic/511150.html
24. Ocean disposal of radioactive waste (2015), Available at https://en.wikipedia.org/wiki/Ocean_disposal_of_radioactive_waste
25. Ocean floor disposal (2015), Available at https://en.wikipedia.org/wiki/Ocean_floor_disposal
26. http://www.barc.gov.in/publications/eb/golden/nfc/toc/Chapter%2017/17.pdf
27. Kalyan Ray (2012), India keen on having nuclear waste repository, Available at http://www.deccanherald.com/content/227293/india-keen-having-nuclear-waste.html
28. Anwesha Borthakur and Pardeep Singh, Electronic waste in India: Problems and policies, http://www.ecsenvironment.com/images/Library/Articles/Electronic%20waste% 20in%20India% 20Problems%20and%20policies.pdf
29. James P. Murray, Joseph, J. Harrington and Richard Wilson, Chemical and Nuclear Waste Disposal: Problems and Solutions, http://object.cato.org/sites/cato.org/files/serials/files/cato-journal/1982/12/cj2n2-11.pdf
30. Fundamentals of the management of radioactive waste (2007), http://www.onr.org.uk/wasteintro.pdf
31. http://www.tos.org/oceanography/archive/10-1_edson.pdf
32. John E. Cantlon (1996), Nuclear Waste Management in the United States: The Nuclear Waste Technical Review Board's Perspective, http://www.nwtrb.gov/reports/wastemgt.pdf
33. Rémi Parmentier, Greenpeace and the dumping of waste in Sea: A case of non-state actors intervention in international affairs, http://www.greenpeace.org/international/PageFiles/25797/odhistory.pdf
34. Nuclear Waste Dumping in the Oceans: Has the Cold War Taught Us Anything?, Available at http://lawschool.unm.edu/nrj/volumes/35/3/09_moody_ogrady_nuclear.pdf
35. Inventory of radioactive waste disposals at sea, Available at http://www-pub.iaea.org/MTCD/publications/PDF/te_1105_prn.pdf
36. David P. Hackett, An Assessment of the Basel Convention on the Control of Transboundary Movements of Hazardous Wastes and Their Disposal, http://digitalcommons.wcl.american.edu/cgi/viewcontent.cgi?article=1583&context=auilr

27

Agricultural Pollution

"The ocean is the lifeblood of our world. If we were to lose our fish that we appreciate so much by overfishing; or if we were to lose some of our favourite beaches to overbuilding and pollution, then how would we feel? It's become a case of not knowing what you've got until it's gone." **-Aaron Peirsol**

Until very recently, the main focus on the impacts that chemicals cause in the environment has been on nutrients heavy metals, 'traditional' active ingredients in pesticide products and persistent organic pollutants. In recent years, there has been increasing concern over the environmental risks of the so called emerging contaminants.[1] For a long time agricultural pollution went almost unnoticed, since most agricultural production took place on proportionately large areas, where animals were pastured and raised for harvest.[2] Agriculture, as the single largest user of freshwater on a global basis and as a major cause of degradation of surface and groundwater resources through erosion and chemical runoff, has cause to be concerned about the global implications of water quality.[3]

Agricultural crops can be injured when exposed to high concentrations of various air pollutants. Injury ranges from visible markings on the foliage, to reduced growth and yield, to premature death of the plant. Air pollution injury to plants can be evident in several ways. Injury to foliage may be visible in a short time and appear as necrotic lesions (dead tissue), or it can develop slowly as a yellowing or chlorosis of the leaf. Major sources of sulphur dioxide are coal-burning operations, especially those providing electric power and space heating. Sulphur dioxide emissions can also result from the burning of petroleum and the smelting of sulphur containing ores.[4] Agriculture is the main source of nitrogen in groundwater, which leaches from excessive fertiliser use. It, including plant production, animal breeding and aquaculture, together with rural villages, are major contributors to this problem.[5]

Meaning

Agricultural pollution refers to biotic and abiotic by-products of farming practices that result in contamination or degradation of the environment and surrounding ecosystems, and/or cause injury to humans and their economic interests. Management techniques range from animal management and housing to the spread of pesticides and fertilisers in global agricultural practices. Pesticides, chemicals and untreated manure are the most dangerous forms of agricultural pollution because they end up in the water supply. Excessive agricultural runoff can prompt the growth of large algal blooms, which starve waterways of oxygen and create dead zones.[6]

Pesticides and herbicides are applied to agricultural land to control pests that disrupt crop production. Pesticide leaching occurs when pesticides mix with water and move through the soil, ultimately contaminating groundwater.[7]

Causes of Pollution

Modern day pesticides and fertilisers have to deal with the local pests that have existed for hundreds of years along with the new invasive species. Contaminated water used for irrigation is one further source of pollution. Much of the water we use comes from ground water reservoirs, canals and through the rain. Further problems are caused by soil erosion and sedimentation. Soil is comprised of many layers and it is only the topmost layer that can support farming or grazing.[8]

Farming operations can contribute to nutrient pollution when not properly managed. Fertilisers and animal manure, which are both rich in nitrogen and phosphorus, are the primary sources of nutrient pollution from agricultural sources. Fertilised soils and livestock can be significant sources of gaseous, nitrogen-based compounds like ammonia and nitrogen oxides.[9] It causes by runoff from barnyards, feedlots and cropland carries away manure, fertilisers, ammonia, pesticides, livestock waste, oil, toxins from farm equipment, soil and sediment.[10]

Effects of the Pollution

According to the researches and studies, the effects of chemical fertilisers on the soil is not immediately obvious. Because soils have strong buffering power due to their components. Over the time, it states that emerged from the pollution, deterioration of soil fertility, soil degradation reactions occurring in the soil leads to deterioration of the balance of the current element. Particularly high level of sodium and potassium containing fertilisers, make a negative impact on soil, pH, soil structure deterioration and the increasing feature of acid irrigation or other agricultural operations or from the benefits derived from it is not possible or very scarce.[11]

Agricultural pollution is the main source of pollution in water and lakes. Chemicals from fertilisers and pesticides make their way into the groundwater that ends up in drinking water. Fertilisers, manure, waste and ammonia turns into nitrate that reduces the amount of oxygen present in water which results in the death of many aquatic animals.[12] Trees and plants are extremely susceptible to damage by chemical pollutants, yet the kind of damage that occurs is not easily predictable. Air, water and soil interact in complex ways, depending upon the chemical or chemicals involved, the kind of vegetative cover, atmospheric conditions and soil types.[13]

Unlike pesticides, fertilisers are not directly toxic. Their presence in freshwater and marine areas alters the nutrient system, and in consequence the species composition of specific ecosystems. Their most dramatic effect is eutrophication – resulting in an explosive growth of algae due to excess nutrients. This depletes water of dissolved oxygen, which in turn can kill fish and other aquatic life. Pesticide pollution of rivers, lakes and wetlands also directly poisons freshwater species, as well as people. Due to inappropriate water management and irrigation technology, fertilisers and pesticides also commonly run-off from fields to adjacent rivers and lakes and contaminate groundwater sources.[14]

The environmental impact of agriculture varies based on the wide variety of agricultural practices employed around the world. The environmental impact of agriculture involves a variety of factors from the soil, to water, the air, animal and soil diversity, people, plants, and the food itself. Climate change and agriculture are interrelated processes, both of which take place on a

Table 1: Categories of major water pollutants

Pollutant category	*Definitions/Examples*
Dioxins	Highly toxic, carcinogenic, petroleum-derived chemicals that are persisten fish tissue, water column, or sediments.
Metals	Substances identified only as 'metals'; also, selenium, lead, copper, ars some cases, include mercury).
Mercury	A toxic metal with neurological and developmental impacts on wildlife column, or sediments. In agriculture, mercury can be associated with merc
Nutrients	Primarily nitrogen and phosphorus; in excess amounts, these nutrients algae and can lead to serious algae blooms and oxygen depletion in ri Agricultural use of fertilizer is a major source of nutrients in rivers, lakes an
Organic enrichment/ oxygen depletion	Low levels of dissolved oxygen; high levels of COD or biochemical oxyg materials such as plant matter, food processing waste, sewage) that use degrade. Runoff from fields contributes to the build up of organic matter in
Pathogens	Bacteria and pathogen indicators E.coli, total coliforms, faecal coliforms, E contamination by sewage, livestock runoff and septic tanks.
Polychlorinated biphenyls (PCBs)	A toxic mixture of chlorinated chemicals that are no longer used in the U are persistent in the environment; used in industry and electrical equi sediments.
Pesticides	Substances identified as 'pesticides'; also, chlordane, atrazine, carbofuran as DDT are banned in China, but are used illegally and are persistent in th
Sediment	Excess sediments, siltation; affects aquatic life by altering and suffocating is a major cause of sediment runoff into rivers, lakes and reservoirs.
Toxic organics	Chemicals identified only as 'toxic organics'; also, priority2 organic comp polycyclic aromatic hydrocarbons (PAH), and others; often persistent in the
Salts	High salt concentrations prevent the uptake of water by plants. The plan those of drought. Agricultural drainage has higher salt concentration than water bodies.

Source: http://www.fao.org/docrep/019/i3536e/i3536e.pdf

worldwide scale. The connection between emissions into the environment and the farming system is indirect, as it also depends on other climate variables such as rainfall and temperature.[15]

Agriculture pollutes the soil, air and water through pesticides, methane, smoke, dust, allergenic pollens, and waste. The systemic damage to the global air, water and soil through genetically engineered crops cannot as yet be quantified. The wastes from agricultural products are a major pollution hazard. They include runoff or effluent from sawmills, pulp manufacture, fruit and vegetable canning, cleaning of dairies, slaughtering of meat animals, tanning, manufacturing of cornstarch and soya protein, sugar refining, distilling, wool processing etc.[16]

Global Perspectives

Polluted water is a major cause of human disease, misery and death. According to the World Health Organisation, as many as four million children die every year as a result of diarrhoea caused by water-borne infection. The bacteria most commonly found in polluted water are coliforms excreted by humans. Surface runoff and consequently non-point source pollution contributes significantly to high level of pathogens in surface water bodies. Improperly designed rural sanitary facilities also contribute to contamination of groundwater. The WHO reports that nitrogen levels in groundwater have grown in many parts of the world as a result of intensification of farming practice. This phenomenon is well known in parts of Europe. The social, economic and ecological disaster that has occurred in the Aral Sea and its drainage basin since the 1960s is the world's largest example of how poorly planned and poorly executed agricultural practices have devastated a once productive region.[17]

The United States has more than 330 million acres of agricultural land that produce an abundant supply of food and other products. American agriculture is noted worldwide for its high productivity, quality and efficiency in delivering goods to the consumer. In the 2000 National Water Quality Inventory, states reported that agricultural non-point source pollution was the leading source of water quality impacts on surveyed rivers and lakes.[18] Good agricultural practices, geared towards the conservation of the major soil functions, are well documented.

Traditional farming practices ensured in many parts of Europe, especially in the Mediterranean region, the long-term conservation of soil fertility. Erosion control measures, integration of organic matter, crop rotation, etc. were all traditional farming practices well known to the European farmers. The European Union, through its Common Agricultural Policy, has well recognised the importance of such beneficial agricultural practices.[19]

Water pollution in China tends to be more narrowly defined than in other countries, and the main targets for control continue to be chemical oxygen demand and ammonia, which are major contributors to water pollution. In China, as elsewhere, a common environmental problem is the occurrence of algae blooms in rivers, lakes and reservoirs. Water quality in Chinese rivers is, generally, very poor – more so in central and northern China where water is scarce. Scientists do not know exactly how much agriculture contributes to surface water pollution. Cultivation practices are major contributors to water quality degradation throughout China. Large-scale irrigation impacts on surface and groundwater quality.[20]

Indian Perspectives

By the 1960s, fears of famine in Asia caused by rapid population growth led to major aid programmes to increase agricultural production though a package of inputs (HYVs, fertilisers, and pesticides) and financial support.[21] The Green Revolution was a period when the productivity of global agriculture increased drastically as a result of new advances. High-yield crops are crops that are specifically designed to produce more overall yield. Multiple cropping is when a field is used to grow two or more crops throughout the year, so that the field constantly has something growing on it. Although the Green Revolution had several benefits, there were also some issues associated with this period that affected both the environment and society. The use of chemical fertilisers and synthetic herbicides and pesticides dramatically influenced the environment by increasing pollution and erosion.[22]

Four decades after the so-called Green Revolution enabled this vast nation to feed itself, some farmers are turning their backs on modern agricultural methods—the use of modified seeds, fertiliser, and pesticides—in favour of organic farming.[23]

Bordering Pakistan in the far northwest of India, Punjab has become the country's most important agricultural region. The green revolution of the 1960s saw great technological advancements and modern farming practices expand, allowing Punjab to become the nation's leader in production of commodities like rice, wheat, and varied general produce. Booming production saw India rise to become the world's second largest producer and exporter of cotton, two-thirds of which is grown in the Punjab region. These 50 years of increased productivity are thought to have been fueled by the excessive use of fertilisers, pesticides and insecticides. The presumed result is of a slow accumulation of toxins within the water, soil, food and ultimately, people of the region.[24]

Preventive Measures

Agriculture disrupts all freshwater systems hugely from their pristine states. The former reductionist concept of pollution was of examining individual effects of particular substances on individual taxa or sub-communities in freshwater systems, an essentially ecotoxicological concept.[25] The key to minimising diffuse pollution is to ensure effective control of the use and fate of potential pollutants. This can be achieved in a number of ways.[26]

Various preventive measures are:

- Use fertilisers sparingly. Test the soil to see the amount of fertiliser needed.
- Don't fertilise before a rain storm.
- Use organic fertilisers that release nutrients more slowly.
- Substitute biological methods for pesticides and never apply them near a well or water
- Recycle oil, antifreeze, batteries, fertiliser, pesticides and other chemicals and materials as much as possible.
- Maintain proper storage of fertilisers, pesticides and other chemicals and monitor containers for leaks.[27]
- Maintain farm equipment and monitor for leaks. Use rags to soak up oils and other chemicals when making repairs.

References

1. New and Emerging Water Pollutants arising from Agriculture, Available at http://www.oecd.org/tad/sustainable-agriculture/49848768.pdf

2. Keith Russell, Agricultural wastes, water pollution and federal regulation, Available at http://repository.law.ttu.edu/bitstream/handle/10601/1782/AgriculturalWastes-Russell. pdf?sequence=1
3. Chapter 1: Introduction to agricultural water pollution, Available at http://www.fao.org/docrep/w2598e/w2598e04.htm
4. Effects of Air Pollution on Agricultural Crops, Available at http://www.omafra.gov.on.ca/english/crops/facts/01-015.htm
5. Guidelines to control water pollution from agriculture in China Decoupling water pollution from agricultural production, Available at http://www.fao.org/docrep/019/i3536e/i3536e.pdf
6. http://www.mnn.com/earth-matters/wilderness-resources/photos/the-10-worst-forms-of-pollution-0/agricultural-pollution-0
7. Agricultural pollution, Available at https://en.wikipedia.org/wiki/Agricultural_pollution
8. Agricultural pollution, Available at http://www.conserve-energy-future.com/causes-and-effects-of-agricultural-pollution.php
9. The Sources and Solutions: Agriculture, Available at http://www2.epa.gov/nutrientpollution/sources-and-solutions-agriculture
10. http://protectingwater.com/agriculture.html
11. Serpil Savci, An Agricultural Pollutant: Chemical Fertiliser, International Journal of Environmental Science and Development, Vol. 3, No. 1, February 2012, Available at http://www.ijesd.org/papers/191-X30004.pdf
12. Agricultural pollution, Available at http://www.conserve-energy-future.com/causes-and-effects-of-agricultural-pollution.php
13. Chemical stress on the biosphere, Available at http://www.fao.org/docrep/q2570e/q2570e01.htm
14. http://wwf.panda.org/what_we_do/footprint/agriculture/impacts/pollution/
15. Environmental impact of agriculture, Available at https://en.wikipedia.org/wiki/Environmental_impact_of_agriculture
16. http://www.equalearth.org/agriculturepollution.htm
17. Chapter 1: Introduction to agricultural water pollution, Available at http://www.fao.org/docrep/w2598e/w2598e04.htm
18. http://water.epa.gov/polwaste/nps/agriculture.cfm
19. Soil at the interface between Agriculture and Environment, Available at http://ec.europa.eu/agriculture/envir/report/en/inter_en/report.htm
20. Guidelines to control water pollution from agriculture in China Decoupling water pollution from agricultural production, Available at http://www.fao.org/docrep/019/i3536e/i3536e.pdf
21. Green revolution, Available at http://www.pollutionissues.com /Fo-Hi/Green-Revolution.html
22. http://study.com/academy/lesson/what-is-the-green-revolution-definition-benefits-and-issues.html
23. The Toxic Consequences of the Green Revolution, Available at http://www.usnews.com/news/world/articles/2008/07/07/the-toxic-consequences-of-the-green-revolution
24. http://pulitzercenter.org/reporting/asia-india-punjab-pesticide-food-production-pollution-chemical-agriculture
25. http://www.ncbi.nlm.nih.gov/pmc/articles/PMC2610176/
26. http://www.gov.scot/Publications/2005/03/20613/51368
27. http://protectingwater.com/agriculture.ht

Bibliography

Books

A. K. Tripathi, S. N. Pandey (1990), *Water pollution,* APH Publishing.

A. Venkat Raman, James Warner Bjorkman (2008), *Public-Private Partnerships in Health Care in India: Lessons for developing countries,* Taylor andFrancis.

Abiodun Alao (2007), *Natural Resources and Conflict in Africa: The Tragedy of Endowment,* University Rochester Press.

Agarwal, S. K. (2005), *Water pollution*, APH Publishing, New Delhi.

Akintola Akintoye, Matthias Beck, Cliff Hardcastle (2003), *Public-Private Partnerships: Managing Risks and Opportunities,* Wiley.

Alan Randall (1987), *Resource Economics: An Economic Approach to Natural Resource and Environmental Policy,* Wiley.

Albert, N. Link (2006), *Public/Private Partnerships: Innovation Strategies and Policy Alternatives,* Springer.

Alberto Paloni, Maurizio Zanardi (2005), *The IMF, World Bank and Policy Reform,* Taylor andFrancis.

Ambuj Gupta (2010), *Non-Performing Assets (Npas) in Indian Banks,* Lambert Academic Publishing.

Anders Åslund, George De Menil (2000), *Economic Reform in Ukraine: The Unfinished Agenda,* M.E. Sharpe.

Anil Kumar De (2006), *Environmental Studies,* New Age International.

Anne E. Maczulak (2010), *Biodiversity: Conserving Endangered Species,* Infobase Publishing.

Anne O. Krueger (2002), *Economic Policy Reforms and the Indian Economy,* University of Chicago Press.

Antonio H. Noblejas (1961), *Philippine law on natural resources,* Central Book Supply.

Arpita Mukherjee, Nitisha Patel (2005), *FDI in Retail Sector, India,* Academic Foundation.

Asish Ghosh (2003), *Natural Resource Conservation and Environment Management,* APH Publishing.

B. Raghavulu Naidu (2009), *Disaster Management,* Sri Venkateswara University Post-Graduate Centre.

B. S. Bhatia, G. S. Batra (2006), *Management of Financial Services*, Deep and Deep Publications.

B. S. Chauhan (2008), *Environmental Studies*, Firewall Media.

B.W. Pandey (2005), *Natural Resource Management*, Mittal Publications.

Benny Joseph (2005), *Environmental studies*, Tata McGraw-Hill Education.

Bishwa Nath Singh, Mohan Prasad Shrivastava, Narendra Prasad (2003), *Economic Reforms in India*, APH Publishing.

Bruce Morgan Campbell, Jeffrey Sayer (2003), *Integrated Natural Resource Management: Linking Productivity, the Environment and Development*, CABI.

C. H. Chai, K. C. Roy 2006), *Economic Reform in China and India: Development Experiences in a Comparative Perspective*, Edward Elgar Publishing.

Charles Gibson (2012), *Financial Reporting and Analysis*, Cengage Learning.

Charles R. Menzies (2006), *Traditional Ecological Knowledge and Natural Resource Management*, U of Nebraska Press.

Christo Fabricius (2004), *Rights, Resources and Rural Development: Community-based Natural Resource Management in Southern Africa*, Earthscan.

D.K. Asthana (2006), *Environmental Studies*, S. Chand Limited.

Dale R. Weigel (1997), *Foreign Direct Investment*, World Bank Publications.

Damon P. Coppola (2011), *Introduction to International Disaster Management*, Butterworth-Heinemann.

Daniel Vallero (2007), *Fundamentals of Air Pollution*, Academic Press, New Delhi.

Darrin Grimsey, Mervyn Lewis (2004), *Public Private Partnerships: The Worldwide Revolution in Infrastructure Provision and Project Finance*, Edward Elgar.

David William Pearce (1994), *The Economic Value of Biodiversity*, Earthscan.

David Williams (1984), *Financial Astrology*, American Federation of Astr.

Debaprosanna Nandy (2010), *Banking Sector Reforms in India and Performance Evaluation of Commercial Banks*, Universal-Publishers.

Donald Grebner, Pete Bettinger, and Jacek Siry (2013), *Introduction to Forestry and Natural Resources*, Academic Press.

Douglas M. Knudson, Ted T. Cable, Larry Beck (2003), *Interpretation of cultural and natural resources*, Venture Pub.

Dr Rajan Misra (2009), *Textbook of Environmental Studies*, Tata McGraw-Hill Education.

Dr Vibha Jain (2007), *Non-performing assets in commercial banks*, Regal Publications.

E S Savas (2000), *Privatisation and Public-Private Partnerships*, CQ Press.

E. R. Yescombe (2011), *Public-Private Partnerships: Principles of Policy and Finance*, Butterworth-Heinemann.

Edward A. Laws (2000), *Aquatic Pollution: An Introductory Text*, John Wiley and Sons.

Edward B. Barbier (2007), *Natural Resources and Economic Development*, Cambridge University Press.

Ellen Marie Pint (2001), *Public-private Partnerships: Background Papers for the U.S.-U.K. Conference on Military Installation Assets, Operations, and Services*, Issue 1309, Rand.

Ernest Aryeetey, Jane Harrigan, Machiko Nissanke (2000), *Economic Reforms in Ghana: The Miracle and the Mirage*, Africa World Press.

Eugene Brigham, Michael Ehrhardt (2010), *Financial Management: Theory and Practice*, Edition 13, Cengage Learning.

Franklin Allen, Douglas Gale (1994), *Financial Innovation and Risk Sharing*, MIT Press.

Gareth Edwards-Jones, Ben Davies, Salman S. Hussain (2000), *Ecological Economics: An Introduction*, Wiley.

Gerald Arthur Best (1999), *Environmental Pollution Studies*, Liverpool University Press.

Gogula Parthasarathy (2003), *Economic Reforms and Rural Development in India*, Academic Foundation.

Graeme A. Hodge, Carsten Greve (2005), *The Challenge of Public-private Partnerships: Learning from International Experience*, Edward Elgar Publishing.

H. K. Yong (2010), *Public-private Partnerships Policy and Practice: A Reference Guide*, Commonwealth Secretariat.

Harsh K. Gupta (2003), *Disaster management*, Universities Press.

Herman E. Daly and Joshua Farley (2010), *Ecological economics: Principles and Applications*, Second edition, Island Press.

Howard A. Frank (2006), *Public Financial Management*, CRC Press.

I.M. Pandey (2009), *Financial Management*, Vikas Publishing House Pvt Ltd.

Ian Nuberg, Brendan Hugh George, Rowan Reid (2009), *Agroforestry for Natural Resource Management*, Csiro Publishing.

Ibrahim A. Mirsal (2004), *Soil Pollution: Origin, Monitoring and Remediation*, Springer Science and Business Media.

Jae K. Shim, Joel G. Siegel (2000), *Financial Management*, Barron's Educational Series.

Jeremy Colls (2002), *Air pollution*, Taylor and Francis.

John I. Spicer (2009), *Biodiversity*, The Rosen Publishing Group.

John Williamson (1994), *The Political Economy of Policy Reform*, Peterson Institute.

José María Fanelli, Lyn Squire (2008), *Economic Reform in Developing Countries: Reach, Range, Reason*, Edward Elgar.

Justin Nelson Michael (2011), *Non Performing Assets in Co-operative Banks*, LAP Lambert Acad. Publ.

Justin Yifu Lin, Fang Cai, Zhou Li (2003), *The China Miracle: Development Strategy and Economic Reform*, Hong Kong Centre for Economic Research and the International Centre for Economic Growth.

K. Seeta Prabhu (2001), *Economic reform and social sector development: a study of two Indian states*, Sage Publications.

Kenneth A. Froot (2008), *Foreign Direct Investment*, University of Chicago Press.

Kevin H. Deal (2002), *Wildlife and Natural Resource Management*, Thomson/ Delmar Learning.

Larry Jay Diamond, Marc F. Plattner (1995), *Economic reform and democracy*, Johns Hopkins University Press.

Manmohan Singh, Isher Judge Ahluwalia, Ian Malcolm David Little (1998), *India's economic reforms and development: essays for Manmohan Singh*, Oxford University Press.

Marco Neuhaus (2006), *The Impact of FDI on Economic Growth: An Analysis for the Transition Countries of Central and Eastern Europe*, Springer Science and Business Media.

Margaret M. Pearson (1997), *China's New Business Elite: The Political Consequences of Economic Reform*, University of California Press.

Marquita K. Hill (2004), *Understanding Environmental Pollution: A Primer*, Cambridge University Press.

Menjor Singh (2001), *Economic Reforms in India: Problems and Prospects*, Mittal Publications.

Miguel A. Altieri (1994), *Biodiversity and Pest Management in Agroecosystems*, Food Products Press.

Mike J. Jeffries (2006), *Biodiversity and Conservation*, Routledge.

Mirjam Bult-Spiering, Geert Dewulf (2007), *Strategic Issues in Public-Private Partnerships: An International Perspective*, Wiley.

Nicholas Avery *et al.* (2006), *Public-Private Partnerships: A Practical Analysis*, Globe Law and Business.

Nico Schrijver (2008), *Sovereignty Over Natural Resources: Balancing Rights and Duties*, Cambridge University Press.

Organisation for Economic Co-operation and Development (2002), *Foreign Direct Investment for Development: Maximising Benefits, Minimising Costs: Overview*, OECD.

Paolo Urio (2010), *Public-Private Partnerships: Success and Failure Factors for In-Transition Countries*, University Press of America.

Parmatam Parkash Arya, B. B. Tandon (2003), *Economic Reforms in India: From First to Second Generation and Beyond*, Deep and Deep Publications.

Pauline Vaillancourt Rosenau (2000), *Public-private Policy Partnerships*, MIT Press.

Philipp H. Pattberg (2012), *Public-private Partnerships for Sustainable Development: Emergence, Influence and Legitimacy*, Edward Elgar Publishing.

Philippa Dee (2012), *Economic Reform Processes in South Asia: Toward Policy Efficiency*, Routledge.

Pradip Baijal (2008), *Disinvestment in India: I Lose and You Gain*, Pearson Education India.

R. Charles Moyer, James McGuigan, Ramesh Rao, William Kretlow (2011), *Contemporary Financial Management*, Cengage Learning.

R. K. Mishra, Bulusu Navin (2002), *Restructuring Public Enterprises in India: Privatisation and Disinvestment*, Mittal Publications.

R. K. Uppal (2005), *Economic Reforms in India: A Sectoral Analysis*, New Century Publications.

Rao (1988), *Air Pollution*, Tata McGraw-Hill Education.

Ricardo Ffrench-Davis (2002), *Economic Reforms in Chile: From Dictatorship to Democracy*, University of Michigan Press.

Richard L. Knight, Sarah F. Bates (1995), *A New Century for Natural Resources Management*, Island Press.

Roger Perman (2003), *Natural Resource and Environmental Economics*, Pearson Education.

Roger Stern (2004), *Good Statistical Practice for Natural Resources Research*, CABI Pub.

Ronald W. Melicher, Edgar A. Norton (2011), *Introduction to Finance: Markets, Investments, and Financial Management*, Edition 14, John Wiley and Sons.

Roy E. Bailey (2005), *The Economics of Financial Markets*, Cambridge University Press.

Roy M. Harrison (2001), *Pollution: Causes, Effects and Control*, Royal Society of Chemistry.

S.M. Shafi (2005), *Environmental Pollution*, Atlantic Publishers and Distribution, New Delhi.

S.N. Bidani (2005), *Managing Non-Performing Assets in Banks,* Vision Books Private, Limited.

Sharad Singh Negi (2001), *Participatory Natural Resource Management,* Indus Publishing.

Stephan Baas (2008), *Disaster Risk Management Systems Analysis: A Guide Book,* Food and Agriculture Organisation of the United Nations.

Stephen Osborne (2002), *Public-Private Partnerships: Theory and Practice in International Perspective,* Taylor and Francis.

Stephen W. Perl (2010), *Public-Private Partnerships: Costs, Benefits and Efficiencies,* Nova Science Publishers.

Steven Heydemann (2004), *Networks of Privilege in the Middle East: The Politics of Economic Reform Revisited,* Palgrave Macmillan.

Sudhindra Bhat (2008), *Financial Management,* Excel Books India.

Sudhir Naib (2004), *Disinvestment in India: Policies, Procedures, Practices,* SAGE Publications India.

Sultan Singh (2007), *Banking Sector Reforms in India,* Kanishka Publ.

Susan L. Shirk (1993), *The Political Logic of Economic Reform in China,* University of California Press.

Susan Robertson, Karen Mundy, Antoni Verger (2012), *Public Private Partnerships in Education: New Actors and Modes of Governance in a Globalising World,* Edward Elgar Publishing.

T. V. Gopalakrishnan (2004), *Management of Non-performing Advances: A Study with Reference to Public Sector Banks,* Northern Book Centre.

Takuya Abe, Simon A. Levin, Masahiko Higashi (1996), *Biodiversity: An Ecological Perspective,* Springer New York.

Tanya M. Shenk, Alan B. Franklin (2001), *Modeling in Natural Resource Management: Development, Interpretation, and Application,* Island Press.

Thomas B. Daugherty (2000), *Managing Our Natural Resources,* Delmar Cengage Learning.

Thomas E. Lovejoy, Lee Jay Hannah (2005), *Climate Change and Biodiversity,* Yale University Press.

Thomas Sterner (2003), *Policy Instruments for Environmental and Natural Resource Management,* Resources for the Future.

Timothy C. Haab, Kenneth E. McConnell (2003), *Valuing Environmental and Natural Resources: The Econometrics of Non-market Valuation,* Edward Elgar.

Tony Prato (1999), *Natural Resource and Environmental Economics,* Wiley.

Uma Kapila (1996), *India's Economic Reforms,* Academic Foundation.

Vandana Shiva (1991), *Biodiversity: Social and Ecological Perspectives,* Zed Books.

Washington Odongo Ochola, P. C. Sanginga, Isaac Bekalo (2010), *Managing Natural Resources for Development in Africa: A Resource Book,* IDRC.

William E. Grant, Sandra L. Marín (1997), *Ecology and Natural Resource Management: Systems Analysis and Simulation,* John Wiley and Sons.

William G. Camp (1997), *Managing Our Natural Resources,* Delmar.

World Bank. Independent Evaluation Group (2008), *Public Sector Reform: What Works and Why? : an IEG Evaluation of World Bank Support,* World Bank Publications.

Articles/Reports

A Brief Introduction to the Narmada Issue (2013), Retrieved from http://www.narmada.org/introduction.html

A. Abdul Jameel, J. Sirajudeen and R. Abdul vahith (2012), Studies on heavy metal pollution of ground water sources between Tamilnadu and Pondicherry, India, *Advances in Applied Science Research,* 3 (1), p.425.

A.K.M. Sadrul Islam and Mazharul Islam (2005), *Status of Renewable Energy Technologies in Bangladesh,* Detailed available at http://www.isesco.org.ma/ISESCO_Technology_Vision/NUM01/A.K.M.%20Sadrul%20Islam/A.K.M.%20Sadrul%20Islam.pdf

A.N.H. Akhtar Hossain, *Flood Management,* Detailed available http://www.apfm.info/pdf/case_studies/bangladesh.pdf

Abiose Adelaja (2007), *Deforestation accelerating in Central Africa,* Retrieved from http://www.scidev.net/en/news/deforestation-accelerating-in-central-africa.html

About Tropical Cyclones (2013), Retrieved from http://www.bom.gov.au/cyclone/about/

Acid Rain (1999), Detailed available at http://library.thinkquest.org/26026/Environmental_Problems/acid_rain.html

Acid rain (2013), See http://library.thinkquest.org/C007231/effect1.htm

Acid Rain In Europe, Detailed available at http://maps.grida.no/go/graphic/acid_rain_in_europe

Acid Rain, Detailed available at http://library.thinkquest.org/CR0215471/acid_rain.htm

Acid Rain, Detailed available at http://www.ecozine.co.uk/AcidRain.htm

Acid Rain: Do you need to start wearing a rainhat?, Detailed available at http://ga.water.usgs.gov/edu/acidrain.html

Acid Rain: Soil Interactions, Detailed available at http://www.elmhurst.edu/~chm/vchembook/196soil.html

Acid Rain-Causes, Detailed available at http://library.thinkquest.org/26026/Environmental_Problems/acid_rain_-_causes.html

Acid rains and the facts, See http://dwb4.unl.edu/chem/chem869v/chem869vlinks/www.ec.gc.ca/acidrain/acidfact.html

Adriana Stuijt (2009), *Africa's soil erosion to be mapped digitally,* Retrieved from http://digitaljournal.com/article/265173
-afficher.do?id=1187276775546&lang=eng

AFGHANISTAN: Thousands affected by floods, landslides, earthquakes, See http://www.irinnews.org/report/84155/afghanistan-thousands-affected-by-floods-landslides-earthquakes

Afghanistan: Water crisis a growing human tragedy, Retrieved from http://www.irinnews.org/indepthmain.aspx?InDepthId=13&ReportId=60533

Africa could reduce greenhouse gases (2013), Retrieved from http://www.fao.org/news/story/en/item/8664/icode/

Africa leads globe in forest fires (2006), Retrieved from http://phys.org/news63169415.html

Africa's deforestation twice world rate, says atlas, Retrieved from http://www.reuters.com/article/2008/06/10/us-africa-environment-idUSL1064180420080610

African coral reefs (2013), Retrieved from http://en.wikipedia.org/wiki/African_coral_reefs

African emissions: African major sources of GHG, emissions per capita, and comparison with emissions from other countries.(2013), Retrieved from http://www.grida.no/publications/vg/africa/page/3113.aspx

Afro tropical Realm (2013), Retrieved from http://www.mongabay.com/rates_africa.htm

Aftershocks: Natural Disaster Risk and Economic Development Policy (2005), Detailed available at http://www.odi.org.uk/resources/docs/2596.pdf

Agnihotri, P. (2003), *Meghalaya's nemesis: Jhum and mines,* Retrieved from http://www.tribuneindia.com/2003/20031116/spectrum/main3.htm

Agricultural Drought scenario in India (2013), Retrieved from http://www.dsc.nrsc.gov.in/DSC/Drought/index.jsp?include1= homelink1_b1.jsp&&include2 =homelink1_b2.jsp

Agricultural scenario (2013), Retrieved from http://kvkmokokchung.in/index.php/2012-03-29-08-20-43/13-agricultural-scenario

Agriculture (2013), Retrieved from http://www.webindia123.com/nagaland/economy/agriculture.htm

Agriculture and irrigation (2013), Retrieved from http://www.webindia123.com/arunachal/economy/economy.htm

Air and Water Pollution in India, Retrieved from http://www.icbse.org/2010/01/air-and-water-pollution-in-india-causes-and-preventions.html

Air Pollution (2012), Retrieved from http://education.nationalgeographic.co.in/education/encyclopedia/air-pollution/?ar_a=1

Air Pollution (2012), Retrieved from http://www.who.int/topics/air_pollution/en/

Air pollution in India (2013), Retrieved from http://en.wikipedia.org/wiki/Air_pollution_in_India

Air pollution prevention, solution and monitoring (2012), Retrieved from http://eschooltoday.com/pollution/air-pollution/air-pollution-prevention.html

Air pollution with special reference to vehicular pollution in urban cities, Retrieved from http://www.rrcap.ait.asia/pub/soe/india_air.pdf

Alexandra Matthews (2009), *Bangladesh's Climate Change Emergency,* Detailed available at http://csis.org/files/publication/sam_136.pdf

Alison Berry, *Forest Policy Up in Smoke: Fire Suppression in the United States,* Retrieved from http://perc.org/sites/default/files/Forest%20Policy%20Up%20in%20 Smoke.pdf

Amanda Brivey, *Acid Rain: The causes, History and effects on Acid rain,* Detailed available at http://geography.about.com/od/globalproblemsandissues/a/acidrain.htm

Amazon (2013), Retrieved from http://www.greenpeace.org/international/en/campaigns/forests/amazon/

Amazon Deforestation and Farming, Detailed available at http://sitemaker.umich.edu/sec005group6/local_problems

Amazon Rainforest Deforestation, Detailed available at http://www.effects-of-deforestation.com/amazon-rainforest-deforestation.php

American forests: Protecting and restoring forests, Retrieved from http://www.americanforests.org/conservation-programs/forests-and-fire/

Amir Dakkak (2013), *Egypt's Water Crisis – Recipe for Disaster,* Retrieved from http://www.ecomena.org/egypt-water/

Ananthanarayanan, S. (2008). *Jhum cultivation under conflict in North-East,* Retrieved from http://www.indiatogether.org/2008/jun/agr-jhum.htm

Andhra Pradesh government declares 234 mandals 'drought-hit' (2013), Retrieved from http://www.ndtv.com/article/south/andhra-pradesh-government-declares-234-mandals-drought-hit-315418

Andy Rowell and Dr Peter F. Moore(2013), *Global review of forest fires,* Retrieved from http://data.iucn.org/dbtw-wpd/edocs/2000-047.pdf

Anirudha Dutta (2013), *Maharashtra Drought: The Worst Man-Made Disaster in Years,* Retrieved from http://forbesindia.com/article/on-assignment/maharashtra-drought-the-worst-manmade-disaster-in-years/35119/1

Annex 6: Size doesn't matter: Why the same-sized cyclone had different impacts in Bangladesh and Burma, Detailed available at http://www.ausaid.gov.au/hottopics/pdf/AIDRF_Feasibility_Study_Report_annex6-10.pdf

Antarctic ice melting at record rate, study shows (2013), Retrieved from http://www.guardian.co.uk/environment/2013/apr/15/antarctic-ice-melt-record-rate

Antarctica (2013), Retrieved from http://en.wikipedia.org/wiki/Antarctica

AP govt urges Centre for drought relief money (2013), Retrieved from http://zeenews.india.com/news/andhra-pradesh/ap-govt-urges-centre-for-drought-relief-money_842428.html

Aragão *et al* (2008), *Interactions between rainfall, deforestation and fires during recent years in the Brazilian Amazonia,* Detailed available at http://www.ncbi.nlm.nih.gov/pmc/articles/PMC2373892/

Argentina floods 'catastrophe' for La Plata, Buenos Aires (2013), Retrieved from http://www.bbc.co.uk/news/world-latin-america-22023196

Argentinian rescuers search for bodies after devastating floods (2013), Retrieved from http://www.guardian.co.uk/world/2013/apr/05/argentinian-rescuers-search-bodies-floods

Arkady A. Tishkov, *Forest Fires and Dynamics of Forest Cover,* Retrieved from http://www.eolss.net/Sample-Chapters/C01/E4-06-02-08.pdf

Arunachal Pradesh- Agriculture (2013), Retrieved from http://www.in.all.biz/regions/?fuseaction=adm_oda.showSection&rgn_id=3&sc_id=6

Asia floods (2013), Retrieved from http://www.worldvision.com.au/issues/emergencies/PastEmergencies/AsiaFloods.aspx

Asia Pacific Allibance (2013), Retrieved from http://apadm.org/activity/

Asia 'will be hit hard by drought in 2020s' (2013), Retrieved from http://www.scidev.net/en/climate-change-and-energy/adaptation/news/asia-will-be-hit-hard-by-drought-in-2020s-.html

Assam (2013), Retrieved from http://www.whereincity.com/india/assam/

Assam earthquake of 1897 (2013), Retrieved from http://en.wikipedia.org/wiki/1897_Assam_earthquake

Atmosphere (2013), Retrieved from http://en.wikipedia.org/wiki/Atmosphere

Atmosphere of Earth (2013), Retrieved from http://en.wikipedia.org/wiki/Atmosphere_of_Earth

Atmosphere of Earth (2013), Retrieved from http://en.wikipedia.org/wiki/Atmosphere_of_Earth

Australia floods leave two dead, thousands evacuated (2012), Retrieved from http://www.bbc.co.uk/news/world-asia-17254966

Australia floods: Brisbane braces for surge (2011), Retrieved from http://www.bbc.co.uk/news/world-asia-pacific-12158608

Australia floods: 'Inland sea' moves across Victoria (2011), Retrieved from http://www.bbc.co.uk/news/world-asia-pacific-12260724

Australia leads advances in disaster managemen (2013), Retrieved from http://app.griffith.edu.au/news/2013/01/02/australia-leads-advances-in-disaster-management/

Australian Coral Reef Society (2013), Retrieved from http://www.australiancoralreefsociety.org/

Australia's Greenhouse Gas Emissions (2013), Retrieved from http://www.carbonneutral.com.au/climate-change/australian-emissions.html

Avoiding heatstroke in dogs and puppies (2013), Retrieved from http://www.dogbreedinfo.com/heat.htm

B. E. Aguirre and Joseph E Trainor, *Emergency Management in Cuba: Disasters Experienced, Lessons Learned, and Recommendations for the Future.*

B.Bolin, J. Jager and B.R. Doos (2013), *The Greenhouse Effect, Climatic Change, and Ecosystems: A Synthesis of Present Knowledge,* Retrieved from http://seri.at/wp-content/uploads/2009/09/SCOPE-29-The-Greenhouse-Effect-Climatic-Change-and-Ecosystems.pdf

Bangladesh rides out weakened storm (2013), Retrieved from http://www.bbc.co.uk/news/world-asia-22564352

Bangladesh: 2004 Flood, Response, Damage and Recovery Needs, Detailed available at http://www.adb.org/Documents/Economic_Updates/BAN/2004/eco-update-ban.pdf

Bangladesh's Comprehensive Approach to Disaster Management: World Resources Report Case Study, Detailed available at http://www.worldresourcesreport.org/case-studies/bangladeshs-comprehensive-approach-disaster-management

Bangladesh-Cyclone Aila (2013), Retrieved from http://www.savethechildren.org.au/what-we-do/emergencies/bangladesh-cyclone-aila

Banglapedia (2013), Retrieved from http://www.banglapedia.org/HT/S_0459.HTM

Barry Smit and Michael Brklacich (1992), *Implications of global warming for agriculture in Ontario,* Retrieved from http://www.uoguelph.ca/gecg/images/userimages/Smit%20and%20Brklacich% 20%281992%29_Canadian%20Geographer.pdf

BBC News England (January 28, 2013), *Air pollution fears in Leicester and Nottingham,* Retrieved from http://www.bbc.co.uk/news/uk-england-21206359

Belize Barrier Reef (2013), Retrieved from http://en.wikipedia.org/wiki/Belize_Barrier_Reef

Belize barrier reef (2013), See http://www.chaacreek.com/belize-barrier-reef/

Bernard Lagan (2013), *Kiribati: A nation going under,* Retrieved from http://www.theglobalmail.org/feature/kiribati-a-nation-going-under/590/

Bernhard G. Gunter, Atiq Rahman and A. F. M. Ataur Rahman (2008), *How Vulnerable are Bangladesh's Indigenous People to Climate Change?* Detailed available at http://papers.ssrn.com/sol3/papers.cfm?abstract_id=1126441

Bishnu Pandey and Kenji Okazaki, Community Based Disaster Management: Empowering Communities to Cope with Disaster Risks, Detailed available at http://unpan1.un.org/intradoc/groups/public/documents/un/unpan020698.pdf

Bo Nordell (2003), *Thermal pollution causes global warming, Global and Planetary Change* 38, 305–312, Retrieved from http://www.ltu.se/cms_fs/1.5035!/nordell%20gpc%20vol%2038%20issue%203-4.pdf

Bolivia (2012), Retrieved from http://rainforests.mongabay.com/20bolivia.htm

Bolivia floods: Emergency declared in Amazon region (2012), Retrieved from http://www.bbc.co.uk/news/world-latin-america-17136500

Bonnie Hamre (2013), *Earthquakes and South America*, Retrieved from http://gosouthamerica.about.com/od/earthquakes/a/earthquakes_2.htm

Brown, D. (2004), *Beyond Boserup: Cameroonian Agroforestry systems in space and time*, Retrieved from http://papers.ssrn.com/sol3/papers.cfm?abstract_id=601278

Brown, D., and Schreckenberg, K. (1998), *Shifting cultivators as agents of deforestation: Assessing the evidence*, Retrieved from http://www.odi.org.uk/sites/odi.org.uk/files/odi-assets/publications-opinion-files/2911.pdf

Bruce A McCarl, Richard M. Adams and Brian H. Hurd (2001), *Global climate change and its impact on agriculture*, Retrieved from http://agecon2.tamu.edu/people/faculty/mccarl-bruce/papers/879.pdf

Bushfires in Australia (2013), Retrieved from http://en.wikipedia.org/wiki/Bushfires_in_Australia

Business Standard (April 11, 2013), *India, Russia to cooperate in disaster management*, Retrieved from http://www.business-standard.com/article/pti-stories/india-russia-to-cooperate-in-disaster-management-113041100446_1.html

Canada quietly pulls out of UN anti-droughts convention (2013), Retrieved from http://www.cbc.ca/news/canada/story/2013/03/27/un-droughts-deserts-convention-canada.html

Carbon dioxide (2013), Retrieved from http://en.wikipedia.org/wiki/Carbon_dioxide

Carl N. Hodges (2007), *Excerpts from: Global warming: effect, solution and opportunity*, Retrieved from http://www.seawaterfoundation.org/articles/Selections_Global%20Warming_7June08.pdf

Carlie Lawson (2013), *The Objectives of Disaster Management*, Retrieved from http://www.ehow.com/list_6788890_objectives-disaster-management.html

Case One. Project Title - Catchment Approach to Managing Soil Erosion in Asia, Retrieved from http://www.fao.org/wairdocs/tac/y4953e/y4953e05.htm

Case study: coastal management – Maldives, Retrieved from http://www.bbc.co.uk/bitesize/ks3/geography/physical_processes/coasts/revision/8/

Causes and Effects of Deforestation, Detailed available at http://www.buzzle.com/articles/causes-and-effects-of-deforestation.html

Causes and Impacts of Global Warming (2013), Retrieved from http://www.greenability.co.za/being-green/causes-and-impacts-of-global-warming/

Causes and types of flood (2013), Retrieved from http://kidlat.pagasa.dost.gov.ph/genmet/floods/cause_types.html

Causes of drought (2013), Retrieved from http://drought.unl.edu/DroughtforKids/WhatisDrought/CausesofDrought.aspx

Causes of Marine Pollution, Detailed available at http://www.tutorvista.com/biology/causes-of-marine-pollution

Causes of Soil Erosion (2013), Retrieved from http://civcal.media.hku.hk/soilerosion/causes/default.htm

Causes of Water Pollution, Retrieved from http://www.buzzle.com/articles/causes-of-water-pollution.html

Causes: Natural and humans, Retrieved from http://www.geology.wisc.edu/courses/g115/projects03/emgoltz/causes.htm

Central America floods and landslides 'leave 80 dead' (2011), See http://www.bbc.co.uk/news/world-latin-america-15331290

Central assistance to drought-hit Karnataka and Maharashtra (2013), Retrieved from http://www.thehindu.com/news/national/central-assistance-to-droughthit-karnataka-and-maharashtra/article4295191.ece

Centre declares 17 districts as drought-hit in Gujarat (2013), Retrieved from http://www.thehindu.com/news/national/centre-declares-17-districts-as-droughthit-in-gujarat/article4529501.ece

Ch 6 Impacts of global warming, Retrieved from http://www.xplora.org/downloads/Knoppix/TREAM/6-chapter6-100505.pdf

Chapter 1 Disaster management: An introductory, Retrieved from http://mizoramdmr.nic.in/ATISchoolSafety/Chap1.pdf

Chapter 22 Soil erosion, Retrieved from http://planningcommission.nic.in/plans/planrel/fiveyr/1st/1planch22.html

Charlotte Benson and Edward Clay (2002), *Bangladesh: Disasters and Public Finance*, Detailed available at http://books.google.co.in/books/about/Bangladesh_disasters_and_public_finance.html?id=DMDZHAAACAAJ&redir_esc=y

Chauhan, R (2011). *Global Warming: An International Issue*, First edition, New Delhi: Saurabh Publishing House, pp.7-9.

China Greenhouse Gas Emissions Set to Rise Well Past U.S, Retrieved from http://www.scientificamerican.com/article.cfm?id=china-greenhouse-gas-emissions-rise-past-us

China Must Exploit Its Shale Gas (2013), Retrieved from http://www.nytimes.com/2013/04/13/opinion/china-must-exploit-its-shale-gas.html?_r=0

China Sichuan landslide 'buries up to 40 people', See http://www.bbc.co.uk/news/world-asia-china-23251188

Christine Lorraine (2011), *Reasons why tropical cyclones occur*, Retrieved from http://www.helium.com/items/2089477-reasons-why-tropical-cyclones-occur

Climate change 101: Overview, Retrieved from http://www.pewtrusts.org/uploadedFiles/wwwpewtrustsorg/Reports/Global_warming/1114_OverviewFinal.pdf

Climate Change and Health programmee (2013), Retrieved from http://www.cdc.gov/climateandhealth/effects/default.htm

Climate change and the pacific islands, Retrieved from http://www.unescap.org/mced2000/pacific/background/climate.htm

Climate change effects on small islands (2013), Retrieved from http://wwf.panda.org/about_our_earth/aboutcc/problems/rising_temperatures/hotspot_map/small_islands.cfm

Climate Change Impact and Disaster Vulnerability in the Coastal Areas of Bangladesh, Detailed available at http://www.unisdr.org/files/4032_DisasterBD.pdf

Climate Change Impacts and Adapting to Change, Retrieved from http://www.epa.gov/climatechange/impacts-adaptation/

Climate Change Impacts and Responses in Bangladesh (2009), http://www.mrfcj.org/news/2011/climate_justice_needed_in_ bangladesh.html?gclid= CMesjamQ0q0CFcEc6wodsHXykw

Climate change impacts on Fiji (2013), Retrieved from http://wwf.panda.org/about_our_earth/aboutcc/problems/rising_temperatures/hotspot_map/fiji.cfm

Climate Change Impacts: South East Asia -, Retrieved from http://www.ifad.org/events/apr09/impact/se_asia.pdf

Climate change, agriculture and water resources in the mid-Atlantic (2010), Retrieved from http://www.mawaterquality.org/capacity_building/documents/Summary-Report_FINAL.pdf

Climate change: A four degree warmer world, Retrieved from http://www.irinnews.org/report/96815/CLIMATE-CHANGE-A-four-degree-warmer-world

Climate Change: River Erosion in Bangladesh, Retrieved from http://www.bangladesch.org/pics/download/river_erosion.pdf

Climate change: The greenhouse effect, Retrieved from http://climate.nasa.gov/causes

Coast Guard Monitoring Pollution, Detailed available at http://www.hindu.com/2011/01/21/stories/2011012161040600.htm

Coastal flooding (2013), Retrieved from http://en.wikipedia.org/wiki/Coastal_flood

Colin Chartres+ and John Williams (2006), Can Australia Overcome its Water Scarcity Problems? *Journal of Developments in Sustainable Agriculture,* Retrieved from http://www.wentworthgroup.org/docs/Chartres_%26_Williams.pdf

Colombia (2013), Retrieved from http://rainforests.mongabay.com/20colombia.htm

Colombia flooding continues with thousands homeless (2010), Retrieved from http://www.bbc.co.uk/news/world-latin-america-12006568

Colombia floods (2012), Retrieved from http://www.oxfam.org/en/emergencies/colombia-floods

Communities Threatened by Sea Level Rise, Retrieved from http://climaterealityproject.org/events/tonga/

Comprehensive Disaster Management Programme (CDMP), Bangladesh (2011), Detailed available at http://www.nset.org.np/nset/html/IK2011/29_CDMP%20Bangladesh.pdf

Conrad Quilty-Harper (2011), *Australia floods: what caused the flooding?* Retrieved from http://www.telegraph.co.uk/news/worldnews/australiaandthepacific/australia/8254976/Australia-floods-what-caused-the-flooding.html

Consequences of Deforestation, Detailed available at http://www.effects-of-deforestation.com/effects-of-deforestation.php

Construction and controversy, Retrieved from http://www.financialexpress.com/old/ie/daily/19970821/23350503.html

Controlling air pollution from vehicles, Detailed available at http://www.dec.ny.gov/chemical/8394.html

Controlling air pollution from vehicles, Detailed available at http://www.dec.ny.gov/chemical/8394.

Cook Islands (2013), Retrieved from http://en.wikipedia.org/wiki/Cook_Islands

Cooperation in disaster management: the European Union and the United States take a major step forward (2011), Retrieved from http://europa.eu/rapid/press-release_IP-11-1365_en.htm

Cumhur Aydinalp and Malcolm S. Cresser (2008), The Effects of Global Climate Change on Agriculture, *American-Eurasian J. Agric. and Environ. Sci.,* 3 (5), pp. 672-676.

Current sea-level rise (2013), Retrieved from http://en.wikipedia.org/wiki/Current_sea_level_rise

Cyclone - Safety Measures (2013), Retrieved from http://en.wikipedia.org/wiki/Hawassa

Cyclone Ali update 2009, Retrieved from ht Cyclone - Safety Measures (2013), Retrieved from http://en.wikipedia.org/wiki/Hawassa

Cyclone Mahasen moving closer,Bangladesh braces for the worst (2013), Retrieved from http://newindianexpress.com/states/odisha/Cyclone-Mahasen-moving-closerBangladesh-braces-for-the-worst/2013/05/15/article1590555.ece

Cyclone Preparedness Programme (CPP) Bangladesh Red Crescent Society, Detailed available at http://www.adrc.asia/publications/TDRM2005/TDRM_Good_Practices/PDF/PDF-2005e/Chapter3_3.1.2-1.pdf

Cyclone preparedness programme: Bangladesh, Retrieved from http://www.cpp.gov.bd/content.php?id=Cyclone_in_Bangladesh

Cyclone Sidr (2013), Retrieved from http://dhaka.usembassy.gov/cyclone_sidr.html

Cyclone Sidr (2013), Retrieved from http://en.wikipedia.org/wiki/Cyclone_Sidr

Cyclone Sidr in Bangladesh: Damage, Loss and Needs Assessment For Disaster Recovery and Reconstruction, Detailed available at Cyclone Sidr in Bangladesh: Damage, Loss and Needs Assessment For Disaster Recovery and Reconstruction, Detailed available at http://www.recoveryp latform.org /outfile.php?id=91&href=http://www.recoveryplatform.org/assets/publication/Cyclone_Sidr_in_ Bangladesh.pdf

Cyclonic Jal (2013), Retrieved from http://en.wikipedia.org/wiki/Cyclone_Jal

Cyclonic Laila (2013), Retrieved from http://en.wikipedia.org/wiki/Cyclone_Laila

Cyclonic Storm Thane (2013), Retrieved from http://en.wikipedia.org/wiki/Cyclone_Thane

D. G. Neary (2004), *An overview of fire effects on soils,* Retrieved from http://www.swhydro.arizona.edu/archive/V3_N5/feature4.pdf

Dan Shapley (2013), *Heat waves,* Retrieved from http://www.thedailygreen.com/living-green/definitions/heat-waves

Dangerous health effects of home burning of plastic and wastes, See http://www.wecf.eu/cms/download/2004-2005/homeburning_plastics.pdf

Dani Alexis Ryskamp (2010), The effects of soil pollution on humans, Retrieved from http://www.livestrong.com/article/176005-the-effects-of-soil-pollution-on-humans/

Darlong, V. (2010), *Traditional community-based fire management among the Mizo shifting cultivators of Mizoram in Northeast India,* Retrieved from http://www.fao.org/docrep/005/AC798E/ac798e0j.htm

David McKenzie and Ed Payne (2013), *China earthquake shears off mountainsides, kills 186 people,* Retrieved from http://edition.cnn.com/2013/04/21/world/asia/china-sichuan-earthquake

David Smith (2011), *South Africa flood death toll rises as government declares 33 disaster zones,* Retrieved from http://www.guardian.co.uk/world/2011/jan/24/south-africa-flood-death-toll

David Werth and Roni Avissar (2002), *The local and global effects of Amazon deforestation,* Detailed available at http://www.agu.org/pubs/crossref/2002/2001JD000717.shtml

David Zilberman, Xuemei Liu, David Roland-Holst and David Sunding (2004), *The economics of climate change in Agriculture,* Retrieved from http://are.berkeley.edu/~dwrh/Docs/Z_Liu_RH_Sunding03.pdf

Daya Kaul, Md. Ayaz, Lohitkumar S N (2013), *Disaster Management In India,* Retrieved from http://unpan1.un.org/intradoc/groups/public/documents/apcity/unpan050292.pdf

De, N. (2012). Partition of India and its immediate effects on Jhum cultivation in Tripura, *International Journal of Social Science and Interdisciplinary Research,* Vol.1 Issue 8, Retrieved from http://indianresearchjournals.com/pdf/IJSSIR/2012/August/15.pdf

Deadly Floods Hit Mozambique (2013), Retrieved from http://www.voanews.com/content/united-nations-reports-devastating-damages-after-mozambique-flood/1595319.html

Deadly floods ravage Brazil's Minas Gerais (2012), Retrieved from http://www.bbc.co.uk/news/world-latin-america-16420098

Deadly heat wave rocks Nigeria (2010), Retrieved from http://news.bbc.co.uk/2/hi/africa/2038164.stm

Debra Ronca, *How Deforestation Works,* Detailed available at http://science.howstuffworks.com/environmental/green-science/deforestation2.htm

Deforestation (2012), Detailed available at http://en.wikipedia.org/wiki/Deforestation

Deforestation and Greenhouse gases (2012), Retrieved from http://www.cbo.gov/publication/42686

Deforestation by region (2012), Detailed available at http://en.wikipedia.org/wiki/Deforestation_by_region

Deforestation in Colombia (2012), Retrieved from http://en.wikipedia.org/wiki/Deforestation_in_Colombia

Deforestation in South America, Retrieved from http://www.mapsofworld.com/south-america/information/deforestation-in-south-america.html

Deforestation in the Congo Rainforest, Retrieved from http://rainforests.mongabay.com/congo/deforestation.html

Deforestation in the rainforests of West Africa reduces rainfall over the rest of the forest (2005), Retrieved from http://www.see.leeds.ac.uk/news/news-inner/?tx_ttnews%5Btt_news%5D=72&cHash=5 056c95782 a8fdde 761050897d1242ad

Deforestation is killing Madagascar's coral reefs (2012), Retrieved from http://news.mongabay.com/2012/0905-deforestation-coral-reefs.html

Deforestation of the Amazon Rainforest (2012), Detailed available at http://en.wikipedia.org/wiki/Deforestation_of_the_Amazon_Rainforest

Deka, S. (2010), *Jhum cultivation in Tribes-A case study in Tripura,* Retrieved from http://ezinearticles.com/?Jhum-Cultivation-of-Tribes—A-Case-Study-in-Tripura&id=5940622

Department of water and soil conservation (2013), *Watershed Development Project in Shifting Cultivation Areas (WDPSCA) in Nagaland,* Retrieved from http://nagaland.nic.in/functionaries/department/agri/soil/wdpsca.htm

Des O'Neill, *Threats to Water Availability in Canada - A Perspective,* Retrieved from http://www.ec.gc.ca/inre-nwri/default.asp?lang=En&n=0CD66675-1&offset=4&toc=show

Devastating fires sweeping through forests across Nepal (2013), Retrieved from http://www.asianewsnet.net/Devastating-fires-sweeping-through-forests-across—45512.html

Devinder Sharma (2010), *Wrong policies behind Rajasthan's water crisis,* Retrieved from http://www.d-sector.org/article-det.asp?id=1244

Disaster risk management, Retrieved from http://www.adb.org/themes/governance/disaster-risk-management

Disaster, Nagaland Board of Secondary Education, Retrieved from http://www.nbsenagaland.com/disaster_management.htm

Disaster (2013), Retrieved from http://en.wikipedia.org/wiki/Disaster

Disaster Management (2013), Retrieved from http://www.iwawaterwiki.org/xwiki/bin/view/Articles/DisasterManagement

Disaster Management (2013), Retrieved from http://www.studymode.com/essays/Disaster-Management-705538.html

Disaster Management (2013), Retrieved from http://www.undp.org.cn/modules.php?op=modload&name=News&file=article&catid=10&sid=44434

Disaster Management :: Flood (2013), Retrieved from http://agritech.tnau.ac.in/agriculture/agri_majorareas_disastermgt_flood.html

Disaster management authority not ready for calamities – CAG (2013), Retrieved from http://in.reuters.com/article/2013/04/24/india-disaster-management-audit-cag-idINDEE93N0F420130424

Disaster Management Bureau Strategic Plan 2005-2006, *Turning Strategic in Action,* Detailed available at http://unpan1.un.org/intradoc/groups/public/documents/apcity/unpan029418.pdf

Disaster Management in Bangladesh, UNOPS, Detailed available at http://www.unops.org/SiteCollectionDocuments/Factsheets/English/Success%20Stories/GBL_PJFS_CDMP_EN.pdf

Disaster Management in Bangladesh, UNOPS, Detailed available at http://www.unops.org/SiteCollectionDocuments/Factsheets/English/Success%20Stories/GBL_PJFS_CDMP_EN.pdf

Disaster Management in India (2013), Retrieved from http://www.undp.org/content/india/en/home/library/crisis_prevention_and_recovery/disaster-management-in-india/

Disaster Management in India. Retrieved from http://www.unisdr.org/2005/mdgs-drr/national-reports/India-report.pdf

Disaster management in India: A status report, Government of India, Home affairs, Retrieved from http://www.ndmindia.nic.in/eqprojects/disaster%20management%20in%20india%20-%20a%20status%20report%20-%20august%202004.pdf

Disaster Management in India-a Status Report (2004), *Government of India, Ministry of Home Affairs, National Disaster Management Division,* Detailed available at http://www.ndmindia.nic.in/eqprojects/disaster%20 management %20in%20india%20-%20a%20status% 20report%20-% 20august%202004.pdf

Disaster Management: Goals and Activities, Retrieved from http://www.uncrd.or.jp/disaster/goal.htm

Disaster Risk Management For Coastal Tourism Destinations Responding to Climate Change: A Practical Guide for Decision makers (2008), Detailed available at http://www.unep.fr/shared/publications/pdf/DTIx1048xPA-DisasterRiskManagementforCoastalTourism.pdf

Displaced Populations in Post-Disaster Reconstruction and Rehabilitation (2013), Retrieved from http://www.unhabitat.org/content.asp?typeid=19&catid=286&cid=868

Dnyanesh Kumar (2013), *Short easy on the concept of disaster management in India,* Retrieved from http://www.preservearticles.com/2011092714226/short-essay-on-the-concept-of-disaster-management-in-india.html

Dominik Fleitmann *et al* (2007), *East African soil erosion recorded in a 300 year old coral colony from Kenya,* Retrieved from http://www.atmos.albany.edu/facstaff/mathias/pubs/Fleitmann_et_al_2007a.pdf

Douglas Southgate and Julian Morris (2011), *Weathering global warming in Agriculture,* Retrieved from http://reason.org/files/weathering_global_warming_ agriculture_food_population.pdf

Doyle Rice (2010), *Antarctic melting due to global warming; sea levels may rise,* Retrieved from http://content.usatoday.com/communities/sciencefair/post/2010/02/antarctic-melting-threatens-worldwide-sea-level-rise/1

Dr A. Krishna Kumari (2007), "An Introduction to Marine Pollution", Dr Areti Krishna Kumari (Ed), *"Water Pollution: Policies and Perspectives",* First edition, Hyderabad: The ICFAI University Press, pp. 2-3.

Dr ChangGil Kim, *The Impact of Climate Change on the Agricultural Sector: Implications of the Agro-industry for Low Carbon, Green Growth Strategy and Roadmap for the East Asian Region,* Retrieved from http://www.unescap.org/esd/environment/lcgg/documents/roadmap/Policy-Papers/The-Impact-of-Climate-Change-on-the-Agricultural-Sector.pdf

Dr Joachim Gross, *The severe impact of climate change on developing countries,* Retrieved from http://ippnw.org/pdf/mgs/7-2-gross.pdf

Dr N.V. Vinith Kumar, "Marine Pollution: A Perspective, Monitoring and Control in India", Dr Areti Krishna Kumari (Ed) *"Water Pollution: Policies and Perspectives",* First edition, Hyderabad: The ICFAI University Press, p. 14.

Drought (2013), Retrieved from http://en.wikipedia.org/wiki/Drought

Drought (2013), Retrieved from http://library.thinkquest.org/16132/html/drought.html

Drought (2013), Retrieved from http://www.thecanadianencyclopedia.com/articles/drought

Drought disasters (2013), Retrieved from http://www.unicef.org/drought/asia.htm

Drought divide is taking shape across the USA (2013), Retrieved from http://www.usatoday.com/story/weather/2013/04/26/drought-divide-usa/2115877/

Drought in Canada (2013), Retrieved from http://en.wikipedia.org/wiki/Drought_in_Canada

Drought in India (2013), Retrieved from http://en.wikipedia.org/wiki/Drought_in_India

Drought mitigation (2013), Retrieved from http://threeissues.sdsu.edu/three_issues_droughtfacts04.html

Drought Trends in Asia (2013), Retrieved from http://scienceandpublicpolicy.org/originals/drought_trends_in_asia.html

Droughts cut Europe's food output, raise fire risks (2002), Retrieved from http://www.euractiv.com/sustainability/european-drought-cuts-food-outpu-news-514331

Dulal Chandra Roy (2011), Vulnerability and Population Displacements due to Climate-induced Disasters in Coastal Bangladesh, Michelle Leighton, Xiaomeng Shen, and Koko Warner (Eds), *Climate Change and Migration: Rethinking Policies for Adaptation and Disaster Risk Reduction*, Detailed available at http://www.ehs.unu.edu/file/get/8468

Dulal Chandra Roy, *Vulnerability and population displacements due to climate-induced disasters in coastal Bangladesh*, Detailed available at http://www.iisd.ca/download/pdf/sd/ymbvol141num2e.pdf

Dulal Chandra Roy, *Vulnerability and population displacements due to climate-induced disasters in coastal Bangladesh*, Detailed available at http://www.ehs.unu.edu/file/get/5410

Duncan K. Foley (2007), *The economic fundamentals of global warming*, Retrieved from http://www.santafe.edu/media/workingpapers/07-12-044.pdf

Dwindling Arctic Ice, Retrieved from http://earthobservatory.nasa.gov/Features/ArcticIce/

Early Warning Signs of Global Warming: Coral Reef Bleaching, Retrieved from http://www.ucsusa.org/global_warming/science_and_i mpacts/impacts/early-warning-signs-of-global-2.html

Earth (2013), Retrieved from http://en.wikipedia.org/wiki/Earth

Earth (2013), Retrieved from http://en.wikipedia.org/wiki/Earth

Earthquake (2010), Retrieved from http://www.disastercenter.com/guide/earth.html

Earthquake (2013), Retrieved from http://en.wikipedia.org/wiki/Earthquake

Earthquake and tsunami in Japan (2013), Retrieved from http://www.ifrc.org/what-we-do/disaster-management/responding/ongoing-operations/japan-earthquake/

Earthquake Effects (2013), Retrieved from http://library.thinkquest.org/03oct/00795/earthquakecauses.html

Earthquake Effects, Retrieved from http://training.fema.gov/emiweb/is/IS8A/pdf/is8a-unit4.pdf

Earthquake Facts (2013), Retrieved from http://earthquake.usgs.gov/learn/facts.php

Earthquake hazard zoning of India (2013), Retrieved from http://en.wikipedia.org/wiki/Earthquake_hazard_zoning_of_India

Earthquake measuring 5.7 strikes northwest Pakistan (2013), Retrieved from http://tvnz.co.nz/world-news/earthquake-measuring-5-7-strikes-northwest-pakistan-5424562

Earthquake prediction (2013), Retrieved from http://en.wikipedia.org/wiki/1935_Quetta_earthquake

Earthquake preparedness: Before, during and after, Retrieved from http://www.embc.gov.bc.ca/em/hazard_preparedness/Directory_Earthquakes.pdf

Earthquake rocks eastern Afghanistan (2013), Retrieved from http://www.aljazeera.com/news/asia/2013/04/2013424143831702 116.html

Earthquake tremors jolt India, Pakistan (2013), Retrieved from http://tribune.com.pk/story/542970/earthquake-tremors-felt-in-punjab-k-p/

East Africa: Deforestation exacerbates droughts, floods, Retrieved from http://www.irinnews.org/Report/61528/EAST-AFRICA-Deforestation-exacerbates-droughts-floods

Ecuador (2013), Retrieved from http://rainforests.mongabay.com/20ecuador.htm

Edawi Wheida, and Ronny Verhoeven (2007), *An alternative solution of the water shortage problem in Libya,* Retrieved from http://link.springer.com/article/10.1007%2Fs11269-006-9067-6

Effect of wildfire on animals (2013), Retrieved from http://oregonexplorer.info/wildfire/WildfireRisk/WildfireEffectsAnimals

Effects of Acid Rain - Surface Waters and Aquatic Animals, Detailed available at http://www.epa.gov/acidrain/effects/surface_water.html

Effects of Acid rain on human health, Detailed available at http://www.epa.gov/acidrain/effects/health.html

Effects of acid rain-Forests, Detailed available at http://www.epa.gov/acidrain/effects/forests.html

Effects of acid rains-Automotive Coastings, Detailed available at http://www.epa.gov/acidrain/effects/auto.html

Effects of Deforestation, Detailed available at http://tomraffoul.tripod.com/id2.html

Effects of Drought (2013), Retrieved from http://library.thinkquest.org/16132/html/droughtinfo/effects1.html

Effects of Earthquakes (2013), Retrieved from http://library.thinkquest.org/16132/html/quakeinfo/effects.html

Effects of flood (2013), Retrieved from http://library.thinkquest.org/03oct/00758/en/disaster/flood/effects.html

Effects of Global Climate Change on Vegetation Distribution, Retrieved from http://www.epa.gov/wed/pages/projects/globalclimat echange / Vegetationredistribution.pdf

Effects of global warming in south Asia (2013), Retrieved from http://en.wikipedia.org/wiki/Effects_of_global_warming_on_South_Asia

Effects of Landslides – When the Earth shakes, rattles and rolls, See http://www.disaster-preparedness-checklist.com/effects-of-landslides/

Effects of Marine Pollution, Detailed available at http://flatplanet.wikispaces.com/Effects+of+Marine+Pollution

Effects of the acid rains-Materials, Detailed available at http://www.epa.gov/acidrain/effects/materials.html

Effects of Tsunamis, Retrieved from http://www.universetoday.com/39319/effects-of-tsunamis/

Effects on Acid rains: Visibility, Detailed available at http://www.epa.gov/acidrain/effects/visibility.html

Ehrlich, P. (2013). *Famine threatens the very survival of human civilisation,* Retrieved from http://www.dailystar.com.lb/Opinion/Commentary/

2013/Feb-28/208192-famine-threatens-the-very-survival-of-human-civilisation.ashx#axzz2Q9QEshXM

Eleanor Fausold (2012), *West Africa: Drought in West Africa Threatens Food Security*, Retrieved fromhttp://allafrica.com/stories/201204190405.html

Elizabeth M Young (2010), *Thermal pollution: Causes, effects and preventives measures*, Retrieved from http://www.helium.com/items/1760188-thermal-pollution-causes-effects-and-preventive-measures

Emergency and Humanitarian Action: Country Report, Detailed available at http://pacificdisastermanagement.kemlu.go.id/Documents/Timor_Leste/Emergency%20Humanitarian%20Action_ %20Country%20Report_%20Timor-Leste.pdf

Empowering communities to prepare for cyclones (2013), Retrieved from http://www.ifrc.org/Global/Publications/disasters/reducing_risks/194300-Empowering-communities-to-prepare-for-cyclones.pdf

Energy savings/prevention of global warming, Retrieved from ftp://texmex.mit.edu/pub/emanuel/PAPERS/wcas_2011.pdf

Engendering Disaster Management: A Review of Policy and Practice in Africa, Detailed available at http://www.unhabitat.org/downloads/docs/1270_1921_RGR.pdf

Entire nation of Kiribati to be relocated over rising sea level threat (2012), Retrieved fromhttp://www.telegraph.co.uk/news/worldnews/australiaandthepacific /kiribati /9127576/Entire-nation-of-Kiribati-to-be-relocated-over-rising-sea-level-threat.html

Environment and pollution: Thermal Pollution, Retrieved from http://agritech.tnau.ac.in/environment/envi_pollution_intro%20-%twentiethermal.html

Environment, Detailed available at http://countrystudies.us/poland/25.htm

Environmental effects (2013), Retrieved from https://fp.auburn.edu/fire/effects.htm

Environmental issues in Peru (2012), Retrieved from http://en.wikipedia.org/wiki/Environmental_issues_in_Peru

Environmental Issues in the Marshall Islands, Retrieved from http://www.rmiembassyus.org/environment.htm

Environmental Management and Disaster Preparedness: Building a multi-stakeholder partnership, Detailed available at http://www.unep.or.jp/ietc/Publications/DM/wcdr_session_report.pdf

Eritrea suffering profound water shortage, UN says, Retrieved from http://www.un.org/apps/news/story.asp?NewsID=11006and Cr=eritrea&Cr1=#.Ua3Hr1KDH3Y

Erosion control (2013), Retrieved from http://en.wikipedia.org/wiki/Erosion_control

Erosion in Bolivia (2013), Retrieved from http://forest.mtu.edu/pcforestry/resources/studentprojects/boliv34.htm

Esmer Golluoglu (2012), *Indonesia lifts tsunami alert after 8.6-magnitude earthquake*, Retrieved from http://www.guardian.co.uk/world/2012/apr/11/indonesia-tsunami-warning-earthquake-aceh

Essential Information on Typhoon Relief and Precautionary Measures (2013), Retrieved from http://www.i-taiwan.nat.gov.tw/en/index.php?option=com_content&view=article&id=306:essential-information-on-typhoon-relief-and-precautionary-measures&catid=18:news-a-events&Itemid=69

Ethiopia profile (2013), Retrieved from http://www.bbc.co.uk/news/world-africa-13349398

EU greenhouse gas emissions and targets (2013), Retrieved from http://ec.europa.eu/clima/policies/g-gas/index_en.htm

Europe swelters in summer heat wave (2012), Retrieved from http://www.cbc.ca/news/world/story/2012/08/21/europe-heatwave-august.html

European drought centre, Retrieved from http://www.geo.uio.no/edc/

European river floods in a changing world (2003), Retrieved from http://www.ncbi.nlm.nih.gov/pubmed/12836849

Everyday life (2013), Retrieved from http://en.wikipedia.org/wiki/Everyday_life

Extreme heat (2013), Retrieved from http://www.ready.gov/heat

F Falchi (2011), Limiting the impact of light pollution on human health and environment, See http://www.sciencedirect.com/science/article/pii/S030147971100226X

Factor Analysis of Water-related Disasters in Bangladesh (2007), Detailed available at http://www.icharm.pwri.go.jp/publication/pdf/pdf_0706/bang_e.pdf

Facts about heat waves (2013), Retrieved from http://www.dosomething.org/tipsandtools/facts-about-heat-waves

Fahmida Aktar (2005), *Disaster Management in Bangladesh: Role of NGOs*, Detailed available at http://drtmc-du.org/userfiles/file/Thesis/Disaster%20Managment%20NGO.pdf

FAQs: West Africa Sahel drought and hunger crisis (2012), Retrieved from http://reliefweb.int/report/niger/faqs-west-africa-sahel-drought-and-hunger-crisis

Farid Uddin Ahmed (2000), *System and National level experiences for protecting traditional knowledge, Innovations and Protections: Experience of Bangladesh*, Detailed available at http://www.unctad.org/trade_env/docs/banglad.pdf

Farming in Arunachal Pradesh (2013), Retrieved from http://www.advanceagriculturalpractice.in/w/index.php/Farming_in_Arunachal_Pradesh

Farming in Nagaland (2013), Retrieved from http://www.advanceagriculturalpractice.in/w/index.php/Farming_in_Nagaland

Farming in Sikkim (2013), Retrieved from http://www.advanceagriculturalpractice.in/w/index.php/Farming_in_Sikkim

Farming: Soil erosion and degradation (2013), Retrieved from http://wwf.panda.org/what_we_do/footprint/agriculture/impacts/soil_erosion/

Festival of air and noise pollution (2012), See http://www.commonfloor.com/guide/festival-of-air-and-noise-pollution-2915.html

Fiji (2013), Retrieved from http://en.wikipedia.org/wiki/Fiji

Fiji's villagers move uphill to escape global warming's rising seas (2013), Retrieved from http://blogs.telegraph.co.uk/news/geoffreylean/100217205/fijis-villagers-move-uphill-to-escape-global-warmings-rising-seas/

Final Climate Management Plan (2009), Detailed available at http://www.ambdhaka.um.dk/NR/rdonlyres/3F63B483-5CB5-4654-8020-6D34CB103CF3/0/FINALClimateManagement Plan_Agriculture.pdf

Fire consequences (2013), Retrieved from http://library.thinkquest.org/07aug/01254/effects.html

Five districts in Rajasthan drought affected (2012), Retrieved from http://www.deccanherald.com/content/268655/F

Flood (2013), Retrieved from http://en.wikipedia.org/wiki/Flood

Flood barrier (2013), Retrieved from http://en.wikipedia.org/wiki/Flood_barrier

Flood control (2013), Retrieved from http://en.wikipedia.org/wiki/Flood_control

Flood Control Act of 1934 (2013), Retrieved from http://en.wikipedia.org/wiki/Flood_Control_Act_of_1934

Flood disasters: Learning from previous relief and recovery operations, Detailed available at http://sheltercentre.org/library/flood-disasters-learning-previous-relief-and-recovery-operations

Flood Havoc by Kosi River in Bihar (2008), Retrieved from http://www.mainstreamweekly.net/article937.html

Flood wall (2013), Retrieved from http://en.wikipedia.org/wiki/Flood_wall

Flooding (2013), Retrieved from http://caracas.usembassy.gov/flooding.html

Flooding (2013), Retrieved from http://www.watersafetykids.co.uk/pdfs/Flooding.pdf

Flooding in Colombia (2011), Retrieved from http://www.abcolombia.org.uk/subpage.asp?subid=402&mainid=76

Floods (2013), Retrieved from http://www.getprepared.gc.ca/cnt/hzd/flds-eng.aspx

Floods and landslides hit Bolivia (2011), Retrieved from http://www.bbc.co.uk/news/world-latin-america-12592408

Floods in Bihar (2013), Retrieved from http://en.wikipedia.org/wiki/Floods_in_Bihar

Floods in India (2013), Retrieved from http://www.indianetzone.com/45/floods_india.htm

Floods leave families in peril in Mexico (2010), Retrieved from http://edition.cnn.com/2010/WORLD/americas/10/02/mexico.flooding/index.html

Florida Keys Reef system (2013), Retrieved from http://www.flkeys-diving.com/DiveSites/reefsystem.html

Fluorinated greenhouse gases (2013), Retrieved from http://ec.europa.eu/clima/policies/f-gas/index_en.htm

Fluvial flood risk management in a changing world (2010), Retrieved from http://www.nat-hazards-earth-syst-sci.net/10/509/2010/nhess-10-509-2010.pdf

Forecasting the effects of global warming on biodiversity, Retrieved from http://www.aibs.org/bioscience-press-releases/resources/03-07.pdf

Forest and other vegetation fires, Retrieved from http://www.fao.org/forestry/firemanagement/en/

Forest conversion and soil erosion, Retrieved from http://wwf.panda.org/about_our_earth/about_forests/deforestation/forest_conversion_agriculture/deforestation_erosion/

Forest Fire (2013), Retrieved from http://www.moa.gov.cy/moa/fd/fd.nsf/DMLprotection_en/DMLprotection_en?OpenDocument

Forest fire and its management (2013), Retrieved from http://agritech.tnau.ac.in/forestry/forest_fire_index.html

Forest fires in Europe (2013), Retrieved from http://ec.europa.eu/commission_2010-2014/georgieva/hot_topics/forest_fires_en.htm

Forest fires in India (2013), Retrieved from http://forestfireindia.org/

Forest fires in India (2013), Retrieved from http://www.fire.uni-freiburg.de/photos/in/in.htm

Forest fires under climate, social and economic changes in Europe, the Mediterranean and other fire-affected areas of the world (FUME), Retrieved from http://www.fumeproject.eu/

Forest fires, Chapter 8, Retrieved from http://www.fao.org/docrep/004/Y1997E/y1997e0d.htm

Forest fires: Causes of fire, Retrieved from http://library.thinkquest.org/C003603/english/forestfires/causesoffire.shtml

Forests and deforestation in Africa- the wasting of an immense resource, Retrieved from http://www.afrol.com/features/10278

French Guiana (2013), Retrieved from http://rainforests.mongabay.com/20frenchg.htm

Frequently Asked Question 1.3, What is the greenhouse effect?, Retrieved from http://www.ipcc.ch/pdf/assessment-report/ar4/wg1/ar4-wg1-faqs.pdf

Funds flow for flood-hit Karnataka, Andhra Pradesh (2009), Retrieved from http://www.dnaindia.com/india/1296088/report-funds-flow-for-flood-hit-karnataka-andhra-pradesh

Future of Africa: Energy and Greenhouse Gas Emissions (2013), Retrieved from http://sustainablebusinessforum.com/sbtoolkit/81921/energy-and-greenhouse-gas-emission-future-africa

Ganges-Brahmaputra Delta, Bangladesh, Retrieved from http://www.climatehotmap.org/global-warming-locations/ganges-brahmaputra-delta-bangladesh.html

Garbyal, S. (1999), *'Jhuming' (Shifting Cultivation) in Mizoram (India) and New Land Use Policy - how Far it has Succeeded in Containing This Primitive Agriculture Practice*, Retrieved from http://www.indianforester.co.in/index.php/indianforester/article/view/55228

Gender Issues in Disaster and Post Conflict Situations (2013), Retrieved from http://www.unhabitat.org/content.asp?typeid= 19&catid= 286&cid=872

Geographical pole (2013), Retrieved from https://en.wikipedia.org/wiki/Geographical_pole

Geography of Bangladesh (2013), Retrieved from http://www.uwec.edu/jolhm/EH4/Coastal%20Erosion/Bangladesh.html

Geological survey of India, See http://www.portal.gsi.gov.in/portal/page?_pageid=127,671641&_dad=portal&_schema=PORTAL

Giant heat wave breaks Australian records (2013), Retrieved from http://www.stuff.co.nz/world/australia/8251297/Giant-heatwave-breaks-Australian-records

Giff Johnson (2010), *Marshall Islands plan seawall to block rising seas*, Retrieved from http://phys.org/news/2010-11-marshall-islands-seawall-block-seas.html

Global Greenhouse Gas Emissions Data, Retrieved from http://www.epa.gov/climatechange/ghgemissions/global.html

Global Platform for Disaster Risk Reduction Bulletin: A Summary Report of the Second Session of the Global Platform for Disaster Risk Reduction, Published by the International Institute for Sustainable Development, Volume 141,

Number 2, Monday, 22 June 2009, Detailed available at http://www.iisd.ca/download/pdf/sd/ymbvol141num2e.pdf

Global warming (2013), Retrieved from http://en.wikipedia.org/wiki/Global_warming

Global Warming (Problem-Solution model essay), Retrieved from http://www.admc.hct.ac.ae/hd1/english/probsoln/tj_run_dict.pdf

Global Warming and Heat Waves (2013), Retrieved from http://www.nwf.org/Wildlife/Threats-to-Wildlife/Global-Warming/Global-Warming-is-Causing-Extreme-Weather/Heat-Waves.aspx

Global warming and its impact on India (2013), Retrieved from http://www.commodityonline.com/news/global-warming-and-its-impact-on-india-24309-3-24310.html

Global warming and its impacts on climate of India, Retrieved from http://www.climateemergencyinstitute.com/uploads/GLOBAL_WARMING_AND_ITS_IMPACTS_ON_CLIMATE_OF_INDIA.pdf

Global Warming And Our Health: Addressing the most serious health impacts of climate change, Retrieved from http://www.nrdc.org/health/effects/globalwarming-map/gwhealth.pdf

Global warming bleaches Australia (2013), Retrieved from http://globalwarming.markey.house.gov/impactzones/australia.html

Global warming changing nature of coral reefs: New Zealand scientist, Retrieved from http://news.xinhuanet.com/english/sci/2013-05/07/c_132365556.htm

Global warming could dry up Indian monsoon (2013), Retrieved from http://www.hindustantimes.com/HTNext/LifeAndUniverse/Global-warming-could-dry-up-Indian-monsoon/Article1-955702.aspx

Global warming exacerbates African conflict (2013), Retrieved from http://globalwarming.markey.house.gov/impactzones/eastafrica.html

Global Warming FAQ (2013), Retrieved from http://www.nmsea.org/Curriculum/Primer/Global_Warming/fossil_fuels_and_global_warming.htm

Global warming impacts in Arctic and Antarctic (2013), Retrieved from http://wwf.panda.org/about_our_earth/aboutcc/problems/impacts/polar_melting/

Global Warming Is Destroying Coral Reefs, Major Study Warns (2007), Retrieved from http://www.sciencedaily.com/releases/2007/12/071213152600.htm

Global Warming Puts the Arctic on Thin Ice, Retrieved from http://www.nrdc.org/globalwarming/qthinice.asp

Global warming threatens the world's largest ice cube (2013), Retrieved from http://globalwarming.markey.house.gov/impactzones/antarctica/

Government of the People's Republic of Bangladesh Ministry of Food and Disaster Management (2004), *Comprehensive Disaster Management Programme,* Detailed available at http://reliefweb.int/sites/reliefweb.int/files/resources/23BEBA005CC4AF 3949257727000773AE-Full_Report.pdf

Great Barrier Reef (2013), Retrieved from http://australia.gov.au/about-australia/australian-story/great-barrier-reef

Great Barrier Reef (2013), Retrieved from http://en.wikipedia.org/wiki/Great_Barrier_Reef

Greenhouse gas abatement cost curves (2013), Retrieved from http://www.mckinsey.com/client_service/sustainability/latest_thinking/greenhouse_gas_abatement_cost_curves

Greenhouse gas emission allowance trading scheme (2013), Retrieved from http://europa.eu/legislation_summaries/energy/european_ energy_policy/l28012_en.htm

Greenhouse gas emission list: India 3rd (2013), Retrieved from http://www.financialexpress.com/news/greenhouse-gas-emission-list-india-3rd/827084

Greenhouse gas emissions by the United States (2013), Retrieved from http://en.wikipedia.org/wiki/Greenhouse_gas_emissions_ by_the_United_States

Greenhouse gas protocol (2013), Retrieved from http://www.ghgprotocol.org/

Greenhouse gases and global warming, Retrieved from http://www.camelclimatechange.org/files/182501_182600/182575/ghg-and-gw.pdf

Greenhouse gases make high temps hotter in China (2013), Retrieved from http://news.yahoo.com/greenhouse-gases-high-temps-hotter-china-073035762.html

Greenhouse gases(2013), Retrieved from http://en.wikipedia.org/wiki/Greenhouse_gas

Growing greenhouse gas emissions due to meat production, Retrieved from http://www.unep.org/pdf/UNEP-GEAS_OCT_2012.pdf

Gujarat Earthquake (2001), See http://www.recoveryplatform.org/countries_and_disasters/disaster/16/gujarat_earthquake_2001

Gupta, R.D. (2006) *'Environmental Pollution: Hazards and Control'*, First edition, Concept Publishing, New Delhi, pp. 6-25.

Gwen Dunnington (2010), *The Potential Impacts of Climate Change on Agriculture in Vermont*, Retrieved from http://www.anr.state.vt.us/anr/climatechange/Pubs/VTCCAdaptAgriculture.pdf

H. E. Dregne (2013), *Erosion and soil productivity in Asia*, Retrieved from http://www.jswconline.org/content/47/1/8.extract

Harmful effects of Soil Pollution (2011), Retrieved from http://www.indiastudychannel.com/resources/135389-Harmful-effects-pollution.aspx

Health and Environmental Effects of Ozone Layer Depletion (2013), Retrieved from http://www.epa.gov/ozone/science/effects/

Health Implications of Global Warming: Impacts on Vulnerable Populations, Retrieved from http://www.psr.org/assets/pdfs/vulnerable-populations.pdf

Heat Stroke in dogs - Know the signs, it can kill rapidly (2013), Retrieved from http://www.petforums.co.uk/dog-health-nutrition/10502-heat-stroke-dogs-know-signs-can-kill-rapidly.html

Heat Wave (2013), Retrieved from http://www.capetown.gov.za/en/DRM/Pages/HeatWave.aspx

Heat Waves and Climate Change: A Science Update from Climate Communication, Retrieved from http://www.climatecommuni cation.org /wpcontent/uploads/2012/06/Heat_Waves_and_ Climate_Change.pdf

Heat waves hits South Africa (2013), Retrieved from http://www.timeslive.co.za/local/2013/01/25/heatwave-hits-south-africa

Heat–health action plans (2013), Retrieved from http://www.euro.who.int/en/what-we-do/health-topics/environment-and-health/Climate-change/activities/prevention,-preparedness-and-response/heathealth-action-plans

Heave metal (2012), Retrieved from http://en.wikipedia.org/wiki/Heavy_metal_%28chemistry%29

Heavy Metal Pollution is More Common Than You Think (2012), Retrieved from http://www.fairfaxcounty.gov/nvswcd/newsletter/heavymetal.htm

Heavy rains and landslides in Bangladesh kill 90 (2012), See http://www.bbc.co.uk/news/world-asia-18605765

Hindustan Times (April 14, 2013), *People battling odds to get drinking water in Gujarat,* Retrieved from http://www.hindustantimes.com/India-news/Gujarat/People-battling-odds-to-get-drinking-water-in-half-of-Gujarat/Article1-1044162.aspx

Hindustan Times (July 17, 2010), *Rajasthan faces severe water crisis,* Retrieved from http://www.hindustantimes.com/India-news/Jaipur/Rajasthan-faces-severe-water-crisis/Article1-573887.aspx

Hindustan Times (May 20, 2013), *Heat wave grips north, central India,* Retrieved from http://www.hindustantimes.com/India-news/NewDelhi/Heat-wave-grips-north-central-India/Article1-1063082.aspx

Hirst, K. (2013). *History of humans on planet earth,* Retrieved from http://archaeology.about.com/od/temporalstudies/u/human_history.htm

Historical Floods and Flash Floods (2013), Retrieved from http://www.weather.com/encyclopedia/flood/history.html

History of Flood in Bihar (2013), Retrieved from http://fmis.bih.nic.in/history.html

History of life on Earth (2013), Retrieved from http://www.bbc.co.uk/nature/history_of_the_earth

History of Sikkim (2010), Retrieved from http://sikkim.nic.in/sws/sikk_his.htm

Hoe acid rain occurs?, Detailed available at http://science.howstuffworks.com/nature/climate-weather/atmospheric/acid-rain.htm

Holly Sims and Kevin Vogelmann (2002), *Polular mobilisation and disaster management in Cuba,* Retrieved from http://www.centerforurbanstudies.com/documents/electronic_library/cuba/disaster/disasterpreparation.pdf

How did civilisation statats? (2013), Retrieved from http://www.wisegeek.com/how-did-civilisation-start.htm

How soil erosion occurs, Retrieved from http://adlib.everysite.co.uk/adlib/defra/content.aspx?doc=110542&id=118409

How to control measures of thermal pollution (2011), Retrieved from http://www.zimbio.com/India+Tours/articles/ptNgMN61v5y/How+Control+Measures+Thermal+Pollution

How to Get Rid of Sunstroke (2013), Retrieved from http://lifestyle.iloveindia.com/lounge/how-to-get-rid-of-sunstroke-4629.html

Human (2013), Retrieved from http://en.wikipedia.org/wiki/Human

Human health and ecological consequences of ozone depletion (2013), Retrieved from http://eesc.columbia.edu/courses/v1003/lectures/ozone_health/

Hurricane Katrina (2013), Retrieved from http://en.wikipedia.org/wiki/Hurricane_Katrina

Hurricane Sandy (2013), Retrieved from http://en.wikipedia.org/wiki/Hurricane_Sandy

Hurricanes and global warming, Retrieved from http://www.toyoda-gosei.com/Information/environment/2011/pdf/18.pdf

Iain Murray and H. Sterling Burnett (2009), *10 cool global warming policies*, Retrieved from http://www.ncpa.org/pdfs/st321.pdf

Ice (2013), Retrieved from https://en.wikipedia.org/wiki/Ice

Impact of Deforestation on Wildlife, Detailed available at http://www.greenleapdelhi.org.in/delhi/impact-of-deforestation-on-wildlife/

Impact of greenhouse effect (2013), Retrieved from http://www.tutorvista.com/content/biology/biology-iv/environmental-changes/green-house-effect-impact.php

Impact of ozone depletion (2013), Retrieved from http://www.ozonedepletion.info/education/part2/ozoneimpact.html

Impacts of drought (2013), Retrieved from http://threeissues.sdsu.edu/three_issues_droughtfacts02.html

Impacts of global warming on corals (2013), Retrieved from http://wwf.panda.org/about_our_earth/aboutcc/problems/impacts/coral_reefs/

Impacts of tropical cyclones (2013), Retrieved from http://www.oas.org/CDMP/hazmap/taos/impacts.htm

Importance of ozone layer in the environment (2012), Retrieved from http://expertscolumn.com/content/importance-ozone-layer-environment

Importance of soil (2013), Retrieved from http://www.thinkwater. act.gov.au/more_information/documents/WRG-GSoil_Web.pdf

India fights curbs on livestock-generated greenhouse gas emissions at Doha (2013), Retrieved from http://clippings.ilri.org/2012/12/12/india-fights-curbs-on-livestock-generated-greenhouse-gas-emissions-at-doha/

'India is inching towards acute water scarcity' (2013), Retrieved from http://www.rediff.com/business/slide-show/slide-show-1-india-is-inching-towards-acute-water-scarcity/20130522.htm

India should spearhead prevention of global warming (2013), Retrieved from http://www.hindu.com/2009/01/16/stories/2009011650 570200.htm

India Today (Sep 27, 2012), *Floods in Assam affect 1,916 villages, 18 killed*, Retrieved from http://indiatoday.intoday.in/story/floods-in-assam-affect-1916-villages-18-killed/1/222408.html

India: Karnataka and Andhra Pradesh flood relief update 9 Oct 2009, Retrieved from http://reliefweb.int/report/india/india-karnataka-and-andhra-pradesh-flood-relief-update-9-oct-2009

Indian landslides leave thousands trapped in valley, See http://www.guardian.co.uk/world/2013/jun/20/indian-landslides-leave-trapped-valley-uttrakhand

Indian ocean sea level rise threatens coastal areas, Retrieved from https://www2.ucar.edu/atmosnews/news/2251/indian-ocean-sea-level-rise-threatens-coastal-areas

India's greenhouse gas emissions rise by 58% (2013), Retrieved from http://www.guardian.co.uk/environment/2010/may/12/india-greenhouse-gas-emissions-rise

Industrialized nations' greenhouse gas emissions dipped in 2011, data shows (2013), Retrieved from http://www.guardian.co.uk/environment/2013/apr/26/carbon-emissions-climate-change

Information on Disaster Risk Reduction of the Member Countries (2013), Retrieved fromhttp://www.adrc.asia/nationinformation.php? NationCode=392&Lang..

Integrated Floodplain Management: How can we save fish from being over fished in Bangladesh floodplains?(2007), Detailed available at http://www.capri.cgiar.org/pdf/capriwp57.pdf

Interesting Ocean Facts, Detailed available at http://savethesea.org/STS%20ocean_facts.htm

International Forum on Tornado Disaster Risk Reduction for Bangladesh ? To Cope with Neglected Severe Disasters ? 13-14 December 2009, Dhaka, Bangladesh, Detailed available at http://www.preventionweb.net/files/11180_ForumTordanoBangladesh.pdf

Introduction to Disaster Management, Virtual University for the Small States of the Commonwealth (VUSSC), *Commonwealth of Learning (COL)*, Detailed available at http://www.col.org/resources/crsMaterials/VUSSCcrsMat/Pages/default.aspx

Introduction to disaster preparedness, Retrieved from http://www.ifrc.org/Global/Publications/disasters/all.pdf

Introduction: Ozone Layer Depletion (2013), Retrieved from http://esl.jrc.ec.europa.eu/envind/pf_intro/pf_int06.htm

Iran rattled by 6.2 quake, aftershocks continue (2013), Retrieved from http://rt.com/news/iran-earthquake-aftershock-134/

Island nation fighting sea level rise (2013), Retrieved from http://www.upi.com/Science_News/2013/02/11/Island-nation-fighting-sea-level-rise/UPI-32581360636139/

Jacob Silverman (2013), *Why is Arctic ice melting 50 years too fast?*, Retrieved from http://science.howstuffworks.com/environmental/earth/geophysics/arctic-ice.htm

Jacqui Hayes (2013), *Heat waves to hit wildlife hard*, Retrieved from http://www.abc.net.au/environment/articles/2013/03/12/3711481.htm

Jaime McLeod (2010), *What Causes a Heat Wave?*, Retrieved from http://www.farmersalmanac.com/weather/2010/04/12/what-causes-a-heat-wave/

James M. Vose, Wayne T. Swank, Chris D. Geron, and Amy E. *Major, Emissions from Forest Burning in the Southeastern United States: Application of a Model Determining Spatial and Temporal Fire Variation*, p. 68.

Javier B. Domínguez (2012), *Soil Contamination Research Trends*, Retrieved from https://www.novapublishers.com/catalog/product_info.php?products_id=6860

Jayaprakash Kakada (2013), Short essay on Soil Erosion in India, Retrieved from http://www.preservearticles.com/2012011320703/short-essay-on-soil-erosion-in-india.html

Jeff Dayton-Johnson (2004), *Natural Disasters and Adoptive Capacity*, Detailed available at http://www.oecd.org/dataoecd/30/63/33845215.pdf

Jefferson Mecham (2001), *Causes and consequences of deforestation in Ecuador*, Retrieved from http://www.rainforestinfo.org.au/projects/jefferson.htm

Jeffrey Masters (2013), *Frequently Asked Questions About The Ozone Hole*, Retrieved from http://www.wunderground.com/resources/climate/holefaq.asp

Jennifer Carpenter (2009), *Consequences of a Global Water Shortage*, See http://voices.yahoo.com/consequences-global-water-shortage-3239191.html

Jhum Cultivation (2011), Retrieved from http://www.arthapedia.in/index.php?title=Jhum_%28Shifting%29_Cultivation

Jhum cultivation (2013), Retrieved from https://sites.google.com/site/efloraofindia/general-eposts/general-efi-posts/scenery-posts/jhum-cultivation

Jhum cultivation in hill tracts (2010), Retrieved from http://discoveringdhaka.wordpress.com/2010/02/12/jhum-cultivation-in-the-hill-tracts/

Jianguo Tan, Youfei Zheng, Xu Tang, Changyi Guo, Liping Li, Guixiang Song, Xinrong Zhen, Dong Yuan, Adam J. Kalkstein, Furong Li, Heng Chen (2010), The urban heat island and its impact on heat waves and human health in Shanghai, *Int J Biometeorol*, 54:75–84.

Joe Ridout, *The Ten Warning Signs of Global Warming,* Retrieved from http://www.citizen.org/documents/10%20Warning%20Signs% 20_text_—final.pdf

Johann G. Goldammer, Peter G.H. Frost, Mike Jurvélius, Evelien M. Kamminga, Teri Kruger, Soo Ing Moody and Manuel Pogeyed (2010), *Community participation in integrated forest fire management: experiences from Africa, Asia and Europe,* Retrieved from http://www.fire.uni-freiburg.de/Manag/CiF-Ch-5-Africa-Asia-Europe.pdf

John Laumer (2012), *Extreme Drought in Mexico: Refugees Will Travel Farther North to Find Water and Work,* Retrieved from http://www.treehugger.com/environmental-policy/drought-still-destroying-texas-and-mexico-agriculture.html

John Vidal (2010), *Soil erosion threatens to leave Earth hungry,* Retrieved from http://www.guardian.co.uk/environment/2010/dec/14/soil-erosion-environment-review-vidal

John Vidal (2011), *Europe's dry spring could lead to power blackouts, governments warn,* Retrieved from http://www.guardian.co.uk/environment/2011/may/31/europe-dry-spring-power-blackouts

John Vidal and Declan Walsh (2010), *Temperatures reach record high in Pakistan,* Retrieved from http://www.guardian.co.uk/world/2010/jun/01/pakistan-record-temperatures-heatwave

John Watkins (2006), *Libya's thirst for fossil water,* Retrieved from http://news.bbc.co.uk/2/hi/science/nature/4814988.stm

Jon Barnett, *Global warming and the security of atoll countries,* Retrieved from http://www.upf.pf/IMG/pdf/12_Barnett.pdf

Jonathan Adams (2007), *Rising sea levels threaten small Pacific island nations,* Retrieved from http://www.nytimes.com/2007/05/03/world/asia/03iht-pacific.2.5548184.html?pagewanted=all&_r=0

Jonathan Kaiman (2012), *China's emissions expected to rise until 2030, despite ambitious green policies,* Retrieved from http://www.guardian.co.uk/environment/2012/nov/26/china-emissions-rise-green-policies

Jones, T. S. *et al.* (1982). "Morbidity and mortality associated with the July 1980 heat wave in St Louis and Kansas City, Mo". *Journal of the American Medical Association* 247 (24): 3327–3331

Jørgen E. Olesen, *Climate change as a driver for European agriculture,* Retrieved from http://ec.europa.eu/research/agriculture/scar/pdf/scar_foresight_climate_change_en.pdf

Joypahash Kakada (2010), *Short essay on thermal pollution: Case Study,* Retrieved from http://www.preservearticles.com/2012011320622/short-essay-on-thermal-pollution-case-study.html

K J Hutchinson (2013), *The causes and effects of wildfires and how people prepare for and respond to them*, Retrieved from http://worldlywise.pbworks.com/w/page/26474623/The%20causes%2 0and%20effects%20of%20wildfires%20and%20how% 20people%20 prepare%20for%20and %20respond%20to %20them

K. Selvavinayagam, Disaster management practices using ArcGIS, ArcIMS, Detailed available at http://www.articlesbase.com/science-articles/disaster-management-practices-using-arcgis-arcims-arcsde-and-sql-403946.html

K.A. Smith, T. Ball, F. Conen, K.E. Dobbie, J. Massheder and A. Rey (2003), Exchange of greenhouse gases between soil and atmosphere: interactions of soil physical factors and biological processes, *European Journal of Soil Science,* December 2003, 54, 779–791.

Kallie Szczepanski (2004), *The 2004 Tsunami in the Indian Ocean,* Retrieved from http://asianhistory.about.com/od/asianenviron mentalhistory/p/The-2004-Tsunami-In-The-Indian-Ocean.htm

Karnataka faces worst drought in 42 years (2012), Retrieved from http://www.livemint.com/Politics/9vhOYH9lqHHuiX7UBARMlI/Karnataka-faces-worst-drought-in-42-years.html

Karunakaran, N. (2013), *Jhum fields forever,* Retrieved from http://business.outlookindia.com/print.aspx?articleid= 2172&editionid=58&catgid=2&subcatgid=973

Katie Kettler (2013), *Coral Reef Conservation,* Retrieved from http://jrscience.wcp.muohio.edu/fieldcourses03/PapersMarineEcology Articles/CoralReefConservation.html

Kenya coral reefs (2013), Retrieved from http://www.letsgokenya.com/kenya-coral-reefs

Khongsai, C. (2013), *Jhum cultivation and its Impact on ecology need for viable,* Retrieved from http://e-pao.net/epSubPageExtractor.asp? src= education.Science_ and_Technology. Jhum_Cultivation_ and_its_impact _on_ Ecology

Kiribati (2013), Retrieved from https://en.wikipedia.org/wiki/Kiribati

Lake Chad: almost gone, Retrieved from http://www.unep.org/dewa/vitalwater/article116.html

Land Pollution (2012), Retrieved from http://lifeofearth.org/2009/08/land-pollution.html

Land Use and Jhum Cultivation in Manipur (2010), Retrieved from http://manipur.nic.in/planning/DraftMSDR/Draft_SDR_pdf/Chapter%206_Land%20Use.pdf

Landslide in Australia (2013), Retrieved from http://lrm.australian geomechanics.org/

Landslide mitigation, See http://en.wikipedia.org/wiki/Landslide_mitigation

Landslide, Seehttp://www.britannica.com/EBchecked/topic/329513/landslide

Landslides (2013), Retrieved from http://en.wikipedia.org/wiki/Landslide

Landslides in Central America (2013), See http://landslides.usgs.gov/research/other/centralamerica.php

Landslides in Europe (2013), Retrieved from http://eusoils.jrc.ec.europa.eu/library/themes/landslides/

Landslides in Sikkim, See http://southsikkim.nic.in/department/disaster/docs/landslides.pdf

Landslides in the Ethiopian highlands and the Rift margins, Retrieved from http://www.sciencedirect.com/science/article/pii/S1464343X 09001113

Landslides Occur in all 50 States, See http://geology.com/usgs/landslides/

Landslides, See http://saarc-sdmc.nic.in/pdf/landslide.pdf

Lansdslide remediation: Take action know, See http://kanat.jsc.vsc.edu/student/dowerr/mainpage.htm

Larry West (2013), *what is the Greenhouse Effect?* Retrieved from http://environment.about.com/od/globalwarming/a/greenhouse.htm

Lars Järup (2012), Hazards of heavy metal contamination. See http://www.ncbi.nlm.nih.gov/pubmed/14757716

Latin America and the Caribbean (2013), Retrieved from http://www.redcross.org/what-we-do/international-services/where-we-help/latin-america-caribbean

Laurence Hecht, *The fraud of global warming: True CO_2 record buried under gore,* Retrieved from http://rense.com/general75/0223_inconvenient_gore.pdf

Lauretta Burke, Liz Selig (WRI), and Mark Spalding (2002), *Reefs at risk in South east Asia,* Retrieved from http://www.wri.org/publication/reefs-risk-southeast-asia

Laurie Uytterlinde, *Flood, Sardar Sarovar Dam: A Case Study of Development-induced Environmental Displacement,* Vol. 16, No. 3 (August 1997).

Leonard F. DeBano (2004), *Fire effects on watersheds: An overview,* Retrieved from http://www.swhydro.arizona.edu/archive/V8_N2/feature5.pdf

Lexi Krock (2013), *The world of fire,* Retrieved from http://www.pbs.org/wgbh/nova/fire/world.html

Lhungdim, J. (2010). *Jhum cultivation: Strategies for North-east India,* Retrieved from http://www.indigenousportal.com/Economic-Development/Jhum-cultivation-Strategies-for-North-East-India.html

Lianzela (1997), *Effects of shifting cultivation on environment: With special reference to Mizoram,* Retrieved from http://dawn.com/2013/04/11/islamist-shot-dead-in-bangladesh-violence-police/

Light pollution (2013), See https://www.iau.org/public/light_pollution/

Light pollution (2013), Seehttp://en.wikipedia.org/wiki/Light_pollution#Light_trespass

Light pollution and human health's, See http://envirolaw.com/light-pollution-and-human-health/

Light pollution awareness groups, See http://www.maltastro.org/lpag/

Light pollution can be prevented, See http://www.klinikum-karlsruhe.com/fileadmin/Medien/Kliniken_und_Medizinische_ Zentren/Kopfkliniken/Augenklinik/SpektAug_267-270.pdf

Light pollution, a growing environmental safety health hazards, See http://www.cooke.id.au/Vision_2020_Submission.pdf

Light pollution-Environmental protection UK, Seehttp://www.environmental-protection.org.uk/neighbourhood-nuisance/light-pollution/

Lisa Friedman and Climate Wire (2012), *India Balks at Greenhouse Gas Emission Cuts,* Retrieved from http://www.scientificamerican.com/article.cfm?id=india-balks-at-greenhouse-gas-emission-cuts

Lisa Friedman and Climate Wire (2013), *Negotiations: US and China pledge 'large-scale cooperative action' to reduce emissions,* Retrieved from http://www.eenews.net/stories/1059979453

Lisa Hayden (2011), *Conservancy Protects Mozambique Coral Reefs and Studies Their Response to Ocean Warming,* Retrieved from http://

change.nature.org/2011/12/08/conservancy-brings-expertise-in-coral-reefs-and-climate-change-to-mozambique/

Lisa Schipper and Mark Pelling, *Disaster risk, climate change and international development: scope for, and challenges to, integration,* Detailed available at http://onlinelibrary.wiley.com/doi/10.1111/j.1467-9523.2006.00304.x/abstract

List of earthquakes in Iran (2013), Retrieved from http://en.wikipedia.org/wiki/List_of_earthquakes_in_Iran

Local and national consequences of local climate regulation, Detailed available at http://rainforests.mongabay.com/0902.htm

Locals worry more Mexican dams could make RGV water shortage worse, Retrieved from http://www.themonitor.com/news/local/article_6da66b60-a3ca-11e2-a63f-0019bb30f31a.html

Lolita Bildan (2013), *Disaster Management in South East Asia - an overview,* Retrieved from http://www.icimod.org/?opg=949&q=drr_document&document=1113

Londani (2013), Retrieved from http://www.londoni.co/index.php/history-of-bangladesh?id=21

M. Heinl, P. Frost, C. Vanderpost and J. Sliva (2007), *Fire activity on drylands and floodplains in the southern Okavango Delta, Botswana, Journal of Arid Environments 68,* Retrieved from www.elsevier.com/locate/jnlabr/yjare

M. Jahangir Alam Chowdhury (2011), *Social Cohesion and Natural Disaster Loss Recovery of Households: Experience from Bangladesh,* Detailed available at http://www.oecd.org/dataoecd/59/25/46880436.pdf

M.V.K. Sivakumar, Natural Disasters and Their Mitigation for Sustainable Agricultural Development, Detailed available at http://www.johannesburgsummit.org/html/documents/backgrounddocs/unisdr%20report.pdf

Madhavi Ariyabandu, *Women: the risk managers in natural disasters,* Detailed available at http://www.ssri.hawaii.edu/research/GDWwebsite/pdf/Ariyabandu.pdf

Maharashtra drought: a story of India's failed water management (2013), Retrieved from http://blogs.hindustantimes.com/ecostani/2013/03/30/maharashtra-drought-a-story-of-india%E2%80%99s-failed-water-management/

Mahbub Robbani, Salah Uddit Siddiquee, Sourovi Zaman, and Hiroshi Nakamura (2007), Agriculture in Bangladesh: Recent Trend and Agro environment towards Sustainability, *Journal of Faculty of Agriculture,* Shinshu University, Vol. 43, No: 1, Detailed available at http://www.undp.org.bd/projects/proj_detail.php?pid=29

Major Areas :: Disaster Management :: Landslide, See http://agritech.tnau.ac.in/agriculture/agri_majorareas_ disastermgt_ landslide.html

Maldives (2013), Retrieved from https://en.wikipedia.org/wiki/Maldives

Maldives country profile (2013), Retrieved from http://www.bbc.co.uk/news/world-south-asia-12651486

Manalisha (2013), *Essay on the harmful effects of ozone depletion,* Retrieved fromhttp://www.publishyourarticles.net/knowledge-hub/environmental-studies/essay-on-the-harmful-effects-of-ozone-depletion.html

Marine Pollution, Detailed available at http://eoedu.belspo.be/en/profs/vgt-europe-marinepollution.asp?section=1.3.1

Marine Pollution, Detailed available at http://www.bcb.uwc.ac.za/envfacts/facts/marinepollution.htm

Marine pollution, Detailed available at http://www.ioseaturtles.org/Education/marinepollutionbooklet.pdf

Marine Pollution: Causes and Consequences, Detailed available at http://envfor.nic.in/news/julsep03/marine.htm

Mark Slingo (2013), *How to Prevent Coral Reefs From Disappearing*, Retrieved from http://www.ehow.com/how_6763099_prevent-coral-reefs-disappearing.html

Marshall Brain (2013), *If the polar ice caps melted, how much would the oceans rise?*, Retrieved from http://science.howstuffworks.com/environmental/earth/geophysics/question473.htm

Martin Khor (2013), *Soil erosion*, Retrieved from http://www.twnside.org.sg/title/land-ch.htm

Mary Simms, *Global Warming Threatens Hawaii's Coral Reefs*, Retrieved from http://www.hawaiinewsnow.com/Global/story.asp?S= 6847592

Md. Safiuddin and Md. Masud Karim, *Groundwater Arsenic Contamination in Bangladesh: Causes, Effects and Remediation*, Detailed available at http://www.eng-consult.com/pub/ArsenicIEB.pdf

Medical problems, See http://www.britastro.org/dark-skies/health.html

Megan Gannon (2012), *Why Heat Waves Can Mean High Death Tolls*, Retrieved from http://www.livescience.com/22050-heat-waves-high-death-tolls.html

Meghalaya (2013), Retrieved from http://vistar.nic.in/document/chapter/87.htm

Metals in aquatic freshwater (2012), Retrieved from http://www.lenntech.com/aquatic/metals.htm

Methane (2013), Retrieved from http://en.wikipedia.org/wiki/Methane

Mexico Threatened with Drought and Food Scarcity (2013), Retrieved from http://larouchepac.com/node/25767

Michael (2013), *30 Facts About The Coming Water Crisis That Will Change The Lives of Every Person on the Planet*, Retrieved from http://theeconomiccollapseblog.com/archives/30-facts-about-the-coming-water-crisis-that-will-change-the-lives-of-every-person-on-the-planet

Michael Acreman (2007), "Principles of Water Management for People and the Environment", Areti Krishna Kumari (Ed), *"Water Pollution: An Overview"*, First edition, Hyderabad: The ICFAI University Press, pp. 41-42.

Middle East and North Africa Water Resources Consortium and Technology Exchange Network, Retrieved from http://www.ercim.eu/medconf/papers/ouazar.html

Mike Bowers and Bernard Lagan (2013), Kiribati enters the end game against climate change - in pictures, Retrieved from http://www.guardian.co.uk/environment/gallery/2013/apr/16/kiribati-end-game-climate-change-in-pictures

Million hit by floods in Africa (2007), Retrieved from http://news.bbc.co.uk/2/hi/africa/6998651.stm

Ministry of Home Affairs, GoI (2013), *State level Programmes for strengthening disaster management in India*, etrieved from http://ndmindia.nic.in/DM-Booklet-080211.pdf

Missing the dark: Health effects of light pollution, See http://www.ncbi.nlm.nih.gov/pmc/articles/PMC2627884/

Missing the dark: Health effects of light pollution, See http://www.ncbi.nlm.nih.gov/pmc/articles/PMC2627884/

Mohammed Asef Iqbal and S.G. Gupta (2009), Studies on Heavy Metal Ion Pollution of Ground Water Sources as an Effect of Municipal Solid Waste Dumping, *African Journal of Basic and Applied Sciences* 1 (5-6): 117, Retrieved from http://idosi.org/ajbas/ajbas1%285-6%2909/6.pdf

Mohit Iasija (2010), *What are the main causes of thermal pollution?*, Retrieved from http://www.preservearticles.com/201101072819/causes-of-thermal-pollution.html

Mohit Iasija (2013), *What are the main causes of soil erosions?*, Retrieved from http://www.preservearticles.com/201101082864/main-causes-of-soil-erosion.html

Mohiuddin Zakaria (2011), *Flood: Some positive effects*, Retrieved from http://archive.thedailystar.net/newDesign/news-details.php? nid=197343

More than 220 forest fires spread across Nepal (2012), Retrieved from http://www.bbc.co.uk/news/world-asia-17859358

Moving closer to more effective disaster management in Europe. See http://europa.eu/rapid/press-release_MEMO-11-927_en.htm

Ms. Arjumand Habib, *Early Warning System for Severe Thunder Storms in Bangladesh*, Detailed available at http://www.iawe.org/WRDRR_Bangladesh/Preprints/S4BMD.pdf

Ms. Salma Rahman and Mr. Shahid Mallick, *Community, Disability and Response to Disaster Mitigation in Bangladesh*, Detailed available at http://www.publicsphereproject.org/events/diac08/proceedings/16.Disaster_Mitigation.Rahman_and_Mallick.pdf

Mukherjee Debashree and Hazra Somnath (Ed) *"Air Pollution and Health"*, First edition, The ICFAI University Press, Hyderabad, pp. 3-12.

Murtem, G., Sinha, G and Dopum, J. (2008), *Jhumias view on shifting cultivation in Arunachal Pradesh, Bulletin of Arunachal Forest Research 24 (1&2)*, Retrieved from http://www.sfri.org/images/pdf/vol24/vol242008.page35-40.pdf

N.G. Menon and C.S.G. Pillai (1996), *Marine Diversity Conservation and Management*, Detailed available at http://www.mendeley.com/research/marine-biodiversity-conservation-management-1/

Nagaland economy (2013), Retrieved from http://www.nagalandonline. in/About/profile/Economy/index.html

Narmada Bachao Andolan (2013), Retrieved from http://en.wikipedia.org/wiki/Narmada_Bachao_Andolan

Nathalie Fiset, The Effect of Deforestation, detailed available at http://ezinearticles.com/?The-Effect-of-Deforestation&id=510236

National Plan for Disaster Management 2008-2015, Detailed available at http://www.preventionweb.net/files/9472_NationalPlanfor Disastermanagement.pdf

National Wildfire Coordinating Group Communicator's Guide for Wild land Fire Management: Fire Education, Prevention, and Mitigation Practices.

Natural disaster (2013), Retrieved from http://en.wikipedia.org/wiki/Natural_disaster

Nature (2013), Retrieved from https://en.wikipedia.org/wiki/Nature

Navin Singh Khadka (2013), *South Asia landslides 'on the rise'*, Retrieved from, See http://www.bbc.co.uk/news/science-environment-18872398

Nearly half the world could face water scarcity by 2030, UN chief warns, Retrieved from http://www.ctvnews.ca/world/nearly-half-the-world-could-face-water-scarcity-by-2030-un-chief-warns-1.1207996

Nena (2001), *6 million environment protection project for Nagaland*, Retrieved from http://www.nenanews.com/OT%20Apr.7-%20%20Apr.21,01/oh1.htm

Nepal floodwaters to be tapped for hydro power in Uttar Pradesh (2013), Retrieved from http://www.infrawindow.com/news/nepal-floodwaters-to-be-tapped-for-hydro-power-in-uttar-pradesh_9182/

Nepal Forest Fire Management Chapter (NFMC), Retrieved from http://www.nffmc.org/

New Devastating Pakistan Floods (2011), Retrieved from http://www.theatlantic.com/infocus/2011/09/new-devastating-pakistan-floods/100152/

Nick Arya (2013), *Write a brief note on Cyclone Preparedness*, Retrieved from http://www.preservearticles.com/201102173913/write-a-brief-note-on-cyclone-preparedness.html

Nick Bryant (2004), *Maldives: Paradise soon to be lost*, Retrieved from http://news.bbc.co.uk/2/hi/south_asia/3930765.stm

Nigeria, SA worst greenhouse gas emitters in Africa (2008), Retrieved from http://mg.co.za/article/2008-08-24-nigeria-sa-worst-greenhouse-gas-emitters-in-africa

Nina Chestney (2012), *Soil erosion increasing global warming threat: UNEP*, Retrieved from http://www.reuters.com/article/2012/02/13/us-unep-soil-idUSTRE81C13J20120213

Ningthoujam Sandhyarani (2011), *Ways to Prevent Air Pollution*, Retrieved from http://www.buzzle.com/articles/ways-to-prevent-air-pollution.html

Nitrous oxide (2013), Retrieved from http://en.wikipedia.org/wiki/Nitrous_oxide

Nitrous oxide (N_2O) (2013), Retrieved from http://en.wikipedia.org/wiki/Greenhouse_gas

No early warning for Nepal's deadly landslides (2013), See http://www.irinnews.org/report/98381/no-early-warning-for-nepal-s-deadly-landslides

No. 102 - Greenhouse Gas Control: Implications for Agriculture (Summary), Retrieved from http://heartland.org/policy-documents/no-102-greenhouse-gas-control-implications-agriculture-summary

NOAA knows tsunami, Retrieved from http://www.noaa.gov/factsheets/new%20version/tsunamis.pdf

Noise pollution (2012), Retrieved from http://en.wikipedia.org/wiki/Noise_pollution

Noise Pollution (2013), Retrieved from *http://www.wdcs.org/stop/pollution/story_details.php?select=57*

North American Drought Monitor, Retrieved from http://www.ncdc.noaa.gov/temp-and-precip/drought/nadm/

North Pole (2013), Retrieved from https://en.wikipedia.org/wiki/North_Pole

Notes on tsunami, Retrieved from http://chuma.cas.usf.edu/~juster/GLY2030-F06/notes-tsunami.pdf

Nyiragongo volcano landslide: 54 'dead' in DR Congo (2010), See http://www.bbc.co.uk/news/10132384

Ocean Pollution, Oceanography 10, T. James Noyes, El Camino College.

Ocean Pollution, Detailed available at http://library.thinkquest.org/CR0215471/ocean_pollution.htm

Omer Farooq (2002), *India's heat wave tragedy*, Retrieved from http://news.bbc.co.uk/2/hi/south_asia/1994174.stm

One Indianews (January 18, 2008), *Jhum cultivation declining in Meghalaya*, Retrieved from http://news.oneindia.in/2008/01/30/jhum-cultivation-declining-in-meghalaya-1201698427.html

On-site effects of soil erosion, Retrieved from http://www.soilerosion.net/doc/on-site.html

Organisations involved in disaster management (2013), Retrieved from http://www.wcpt.org/node/36994

Over 20 sunstroke deaths reported in Andhra Pradesh's Krishna district (2012), Retrieved from http://www.ndtv.com/article/south/over-20-sunstroke-deaths-reported-in-andhra-pradesh-s-krishna-district-223013

Ozone (2013), Retrieved from http://en.wikipedia.org/wiki/Ozone

Ozone depletion (2013), Retrieved from http://en.wikipedia.org/wiki/Ozone_depletion

Ozone depletion (2013), Retrieved from http://library.thinkquest.org/26026/Environmental_Problems/ozone_depletion.html

Ozone depletion and UVB radiation: Impact on plant DNA damage in southern South America (1999), Retrieved from http://www.ncbi.nlm.nih.gov/pmc/articles/PMC24816/

Ozone depletion-causes (2013), Retrieved from http://library.thinkquest.org/26026/Environmental_Problems/ozone_depletion.html

Ozone layer (2013), Retrieved from http://en.wikipedia.org/wiki/Ozone_layer

Ozone Layer Depletion: Effects and Causes of Ozone Depletion, Retrieved from http://www.buzzle.com/articles/ozone-layer-depletion-effects-and-causes-of-ozone-depletion.html

P.G. Dhar Chakrabarti (2013), *Challenges of Disaster Management in India: Implications for the Economic, Political, and Security Environments*, Retrieved fromhttp://www.nbr.org/publications/element.aspx?id=549#.UZ8l9VKDH3Y

Pakistan: Humanitarian responses (2013), Retrieved from http://pakresponse.info/

Panda D.S., Behera R.K., Sahu R.K. and Bandhopadhya S.N. (2012), *Heavy Metal Pollution in Chilika Lake, A Tropical Lagoon*, Retrieved from http://ces.iisc.ernet.in/energy/Lake2002abs/ses145.html

Pankaj Sekhsaria, *Deforestation in India: Overview and proposed case studies*, Detailed available at http://enviroscope.iges.or.jp/modules/envirolib/upload/1508/attach/1ws-9-pankaji.pdf

Pashupati Chaudhary and Kamal P. Aryal (2009), *Global Warming in Nepal: Challenges and Policy Imperatives*, Retrieved from http://forestaction.org/app/webroot/js/tinymce/editor/plugins/filemanager/files/images/stories/pdfs/journal_of_forest_and_livelihood/vol_8_1/1_Chaudhary_and_ Aryal_Global_warming_ in_Nepal.pdf

Paul, I (2008), *Shifting cultivation: a means of subsistence among the Naga tribes of India and the associated environmental impacts,* Retrieved from http://www.cabdirect.org/abstracts/20083225481.html;jsessionid=71F12346A055FEA41 A1DF8F690E9E1E9? gitCommit=4.13.29

Peru (2013), Retrieved from http://rainforests.mongabay.com/20peru.htm

Peru, Chile and Bolivia hit by floods after heavy rain (2013), Retrieved from http://www.bbc.co.uk/news/world-latin-america-21399408

Peter Tatham, Karen Spens and Richard Oloruntoba (2009), *Cyclones in Bangladesh: A Case Study of a Whole Country Response to Rapid onset Disasters,* Detailed Available at http://nova.newcastle.edu.au/vital/access/manager/Repository/uon:9024

Petra Wakefield (2013), *Harmful Effects of Soil Erosion,* Retrieved from http://www.ehow.com/info_8597181_harmful-effects-soil-erosion.html

Philip M. Fearnside (2007), *Deforestation in Amazon,* Detailed available at http://www.eoearth.org/article/Deforestation_in_Amazonia

Philippa McDonald (2010), *Pacific islands growing, not sinking,* Retrieved from http://www.abc.net.au/news/2010-06-03/pacific-islands-growing-not-sinking/851738

Plastic pollution (2013), See http://www.britannica.com/EBchecked/topic/1589019/plastic-pollution

Plastic pollution: A cancer in nature (2013), See http://vinesh777.hubpages.com/hub/Plastic-Pollution—A-Cancer-in-Nature

Plastic recycling (2013), See http://en.wikipedia.org/wiki/Plastic_recycling

Poland fights acid rain (2001), Detailed available at http://www.iaea.org/newscenter/news/2001/03062001_news01.shtml

Potential impact of sea-level rise on Bangladesh, Retrieved from http://www.grida.no/publications/vg/climate/page/3086.aspx

Prabal Barua1, Md. Shah Nawaz Chowdhury and Subrata Sarker, *Climate Change and Its risk reduction by mangrove Ecosystem of Bangladesh,* Vol. 4, Issue: 3, pp. 208-225, September - October, 2010, Detailed available at http://www.bdresearchpublications. com/admin/journal/upload/09168/09168.pdf

Pradeep Kurukulasuriya and Shane Rosenthal (2003), *Climate change and agriculture: A review of impacts and adaptations,* p. 7, Retrieved from http://www.c-ciarn.uoguelph.ca/updates_archived/World_Bank_Paper.pdf

Precautionary Measures Before, During and After a Typhoon (2013), Retrieved from http://guides.wikinut.com/Precautionary-Measures-Before,-During-and-After-a-Typhoon/x1cwj3g5/

Precautionary measures, Before, During and After a Typhoon (2013), Retrieved from http://expertscolumn.com/content/precautionary-measures-during-and-after-typhoon

Prevention of Air Pollution from Ships (2012), Retrieved from http://www.imo.org/ourwork/environment/pollutionprevention/airpollution/pages/air-pollution.aspx

Prevention of vehicular pollution to save the environment, Detailed available at http://www.controllingpollution.com/prevention-of-vehicular-pollution

Priestley Habru (2010), *The view from beneath the waves: climate change in the Solomon Islands,* Retrieved from http://www.guardian.co.uk/world/2010/nov/09/solomon-islands-climate-change

Professor (Dr) K.C.Jena and Moon Rani Mishra (2011), *Effect of global warming and climate change on coastal zones and sea level*, Retrieved from http://orissa.gov.in/e-magazine/Orissareview/2011/sep-oct/engpdf/83-95.pdf

Professor M Alimullah Miyan, *Cyclone Disaster Mitigation in Bangladesh*, Detailed available at http://www.fao.org/forestry/11285-03611be0ad43d80eefb3de4a8ee2e1fd0.pdf

Progress Report on Community Based Fire Management Initiatives in the Hills of Nepal (CBFiM) (2010). See http://www.fire.uni-freiburg.de/GlobalNetworks/South_Asia/Community-Level-Fire-Management-Planning.pdf

Project Amazonia: Threats – Deforestation, Detailed available at http://web.mit.edu/12.000/www/m2006/final/threats/threat_ deforest.html

Quazi Shahabuddin and Zulfiqar Ali (2006), *Natural Disasters, Risks, Vulnerability and Persistence of Poverty: An Analysis of Household Level Data*, Detailed available at http://www.chronicpoverty.org/publications/details/natural-disasters-risks-vulnerability-and-persistence-of-poverty-an-analysis-of-household-level-data

Quick Facts on Ice Sheets (2013), Retrieved from http://nsidc.org/cryosphere/quickfacts/icesheets.html

R Sari Kovats and L.Ebi Kristie (2006), *Heat waves and public health in Europe*, Retrieved from http://eurpub.oxfordjournals.org/content/16/6/592.full

R. D. Gupta (2006), *Environmental Pollution: Hazards and Control*, First edition, Concept Publishing Company, New Delhi, p.6.

R. Gomme and F. Petrassi (1996), *Rainfall Variability and Drought in Sub-Saharan Africa*, Retrieved from http://www.fao.org/sd/eidirect/eian0004.htm

R. Lal and J.P. Bruce (1999), The potential of world cropland soils to sequester C and mitigate the greenhouse effect, *Environmental Science and Policy* 2, pp. 177-185, Retrieved from http://controverses.sciences-po.fr/climatewiki/images/5/55/99_Lal_-_potential_of_world_cropland_to_sequester_and_mitigate.pdf

R. Nasi, R. Dennis, E. Meijaard, G. Applegate and P. Moore (2013), *Forest fire and biological diversity*, Retrieved from http://www.fao.org/docrep/004/y3582e/y3582e08.htm

R.C. Chandna (2005), *"Environmental Geography"*, First edition, Ludhiana: Kalyani Publishers, pp.164-65.

R.D. Gupta (2006), *"Environmental Pollution: Hazards and Control"*, First edition, New Delhi: Concept Publishing Company, pp. 1-5.

Rae Zimmerman (2013), *Global climate change and transportation infrastructure: Lessons from the New York areas*, Retrieved from http://climate.dot.gov/documents/workshop1002/zimmermanrch.pdf

Rahman, S.; Rahman, M.; Sunderland, T (2012), *Causes and consequences of shifting cultivation and its alternative in the hill tracts of eastern Bangladesh*, Retrieved from http://www.cifor.org/online-library/browse/view-publication/publication/3743.html

Rajasthan has the highest probability of drought: Report (2013), Retrieved from http://articles.timesofindia.indiatimes.com/2012-06-08/jaipur/32123682_1_groundwater-water-pollution-sewage-water

Ranjan, R. and Upadhyay, V. (1999), *Ecological impact due to shifting cultivations*, Retrieved from http://www.iisc.ernet.in/currsci/nov25/articles12.htm

Ranjita (2013), *Essay on the main causes of earthquake,* Retrieved from http://www.preservearticles.com/2011090212686/essay-on-the-main-causes-of-earthquake.html

Rasoul Sorkhabi (2011), *Japan's megaquake and killer tsunami: How did this happen?,* Retrieved from http://www.earthmagazine.org/article/japans-megaquake-and-killer-tsunami-how-did-happen

Rehabilitation and Reconstruction, Disaster Management Training Programme, Detailed available at http://ocha.unog.ch/drptoolkit/PreparednessTools/Coordination/role%20and%20 responsibilities%20of%20UNDMT.pdf

Remote sensing of land/forest fires (2013), Retrieved from http://www.crisp.nus.edu.sg/forest_fire/fire.html

Republic of Maldives (2013), Retrieved from http://www.climatehotmap.org/global-warming-locations/republic-of-maldives.html

Responding to the Earthquake and Tsunami (2013), Retrieved from http://www.redcross.org/what-we-do/international-services/where-we-help/asia/japan

Rhett Butler (2012), *Soil erosions and its effects,* Retrieved from http://rainforests.mongabay.com/0903.htm

Rhett. A.Butler (2013), *The Amazon: The World's Largest Rainforest,* Retrieved from http://rainforests.mongabay.com/amazon/

Rising CO_2 Levels Disrupt Rain Forest Growth Patterns (2013), Retrieved from http://globalwarming.markey.house.gov/impactzones/amazon.html

Risk and Disaster Management: Overview (2013), Retrieved from http://www.unhabitat.org/content.asp?cid=2711&catid= 286&typeid=24&subMenuId=0

Risk reduction and emergency preparedness: WHO six-year strategy for the health sector and community capacity development (2007), World Health Organisation, Detailed available at http://www.who.int/hac/techguidance/preparedness/emergency_preparedness_eng.pdf

Risks from urban flooding rise in East Asia, says World Bank (2012), Retrieved from http://www.abs-cbnnews.com/business/02/13/12/risks-urban-flooding-rise-east-asia-says-world-bank

Rita Putatunda, *Causes and effects of acid rains,* Detailed available at http://www.buzzle.com/articles/causes-and-effects-of-acid-rain.html

Robert J A Jones and Luca Montanarella (2013), *Soil Erosion in Europe,* Retrieved from http://eusoils.jrc.ec.europa.eu/esdb_archive/pesera/pesera_cd/sect_h6.htm

Robert Mburia (2011), *Climate Change and Food Security Issues in Sub-Saharan Africa,* Retrieved from http://www.climateemergency institute.com/food_sec_subsaharan_ mburia.html

Robert Nolin (2013), *South Florida Coral Reefs In 'Extremely Alarming' Decline: Study,* Retrieved from http://www.huffingtonpost.com/2013/02/01/florida-coral-reefs-alarming-decline_n_2594504.html

Rod Jenkins (1998), *A Summary of the Biological and Human Health Risks of Stratospheric Ozone Depletion,* Retrieved from http://www.ozonedepletion.info/health_report/ozone.html

Ross W. Gorte and Kelsi Bracmort (2012), *Forest Fire/Wildfire Protection,* Retrieved from http://www.fas.org/sgp/crs/misc/RL30755.pdf

Russia mulls ozone actions (2013), Retrieved from http://www.upi.com/Business_News/Energy-Resources/2013/04/01/Russia-mulls-ozone-actions/UPI-40941364819111/

Russia to cut greenhouse gas emissions by 50% by 2050 - Medvedev (2009), Retrieved from http://en.rian.ru/russia/20090710/155493615.html

Russia will not cut emissions under extended Kyoto climate pact (2013), Retrieved from http://www.reuters.com/article/2012/09/13/us-russia-kyoto-idUSBRE88C0QZ20120913

Russia wins new greenhouse gas emissions rights (2008), Retrieved from http://usatoday30.usatoday.com/weather/climate/2008-05-29\

Russia, China to set up regional disaster management centre (2008), Retrieved from http://en.rian.ru/russia/20080523/108181773.html

S.C. Gulati and Suresh Sharma, *Population pressure and deforestation in India*, Detailed available at http://www.corecentre.co.in/database/docs/docfiles/population_pressure.pdf

S.C. Santra (2001), "*Environmental Science*", First edition, Kolkata: New Central Book Agency (P) Ltd., pp.1001-1018.

S.M. Enzler (2013), *History of the greenhouse effect and global warming*, Retrieved from http://www.lenntech.com/greenhouse-effect/global-warming-history.htm

Safety During Typhoons (2013), Retrieved from http://www.healthypinoy.com/health/articles/disaster-preparedness-typhoon.html

Sahasrabuddhe, V. (2013), *Arunachal's green could soon turn brown*, Retrieved from http://www.indiaenvironmentportal.org.in/opinion/arunachals-green-could-soon-turn-brown

Sakthi Vel Shankar (2010), *Deforestation causes and effects*, Detailed available at http://www.indiastudychannel.com/resources/106827-Deforestation-causes-effects.aspx

Salek M. Seraj, *Disaster Management in Metropolitan Dhaka*, Detailed available at http://desastres.usac.edu.gt/documentos/pdf/eng/doc5838/doc5838.pdf

Samir M. Saeed and Ibrahim M. Shaker (2008), *Assessment of heavy metals pollution in water and sediments and their effect on Oreochromis Niloticus in the Northern Delta Lakes, Egypt*, pp. 475-476, 8th International Symposium on Tilapia in Aquaculture, Retrieved from http://ag.arizona.edu/azaqua/ista/ISTA8/FinalPapers/PDF%20Files/37%20SAMIR%20M.%20SAEED.pdf

Samuela Bassi, Marianne Kettunen (2008), *Forest fires: causes and contributing factors in Europe*, Retrieved from http://climate-adapt.eea.europa.eu/viewaceitem?aceitem_id=5928

Sangma, S. (2013), *The 'Problem' of Shifting Cultivation in the Garo Hills*, Retrieved from http://samgar2007.blogspot.in/2010/08/problem-of-shifting-cultivation-in-garo.html

Santi Nindang and Teigan Allen (2012), *Ahead of Flood Season, Thailand's Communities Demand Greater Preparedness*, Retrieved from http://asiafoundation.org/in-asia/tag/thailand-floods/

Santra, S.C. (2008), '*Environmental Science*', First edition, New Central Book Agency (P) Ltd., Kolkata, pp. 169-177.

Sci/Tech Islands disappear under rising seas, Retrieved from http://news.bbc.co.uk/2/hi/science/nature/368892.stm

Sea (2013), Retrieved from http://en.wikipedia.org/wiki/Sea

Sea level rise forces Fiji villages to move (2013), Retrieved from http://www.radioaustralia.net.au/international/radio/program/pacific-beat/sea-level-rise-forces-fiji-villages-to-move/1114224

Sea level rise in Bangladesh and The Netherlands, Retrieved from http://germanwatch.org/download/klak/fb-ms-e.pdf

Sea levels rising, Marshall Islands appeal for help (2013), Retrieved from http://unearthnews.org/sea-levels-rising-marshall-islands-appeal-for-help/

See level rise (2012), Retrieved from http://www.greenpeace.org/international/en/campaigns/climate-change/impacts/sea_level_rise/

Shanti (2012), Retrieved from http://www.preservearticles.com/2012032228647/here-is-your-short-article-on-soil-erosion.html

Shardul Agrawala, Tomoko Ota, Ahsan Uddin Ahmed, Joel Smith and Maarten van Aalst (2003), *Development and Climate Change in Bangladesh: Focus on Coastal Flooding and The Sundarbans,* Detailed available at http://www.oecd.org/dataoecd/46/55/21055658.pdf

Sheo Nandan Pandey (2013), *The Chinese Disaster Management Mechanism,* Retrieved from http://idsa.in/system/files/jds_6_1_NandanPandey.pdf

Shifting cultivation (2013), Retrieved from http://megsoil.nic.in/shifting_cul.htm

Shobha Rani, Environment: Quality and Control, Jiwitesh Kumar Singh and Debendra Kumar Das (Ed), *'Environmental Economics and Development',* First edition, Deep and Deep Publications Pvt. Ltd., New Delhi, 2004, pp.248-253.

Sikkim (2013), Retrieved from http://en.wikipedia.org/wiki/Sikkim

Silvia Milanova (2011), *Environmental impact of forest fires,* Retrieved from http://www.ecoplum.com/greenliving/view/274?category_id=&author=&month=&searchtext=

Singapore's International Actions, Retrieved from http://app.nccs.gov.sg/page.aspx?pageid=55&AspxAutoDetectCookieSupport=1

Singh, J.,Borah, I., Barua, A and Barua, K. (2002), *Shifting cultivation in North-East India: An overview,* Retrieved from http://www.icfre.org/UserFiles/File/rfri/rpap23.htm

Singh, N. (2010), *14 Shifting cultivation practices in Manipur,* Retrieved from http://www.ncap.res.in/upload_files/workshop/wsp10/html/chapter14.htm

Sirajur Rahman Khan, *Cyclone Hazard in Bangladesh,* Detailed available at http://www.adpc.net/casita/case_studies/coastal%20hazard%20assessment/modelling%20cyclone%20hazard%20in% 20bangladesh/background_information_ on_the_storm_surge_ modelling.pdf

Slash-and-burn (2013), Retrieved from http://en.wikipedia.org/wiki/Slash-and-burn

Slope Stability - Landslide Prevention, See http://www.geotechnical-engineer.com/landslide-prevention.html

SME News (Nov 05, 2012), *Mizoram gets Rs. 370 crores for shift to permanent farming,* Retrieved from http://news.indiamart.com/story/mizoram-gets-rs370-crore-shift-permanent-farming-170741.html

Soil (2013), Retrieved from http://en.wikipedia.org/wiki/Soil

Soil and Sediment Erosion, Retrieved from http://www2.nature.nps.gov/geology/monitoring/soil_erosion.pdf

Soil Erosion – Causes and Effects (2013), Retrieved from http://www.omafra.gov.on.ca/english/engineer/facts/12-053.htm

Soil erosion (2013), Retrieved from http://www.botany.uwc.ac.za/envfacts/facts/erosion.htm

Soil erosion (2013), Retrieved from http://www.nda.agric.za/docs/Infopaks/Soilerosion.pdf

Soil Erosion and Human Impact, Retrieved from http://www.mesd.k12.or.us/os/OutdoorSchool/Soil_files/Soil%20Erosion%20and %20Human%20Impact.pdf

Soil Erosion Causes and Effects, Retrieved from http://www.envirothon.org/pdf/CG/soil_erosion.pdf

Soil Erosion in Brazil from Coffee to the Present-day Soy Bean Production, Retrieved fromhttp://www.sciencedirect.com/science/article/pii/S0928202508100116

Soil Erosion in India (2012), Retrieved from http://www.indianetzone.com/41/soil_erosion_india.htm

Soil erosion poses grave threat to wildlife sanctuary in West Bengal (2009), Retrieved from http://news.oneindia.in/2009/09/05/soilerosion-poses-grave-threat-to-wildlife-sanctuary-inwes.html

Soil erosion site (2013), Retrieved from http://www.soilerosion.net/

Soil Pollution (2012), Retrieved from http://www.environmental pollutioncenters.org/soil/

Solomon Islands (2013), Retrieved from https://en.wikipedia.org/wiki/Solomon_Islands

Solomon Islands and Sea Level Rise, Retrieved from http://www1.american.edu/ted/ice/solomon-sealevel.htm

Solution to deforestations, Retrieved from http://www.greenpeace.org/usa/en/campaigns/forests/solutions-to-deforestation/

Solutions to Global Warming for the Small Islands (2013), Retrieved from http://www.climatehotmap.org/global-warming-solutions/small-islands.html

Solutions to Global Warming in Africa (2013), Retrieved from http://www.climatehotmap.org/global-warming-solutions/africa.html

Solutions to Global Warming in Latin America (2013), Retrieved from http://www.climatehotmap.org/global-warming-solutions/latin-america.html

Some 100,000 people hit by rains, floods in Mexico and Central America – UN (2011), Retrieved from http://reliefweb.int/report/mexico/some-100000-people-hit-rains-floods-mexico-and-central-america-%E2%80%93-un

Sorcha Pollak (2012), *Cyclone Nilam Hits the Southeastern Coast of India*, Retrieved from http://newsfeed.time.com/2012/10/31/cyclone-nilam-hits-the-south-eastern-coast-of-india/

South Africa's coral reef MPAs (2013), Retrieved from http://www.tritondiving.co.za/Latest/south-africas-coral-reef-mpas.php

South African crocodiles 'in mass escape' during floods (2013), Retrieved from http://www.bbc.co.uk/news/world-africa-21178793

South America drought hits corn yields (2013), Retrieved from http://www.upi.com/Business_News/Energy-Resources/2012/01/31/South-America-drought-hits-corn-yields/UPI-13741328007422

South east Asian coral reefs (2013), Retrieved from http://www.sciencedaily.com/articles/s/southeast_asia_coral_reefs.htm

Southeast Asian coral reefs (2013), Retrieved from http://en.wikipedia.org/wiki/Southeast_Asian_coral_reefs

Southeast India braces for Cyclone Nilam (2012), Retrieved from http://www.aljazeera.com/news/asia/2012/10/2012103182047739 106.html

Status of the vehicular pollution control programme in India, Retrieved from http://www.cpcb.nic.in/upload/NewItems/NewItem_157_VPC_REPORT.pdf

Stephen Kurczy (2011), *What's causing the Australia flooding,* Retrieved from http://www.csmonitor.com/World/Asia-Pacific/2011/0111/What-s-causing-the-Australia-flooding

Steve Connor (2000), Soil crisis is holding back African recovery, Retrieved from http://www.independent.co.uk/news/world/africa/soil-crisis-is-holding-back-african-recovery-472161.html

Steven Kinsella (2008). *The Impacts of Global Warming on Trout in the Interior West,* Retrieved from http://www.defenders.org/publication/effects-global-warming-trout-and-salmon-us-streams

Stewart Smith (2011), *The Effects of Deforestation on Animals,* Detailed available at http://www.ehow.com/info_8457227_effects-deforestation-animals.html

Strategic Priorities of Digital Bangladesh, Section 4.5: Disaster Management, Environment and Climate Change, Detailed available at http://geoportal.icimod.org/symposium2010/PPT/Theme-VI/Shahidul%20Islam.pdf

Strong quake hits southern Africa (2006), Retrieved from http://news.bbc.co.uk/2/hi/africa/4742266.stm

Strukova E, Alexander G and Markandya A., (2008), 'Air Pollution Costs in Ukraine', Mukherjee Debashree and Hazra Somnath (Ed), *"Air Pollution and Health"*, First edition, The ICFAI University Press, Hyderabad, p. 128.

Stubborn drought expected to tax Mexico for years, Retrieved from http://www.reuters.com/article/2012/03/21/us-mexico-drought-idUSBRE82K1E520120321

Sudan Drought Breeds Violence (2012), Retrieved from http://www.thedailybeast.com/articles/2011/07/03/african-drought-in-sudan-and-somalia-breeds-famine-and-bloodshed.html

Sugarcane acreage in India seen at four-year low on drought (2013), Retrieved from http://www.business-standard.com/article/markets/sugarcane-acreage-in-india-seen-at-four-year-low-on-drought-113051100608_1.html

Sule, S. (2006), *Jhum cultivation under sharper scrutiny,* Retrieved from http://www.indiatogether.org/2006/dec/agr-jhum.htm

Sun (2013), Retrieved from http://en.wikipedia.org/wiki/Sun

Sun stroke : 3-hour rest for outdoor workers in Kerala (2013), Retrieved from http://www.deccanchronicle.com/130411/news-current-affairs/article/sun-stroke-3-hour-rest-outdoor-workers-kerala

Sun stroke claims one life in Jharkhand (2013), Retrieved from http://zeenews.india.com/news/jharkhand/sun-stroke-claims-one-life-in-jharkhand_778781.html

Sunstroke can cause instant death (2013), Retrieved from http://www.nation.com.pk/pakistan-news-newspaper-daily-english-online/lahore/20-May-2013/sunstroke-can-cause-instant-death

Sunstroke or Heatstroke (2013), Retrieved from http://www.indg.in/india/sitemap-1/health/diseases/sunstroke-or-heatstroke

Sunstroke: Prevention and Prevalence (2013), Retrieved from http://www.mdhil.com/sunstroke/

Suranjana (2012), *What are the causes of soil pollution?*, Retrieved from http://voices.yahoo.com/what-causes-soil-pollution-10847033.html?cat=57

Surging waters, floods, erosion, and Assam Government's track record, Retrieved from http://www.indiaenvironmentportal.org.in/news/surging-waters-floods-erosion-and-assam-government%E2% 80%99s-track-record

Surinam (2012), Retrieved from http://rainforests.mongabay.com/20suriname.htm

Surinam Forest Information and Data, Retrieved from http://rainforests.mongabay.com/deforestation/2000/Suriname.htm

Surviving Cyclones: Preparation and Safety Procedures, Retrieved from http://www.bom.gov.au/cyclone/about/tc-checklist.shtml

Susmita Dasgupta, Mainul Huq, Zahirul Huq Khan, Manjur Murshed Zahid Ahmed, Nandan Mukherjee, Malik Fida Khan and Kiran Pandey (2010), *Vulnerability of Bangladesh to Cyclones in a Changing Climate: Potential Damages and Adaptation Cost,* Detailed available at http://papers.ssrn.com/sol3/papers.cfm?abstract_id=1596490

Suvit Yodmani (2001), *Disaster Risk Management and Vulnerability Reduction: Protecting the Poor,* Detailed available at http://www.adb.org/poverty/forum/pdf/Yodmani.pdf

T. Kala and Ram Kumar (2005), *India: floods kill hundreds in Tamil Nadu,* Retrieved from http://www.wsws.org/en/articles/2005/12/madr-d06.html

Technical annex to cost action 623: Soil erosion and global change, Retrieved from http://www.soilerosion.net/cost623/annex.html

Tehri dam (2013), Retrieved from http://en.wikipedia.org/wiki/Tehri_Dam

Temperatures Rising: Global Warming Turns up the Heat on Human Health, Retrieved from http://www.nrdc.org/health/files/temperatures. pdf

Ten top coral refs/USA Today (2013), See http://traveltips.usatoday. com/top-ten-largest-coral-reefs-100603.html

The Acid Rain Report, Detailed available at http://www.angelfire.com/ks3/acidrainreport/acid.html

The cause of global warming (2001), Retrieved from http://www.wmo.int/pages/themes/climate/causes_of_global_ warming.php

The Causes of Ozone Depletion (2013), Retrieved from http://www.bcairquality.ca/101/ozone-depletion-causes.html

The Disaster Management and Resiliency in the Asia Pacific Journalism Fellowship, Retrieved from http://www.eastwestcenter.org/seminars-and-journalism-fellowships/journalism-fellowships/disaster-management-and-resiliency

The drought and humanitarian crisis in Central and Southwest Asia: A climate perspective (2001), Retrieved from http://reliefweb.int/report/afghanistan/drought-and-humanitarian-crisis-central-and-southwest-asia-climate-perspective

The Economic Times (May 30, 2013), *State run thermal power plants responsible of water scarcity: Study,* Retrieved from http://articles.economictimes.indiatimes.com/2013-05-30/news/39628923_1_scarcity-water-stocks-drinking-purpose

The effect of seasonal rainfall on landslides in the highlands of Ethiopia, See http://link.springer.com/article/10.1007%2Fs100640050065

The effects of earthquakes, Retrieved from http://www.geographylwc. org.uk/A/A2/A2tectonics/eqeffect.html

The effects of global warming in Africa (2013), Retrieved from http://news.softpedia.com/news/The-Effects-of-Global-Warming-in-Africa-41077.shtml

The Effects of Landslides on Structures (2013), Retrieved *from* http://www.stfrancis.edu/content/ns/bromer/earthsci/student10/Landslides%20affect%20structures%20in%20nature.htm

The effects of plastic bags on environments (2013), See http://www.healthguidance.org/entry/14901/1/The-Effects-of-Plastic-Bags-on-Environment.html

The Financial Express (Feb 06, 2006), *Jhum cultivation helps maintain ecological balance*, Retrieved from http://www.financialexpress.com/news/jhum-cultivation-helps-maintain-ecological-balance/149209/0

The Greenhouse Effect (2013), Retrieved from http://www.dnrec.delaware.gov/ClimateChange/Pages/Greenhouse% 20Effect.aspx

The greenhouse effect, Bio Factsheet (January 1998, Number 15), Retrieved from http://www.nwvle.net/file.php/374/15_greenhouse_ effact.pdf

The greenhouse gas effect (2013), Retrieved from http://www.infoplease.com/ipa/A0004686.html

The harmful effects of plastic on human health's and the environments. See http://www.motherearthliving.com/health-and-wellness/harmful-effects-of-plastic-ze0z1205zsch.aspx

The Hindu (Aug 04, 2012), *Ghaghra, Saryu flooded; dozens of villages hit*, Retrieved from http://www.thehindu.com/news/national/ghaghra-saryu-flooded-dozens-of-villages-hit/article3727310.ece

The Hindu (February 15, 2013), *UN report rings alarm on water scarcity in India*, Retrieved from http://www.thehindu.com/news/national/un-report-rings-alarm-on-water-scarcity-in-india/article4415356.ece

The Hindu (Jan 21-2011), *Coast Guard Monitoring Pollution*, Detailed available at http://www.hindu.com/2011/01/21/stories/2011012161040600.htm

The Hindu (June 30, 2011), *Russia for sharing its experience in disaster management*, Retrieved from http://www.thehindu.com/news/national/russia-for-sharing-its-experience-in-disaster-management/article2148007.ece

The Hindu (March 13, 2013), *Most Asia-Pacific countries face water crisis: ADB*, Retrieved from http://www.thehindu.com/sci-tech/energy-and-environment/most-asiapacific-countries-face-water-crisis-adb/article4504627.ece

The Hindu (May 9, 2013), *Heatstroke can kill your pets*, Retrieved from http://www.thehindu.com/news/cities/Hyderabad/heatstroke-can-kill-your-pets/article4699715.ece

The Hindu (November 26, 2010), *India losing 5,334 million tonnes of soil annually due to erosion: Govt*, Retrieved from http://www.thehindu.com/sci-tech/agriculture/india-losing-5334-million-tonnes-of-soil-annually-due-to-erosion-govt/article915245.ece

The history of flooding (2013), Retrieved from http://en.wikipedia.org/wiki/History_of_flooding_in_Canada

The human impact of tropical cyclones: a historical review of events 1980-2009 and systematic literature review (2013), Retrieved from http://currents.plos.org/

disasters/article/the-human-impact-of-tropical-cyclones-a-historical-review-of-events-1980-2009-and-systematic-literature-review/

The Impacts of Ozone Depletion (2013), Retrieved from http://www.bcairquality.ca/101/ozone-depletion-impacts.html

The importance of water (2013), Retrieved from http://www.aomega.com/mpure/water.htm

The Indian Express (July 19, 2013), *Uttarakhand: Heavy rainfall lashesKumaon, landslides damage houses,* See http://www.indianexpress.com/news/uttarakhand-heavy-rainfall-lashes-kumaon-landslides-damage-houses/1144008/

The Indian Express (Sep 27, 2011), *Kanpur second most polluted city: Lucknow fifth: WHO,* Retrieved from http://www.indianexpress. com/news/kanpur-second-most-polluted-city-lucknow-fifth-who/852395

The Indian Forest Fire Response and Assessment System (INFFRAS), Retrieved from http://applications.nrsc.gov.in/fire/

The Medical and Public Health Impacts of Global Warming, Retrieved from http://www.psr.org/resources/the-medical-and-public-health-impacts-of-global-warming.pdf

The Need for the Desert Rainwater Harvesting Initiative, Retrieved from http://www.omashram.com/projects/rainwater-harvesting-talab

The night sky in the world, See http://www.lightpollution.it/dmsp/

The ozone layer (2013), Retrieved from http://www.research.noaa.gov/climate/t_ozonelayer.html

The problem of soil erosion in Europe (2013), Retrieved from http://www.glyphosate.eu/problem-soil-erosion-europe

The Shillong Times (7 Dec 2011), *Tripura practices jhum in 17000 hectares for paddy,* Retrieved from http://www.theshillongtimes.com/2011/12/07/tripura-practises-jhum-in-17000-hectares-for-paddy/

The sun in culture (2013), Retrieved from http://en.wikipedia.org/wiki/The_Sun_in_culture

The Supreme Court Ruling: Friends of River Narmada (2013), Retrieved from http://www.narmada.org/sardar-sarovar/sc.ruling/

The Telegraph (Aug 08, 2012), *Landslides raise death toll in Pakistan,* See http://www.telegraph.co.uk/news/worldnews/asia/pakistan/7933395/Landslides-raise-death-toll-in-Pakistan.html

The Telegraph (Aug 25, 2011), *Hurricane Irene: Top five hurricanes to hit the US,* Retrieved from http://www.telegraph.co.uk/news/worldnews/northamerica/usa/8722957/Hurricane-Irene-Top-five-hurricanes-to-hit-the-US.html

The Telegraph (Nov 04, 2011), *Noise pollution: why the silence?* Retrieved from http://www.telegraph.co.uk/earth/environment/8870228/Noise-pollution-why-the-silence.html

The Times of India (July 4, 2013), *Landslides, floods kill 50, displace 12,000 in Nepal,* See http://articles.timesofindia.indiatimes.com/2013-07-04/south-asia/40370714_1_landslides-incessant-rain-nepal

The Times of India (June 01, 2013), *World Bank report suggests measures to combat water scarcity,* Retrieved from http://articles.timesofindia.indiatimes. com/2013-06-01/india/39674059_1_water-scarcity-water-bodies-drinking-water-availability

The Times of India (June 18, 2007), *Vehicular pollution on the rise*, Retrieved from http://articles.timesofindia.indiatimes.com/2007-06-18/patna/27996208_1_vehicle-owners-puc-certificate-vehicular-pollution

The Times of India (May 1, 2013), *Earthquake rattles buildings in north India*, Retrieved from http://articles.timesofindia.indiatimes.com/2013-05-01/india/38956798_1_jammu-and-kashmir-5-8-magnitude-quake-srinagar

The Times of India (May 18, 2012), Retrieved from http://articles.timesofindia.indiatimes.com/2012-05-18/bhubaneswar/31765010_1_sunstroke-disaster-management-minister-odisha

The Times of India (May 21, 2013), *Three die of sunstroke*, Retrieved from http://articles.timesofindia.indiatimes.com/2013-05-21/bhubaneswar/39417445_1_sunstroke-severe-heat-heat-wave

The United Nations Disaster Management Team (UNDMT) India, Retrieved from http://www.un.org.in/_layouts/CMS/undmt.aspx

The World Water Crisis, Retrieved from http://www.thewatergeeks. com/The-World-Water-Crisis-sp-3.html

Thermal Pollution (2012), Retrieved from http://www.eoearth.org/article/Thermal_pollution?topic=49471

Thermal Pollution (2013), Retrieved from http://en.wikipedia.org/wiki/Thermal_pollution

Thermal pollution from coal plants, Retrieved from http://www.sourcewatch.org/index.php/Thermal_pollution_from_ coal_plants

Thermal Pollution, Retrieved from http://library.thinkquest.org/C0111040/Types/thermal.php

Thermal Pollution, Retrieved from http://www.allsubjects4you.com/thermal-pollution.htm

Thermal Pollution, Retrieved from http://www.ukm.my/ahmadukm/images/stories/data/kuliah/manusia/artikel/thermal.htm

Tidal barrage (2013), Retrieved from http://en.wikipedia.org/wiki/Tidal_barrage

To Escape Rising Seas, Maldives President May Move His Entire Island Nation to Australia, Retrieved from http://www.treehugger.com/climate-change/sea-levels-rise-maldives-president-may-move-his-entire-island-nation-australia.html

Toni Vernetti (2005), *Are u wildfire aware?*, http://www.googobits.com/articles/p2-547-are-you-wildfire-aware.html

Top 50 Things To Do To Stop Global Warming, Retrieved from http://globalwarming-facts.info/50-tips.html

Tornadoes in the United States (2013), Retrieved from http://en.wikipedia.org/wiki/Tornadoes_in_the_United_States

Torrential rain causes flood in Peru's 2nd-largest city; at least 6 dead, many homes swamped (2013), Retrieved from http://www.foxnews.com/world/2013/02/09/torrential-rain-causes-flood-in-peru-2nd-largest-city-at-least-6-dead-many/

Transantarctic Mountains (2013), Retrieved from http://en.wikipedia.org/wiki/Transantarctic_Mountains

Tropical Storm Mahasen strikes southern Bangladesh (2013), Retrieved from http://www.bbc.co.uk/news/world-asia-22537615

Tsunami (2013), Retrieved from http://en.wikipedia.org/wiki/Tsunami

Tsunami Awareness and Safety, Retrieved from http://nthmp.tsunami.gov/taw/downloads/tsunami-factsheet.pdf

Tsunami Fast Facts, Retrieved from http://www.stopdisastersgame.org/en/pdf/Tsunami_fact-sheet.pdf

Tsunami information sheet, Retrieved from http://www.em.gov.au/Documents/Tsunami%20Information%20Sheet.PDF

Tuvalu (2013), Retrieved from http://en.wikipedia.org/wiki/Tuvalu

Types of damages caused by earthquakes, Retrieved from http://www.stfrancis.edu/content/ns/bromer/earthsci/student2/damage.htm

Types of Drought Impacts (2013), Retrieved from http://drought.unl.edu/DroughtforKids/HowDoesDroughtAffectOurLives/TypesofDroughtImpacts.aspx

Types of earthquake waves, Retrieved from http://www.allshookup.org/quakes/wavetype.htm

Typhoon (2013), Retrieved from http://en.wikipedia.org/wiki/Typhoon

Typhoon Fengshen (2008), Retrieved from http://en.wikipedia.org/wiki/Typhoon_Fengshen_%282008%29

Typhoon Ketsana (2013), Retrieved from http://en.wikipedia.org/wiki/Typhoon_Ketsana

Typhoon Megi (2010), Retrieved from http://en.wikipedia.org/wiki/Typhoon_Megi_%282010%29

Typhoon Nesat (2011), Retrieved from http://en.wikipedia.org/wiki/Typhoon_Nesat_%282011%29

UGANDA: After landslides in the east, now flooding, See http://www.irinnews.org/report/88319/uganda-after-landslides-in-the-east-now-flooding

Ujwal Deshmukh (2012), *Soil pollution causes and effects,* Retrieved from http://www.buzzle.com/articles/soil-pollution-causes-and-effects.html

Umendra Dutt (2006), *Land of Five Rivers in Water Crisis and Water Chaos,* Retrieved from http://www.countercurrents.org/en-dutt051006.htm

Umendra Sharma (2011), *The effect of global warming on biodiversity in India, National Conference on Forest Biodiversity: Earth's Living Treasure.* Retrieved from http://www.cbd.int/idb/doc/2011/idb-2011-booklet-en.pdf

UN agencies voice concern at impact of South-East Asian floods on children (2012), Retrieved from http://www.un.org/apps/news/story.asp?Cr1=flood&Cr=asia&NewsID=40156#.Uac4NVKDH3Y

UN says Somalia famine killed nearly 260,000 (2013), Retrieved from http://www.aljazeera.com/news/africa/2013/05/201352113337568731.html

UN warns Asia Faces Marine Pollution (2006), Detailed available at http://www.ens-newswire.com/ens/oct2006/2006-10-17-02.html

Understanding fire effects on the environment (2013), Retrieved from http://www.fs.fed.us/pnw/research/fire/fire-effects.shtml

US lead world in Greenhouse gas emission, Retrieved from http://www.newgeography.com/content/001682-us-leads-world-greenhouse-gas-reduction

Uthpal Kumar, Mohammed Abdul Baten, Abdullah Al Masud, Khandakar Showkat Osman and M. Mizanur Rahman (2010), *Cyclone Aila: One Year on Natural Disaster to Human Sufferings,* Detailed available at http://www.unnayan.org/reports/climate/ailareport_final.pdf

Uttarakhand: Hydropower, mining projects behind landslides, floods, See http://ibnlive.in.com/news/uttarakhand-hydropower-mining-projects-behind-landslides-floods/399989-3-243.html

Vaitoti Tupa, The Cook Islands - an Ocean and Coastal Environment, Retrieved from http://www.tiempocyberclimate.org/newswatch/feature 070527.htm

Valentina Vasile and Mariana Balan, *Impact of greenhouse effect gases on climate changes, measurement indicators and forecast models,* Retrieved from http://econpapers.repec.org/article/alujournl/v_3a2_3ay_ 3a2008_ 3ai_3a10_3ap_3a19.htm

Vehicular Pollution in India, Detailed available at http://dezi9or.com/c4n/ecoinfo/vehicular/archivevehicular3.htm

Vehicular Pollution, Detailed available at http://www.pollutionissues. com/Ve-Z/Vehicular-Pollution.html

Vehicular pollution, Detailed available at http://www.allfreeessays. com/essays/Vehicle-Pollution/16027.html

Vehicular pollution, Detailed available at http://www.cyberessays.com/Term-Paper-on-Vehicular-Pollution/26470/

Venezuela (2013), Retrieved from http://rainforests.mongabay.com/deforestation/archive/Venezuela.htm

Venezuela: Overview, Retrieved from http://www.globalforestwatch.org/english/venezuela/index.htm

Vulnerability, Risk Reduction, and Adaptation to Climate Change: Bangladesh (2011), Detailed available at http://sdwebx.worldbank.org/climateportalb/doc/GFDRRCountryProfiles/wb_gfdrr_ climate_change_ country_ profile_for_BGD.pdf

Water - its importance and source (2013), Retrieved from http://www.health.gov.au/internet/publications/publishing.nsf/Content/ohp-enhealth-manual-atsi-cnt-l~ohp-enhealth-manual-atsi-cnt-l-ch6~ohp-enhealth-manual-atsi-cnt-l-ch6.1

Water (2012), Detailed available at http://en.wikipedia.org/wiki/Water

Water (2013), Retrieved from https://en.wikipedia.org/wiki/Water

Water Crisis - Effects and Causes, Retrieved from http://www.indiastudy channel.com/resources/122105-Water-Crisis-Effects-Causes.aspx

Water Crisis (2012), Detailed available at http://en.wikipedia.org/wiki/Water_crisis

Water crisis (2013), Retrieved from http://archive.unu.edu/env/water/water.html

Water crisis I South Africa (2013), Retrieved from http://thewaterproject.org/water-in-crisis-south-africa.php

Water crisis in Rajasthan (2013), Retrieved from http://www.gits4u.com/water/water4.htm

Water crisis in Sudan, Retrieved from http://thewaterproject.org/water-in-crisis-sudan.asp

Water in crisis: Ethiopia, Retrieved from http://thewaterproject.org/water-in-crisis-ethiopia.php

Water Resources Impacts and Adaptation, Retrieved from http://www.epa.gov/climatechange/impacts-adaptation/water.html

Water restrictions in Australia (2013), Retrieved from http://en.wikipedia.org/wiki/Water_restrictions_in_Australia

Water scarcity (2008), Retrieved from http://www.eea.europa.eu/themes/water/featured-articles/water-scarcity

Water scarcity (2013), Retrieved from http://en.wikipedia.org/wiki/Water_scarcity

Water scarcity (2013), Retrieved from http://www.un.org/waterforlifedecade/scarcity.shtml

Water Scarcity (2013), Retrieved from http://www.worldnature.org/water-scarcity

Water scarcity and development (May 26, 2009), *The Economic Times,* retrieved from http://articles.economictimes.indiatimes.com/2009-05-26/news/29403857_1_water-scarcity-safe-drinking-water-water-management

Water Scarcity and Drought in the European Union, Retrieved from http://ec.europa.eu/environment/water/quantity/pdf/brochure.pdf

Water Scarcity in Delhi (2013), Retrieved from http://www.delhijalboard.nic.in/djbdocs/r_w_harvesting/harvesting1.htm

Water scarcity in Mexico (2013), Retrieved from http://en.wikipedia.org/wiki/Water_scarcity_in_Mexico

Water scarcity: Threats, Retrieved from http://worldwildlife.org/threats/water-scarcity

Water vapour (2013), Retrieved from http://en.wikipedia.org/wiki/Water_vapour

Water, Air and Soil Pollution Causes 40 per cent of Deaths Worldwide, Cornell Study Finds, See http://www.enn.com/pollution/article/21740

Weathering the drought in Africa (2013), Retrieved from http://planetearth.nerc.ac.uk/features/story.aspx?id=1382

Weddell Sea (2013), Retrieved from http://en.wikipedia.org/wiki/Weddell_Sea

Welcome to Floods Portal (2013), Retrieved from http://floods.jrc.ec.europa.eu/

West Bengal declares 11 districts as drought-hit (2010), Retrieved from http://www.dnaindia.com/india/1424214/report-west-bengal-declares-11-districts-as-drought-hit

What are greenhouse gases? (2013), Retrieved from http://www.ncdc.noaa.gov/oa/climate/gases.html

What are Some of the Effects of Deforestation?, Detailed available at http://www.wisegeek.com/what-are-some-of-the-effects-of-deforestation.htm

What are Symptoms of Sunstroke?, Retrieved from http://www.wisegeek.org/what-are-symptoms-of-sunstroke.htm

What are the effects of Tsunami? Retrieved from http://www.ask.com/question/what-are-the-effects-of-a-tsunami

What are the Effects of Drought? (2013), Retrieved from http://environment.about.com/od/environmentalevents/a/droughteffects.htm

What are the main causes of Noise pollution? See http://www.preservearticles.com/2012011320628/what-are-the-main-causes-of-noise-pollution.html

What can I do in hot weather to prevent heatstroke in my pet? (2013), Retrieved from http://kb.rspca.org.au/What-can-I-do-in-hot-weather-to-prevent-heatstroke-in-my-pet_353.html

What causes a tsunami? Retrieved from http://embc.gov.bc.ca/em/tsunamis/causes_1.htm

What Causes a Tsunami? Retrieved from http://www.voanews.com/content/what-causes-a-tsunami-117813908/167170.html

What causes acid rain?, Detailed available at http://www.epa.gov/acidrain/education/site_students/whatcauses.html

What causes Cyclones? See http://www.ga.gov.au/hazards/cyclone/cyclone-basics/causes.html

What causes Floods? Retrieved from http://www.ga.gov.au/hazards/flood/flood-basics/causes.html

What causes forest fire? Retrieved from http://www.letusfindout.com/what-causes-forest-fires/

What causes forest fire?, Retrieved from http://www.buzzle.com/articles/what-causes-forest-fires.html

What causes landslides? See http://www.ga.gov.au/hazards/landslide/landslide-basics/causes.html

What effects does acid rain have on the environment, Detailed available at http://library.thinkquest.org/C007231/effect1.htm

What is a coral reef?, See http://www.msc.ucla.edu/sswims/links_files/FrankLessonPlan.pdf

What is a Cyclone? See http://www.gmat.unsw.edu.au/currentstudents/ug/projects/darmawan/cyclone.html

What is Acid Rain?, Detailed available at http://www.pavilion.co.uk/dwakefield/curriculum/ks4/letts/acidrain.htm

What is Acid Rain?, Detailed available at http://www.pavilion.co.uk/dwakefield/curriculum/ks4/letts/acidrain.htm

What is Acid Rains and What causes of it? (2002), Detailed available at http://www.policyalmanac.org/environment/archive/acid_rain.shtml

What is causing Australia's heat wave?(2013), Retrieved from http://www.guardian.co.uk/environment/blog/2013/jan/21/what-is-causing-australia-heatwave

What is light pollution? See http://greenliving.nationalgeographic.com/light-pollution-2221.html

What is light pollution? See http://www.lrc.rpi.edu/programs/nlpip/lightinganswers/lightpollution/lightpollution.asp

What is Marine Pollution? and How does it Affect Marine Life, Detailed available at http://www.grida.no/publications/rr/our-precious-coasts/page/1292.aspx

What is noise pollution?, Retrieved from http://www.thebigger.com/biology/pollution/what-is-noise-pollution/

What is sky grow?, See http://www.lrc.rpi.edu/programs/nlpip/lightinganswers/lightpollution/skyGlow.asp

What is the EU doing about climate change?, Retrieved from http://ec.europa.eu/clima/policies/brief/eu/index_en.htm

What kind of droughts does South Africa experience? Retrieved from http://www.weathersa.co.za/web/index.php/corporate?id=164

What's Problem?, Detailed available at http://www.maine.gov/dep/air/lev4me/effects.htm

Where the Sea Has Risen Too High Already, Retrieved from http://www.ipsnews.net/2013/04/where-the-sea-has-risen-too-high-already/

White House warned on imminent Arctic ice death spiral, Retrieved from http://www.guardian.co.uk/environment/earth-insight/2013/may/02/white-house-arctic-ice-death-spiral

White paper: Roads and greenhouse effects, p. 7, Retrieved from http://download.intel.com/pressroom/archive/reference/IDCWP31R.pdf

Why is soil important?, Retrieved from http://www.envirothon.org/pdf/CG/Why_Soil_is_Important.pdf

Why people needed help after Cyclone Aila (2011), Retrieved from http://www.redcross.org.uk/What-we-do/Emergency-response/Past-emergency-appeals/Bangladesh-cyclone/Why-people-need-help-after-Cyclone-Aila

Why soil is important (2013), Retrieved from http://www.sepa.org.uk/land/soil/why_soil_is_important.aspx

Wildfires (2013), Retrieved from http://ajwaters.myweb.uga.edu/

Wildfires (2013), Retrieved from http://en.wikipedia.org/wiki/Wildfire

Wildfires (2013), Retrieved from http://www.weatherwizkids.com/weather-wildfire.htm

Wildlife flee Kenyan forest fires (2009), Retrieved from http://news.bbc.co.uk/2/hi/africa/7959230.stm

Will Grant (2009), *Venezuela flood victims still live in ruins 10 years on*, Retrieved from http://news.bbc.co.uk/2/hi/americas/8412249.stm

William Ladrach (2009), *The effects of fire in agriculture and forest ecosystems*, Retrieved from http://www.istf-bethesda.org/specialreports/fuego_fire/fire_ecology-eng.pdf

Working Group II: Impacts, Adaptation and Vulnerability, Retrieved from http://www.ipcc.ch/ipccreports/tar/wg2/index.php?idp=671

Yasuko Kamiizumi and Martin Fackler (2011), *Powerful Quake and Tsunami Devastate Northern Japan*, Retrieved from http://www.nytimes.com/2011/03/12/world/asia/12japan.html?pagewanted=all&_r=0

Yvonne Agyei (1998), *Deforestation in Sub-Saharan Africa*, Detailed available at http://web.mit.edu/africantech/www/articles/Deforestation.htm

Zeeshan Amin (2010), *Causes and impacts of thermal pollution*, Retrieved from http://suite101.com/article/causes-and-impacts-of-thermal-pollution-a291023

Websites

http://earthobservatory.nasa.gov/IOTD/view.php?id=7261

http://earthobservatory.nasa.gov/NaturalHazards/view.php?id=76216

http://earthobservatory.nasa.gov/NaturalHazards/view.php?id=76291

http://web.mit.edu/12.000/www/m2012/finalwebsite/

http://www.climatechoices.org/impacts_wildfires/

http://www.fao.org/emergencies/emergency-types/landslides/en/

http://www.mde.state.md.us/programs/ResearchCentre/FactSheets/AirFactSheets/Documents/www.mde.state.md.us/assets/document/factsheets/acidrain.pdf

http://www.motherearthliving.com/health-and-wellness/harmful-effects-of-plastic-ze0z1205zsch.aspx

http://www.telegraph.co.uk/earth/environment/8870228/Noise-pollution-why-the-silence.html

http://www.thenational.ae/news/world/south-asia/worst-drought-in-india-in-decades-blamed-on-official-incompetence

Index